ADVANCE PRAISE

The existence of Willy Rosen ended years ago in a place synonymous with Hell, KL Auschwitz-Birkenau. The mere mention of this place conjures images of man's depravity towards others who were intended to disappear and be forgotten, as is they never existed. Professor Hayes in this book *When The Music Stopped - Willy Rosen's Holocaust*, will bring to you the memories of many people who the Nazis had labelled as "Untermensch" and members of "Entartete Kunst", degenerate inferior artists.

The characters in the book are real people who were the toast of Berlin one year then rejected and finally murdered. Professor Hayes is perhaps the world's leading authority on the life and works of Willy Rosen, a composer and lyricist of over 600 popular songs, sung on radio, film and recorded thousands of times, during the Weimar Republic and the very early years of the Third Reich. Hayes tells the story of Rosen from his early years, through to the high years of Cabaret and fame in Berlin and to his imprisonment and exile in the Netherlands, with his death in a gas chamber.

Hayes answers the question: "Whatever happened to Willy Rosen?" He tells in story form, his own years of research not only into Rosen's life but also his music and performances, ending in a

Transit Camp, which produced the "Best Cabaret in Europe," for the entertainment of such men as Adolf Eichmann, as well as the thousands due to board trains to their deaths.

This is the definitive story of the life of Willy Rosen where you can travel with Rosen and his friends through a time of fame and celebration to one where death could come quickly on a whim. This book will restore Willy Rosen to his place in the world's memory.

Jonathan Gardiner MA, Author *One-Way Ticket from Westerbork,* 2021

Casey Hayes' book tells the exciting and eventful story of one of the most important and popular musicians from the time of the Weimar Republic. Willy Rosen's career and his bitter fate represents as well the many other Jewish artists who significantly influenced and shaped culture in Germany at the time. Willy Rosen also occupies an important part in my feature-length documentary *I Dance, but my Heart is Crying,* which will be released in the fall of 2022 and focuses on the music of German-Jewish artists in Nazi Berlin. The publication of *When The Music Stopped - Willy Rosen's Holocaust* was long overdue and is an asset to anyone interested in culture and especially the music scene in Germany in the 1920s and 30s.

Christoph Weinert, Film director based in Berlin, Germany

We must never forget. Perhaps we are often tempted to think we have more than enough to learn from and about the tragedies of the Shoah. Then riveting research like Dr. Hayes' into the life of Weimar Cabaret performer Willy Rosen appears. We are left speechless in the face of ever more far-reaching glimpses of evil and of good. What an amazing gift we are given in this book about Germany's most celebrated one-man show leading up to and into the catastrophe of Nazi Germany. How can the finest cabaret in Europe unveil some of the horrors of the Shoah? Dr. Hayes carefully opens up this fascinating new perspective!

Dr. David Chandler, Professor Emeritus & Holocaust Researcher, Franklin, IN & Münster, Germany

---

For the longest time, researchers have ignored the history of popular musical theater when researching the Holocaust; as if the horrors of the latter couldn't be associated with "entertainment", even though many famous artists from the world of operetta, cabaret, Schlager and revue were sent to concentration camps and died there. Only in the past 20 years have German language publications addressed this openly in a wider analysis of the Nazi era. However, the English-speaking world has so far not taken note of these groundbreaking studies, with the possible exception of the 2020 *Cambridge Companion to Operetta*, which included a single essay on the topic. This makes *When the Music Stopped - Willy Rosen's Holocaust* the first big English language study on one of the famous figures of the German entertainment world of the 1920s. Willy Rosen emigrated to The Netherland, like so many others who hoped to escape the antisemitic terror of the National Socialists. He hoped in vain. After his arrest, Rosen performed his quirky song repertoire in the Dutch transit camp Westerbork he even wrote new shows for Westerbork before being transported to Auschwitz. Until now, only Katja Zaich has covered this story in her 2001 book *Ich bitte dringend um ein Happyend: Deutsche Bühnenkünstler im niederländischen Exil 1933-1945*. The new English publication by Casey J. Hayes will hopefully alert more international readers to the forgotten histories of these once-celebrated artists and also remind them of their life-embracing music, which should not be overlooked because of the backdrop of so much tragedy. Even if the Nazis killed people like Rosen, his music deserves to live on. And his story should be told, after the many decades of silence. So, the Nazis don't win in the end.

Dr. Kevin Clarke, Director of the Operetta Research Center Amsterdam

WHEN THE MUSIC STOPPED

WILLY ROSEN'S HOLOCAUST

CASEY J. HAYES

a|p

ISBN: 9789493276093 (ebook)

ISBN: 9789493276079 (paperback)

Publisher: Amsterdam Publishers, The Netherlands

info@amsterdampublishers.com

When the Music Stopped is Book 2 in the series **New Jewish Fiction**

CONTENTS

For my husband,
Joseph R. Morris

FOREWORD

The time between the world wars in Germany, known by its sobriquet the "Weimar Republic," was a glorious time of cultural awakening: artists, musicians, and cabaret performers created in seemingly unregulated waters. The German government, busily rebuilding itself after the elimination of the monarchy, found itself faced with challenges at every turn. There were communist revolts in the streets of Berlin and the beer halls of Munich, hyperinflation from a crumbling Reichsmark, and an unrealistic demand from the Allied victors that Germany take full responsibility for the Great War and repay billions in reparations that it did not have. These distractions allowed for a loosening of moral regulations and the explosion of a burgeoning cultural scene. Berlin became the center of a voluptuous depravity and a night life unparalleled on the continent. It was within this blossoming Zeitgeist that Willy Rosen became a household name.

Known throughout Europe as an *Alleinunterhaltungskünstler*, a consummate solo performer, Rosen was a versatile entertainer who would sing in his own unique timbre the songs that he so carefully crafted. *Text und Musik von Mir!* (Text and music by me!) became his beloved calling card across Europe, and his songs filled the airwaves as hit after hit made him a shining star across the continent on the cabaret stage, the screen, and the radio. He acted alongside the finest talent the Roaring Twenties and the 1930s ever produced: Paul Morgan, Max Hansen, Sig Arno, Szöke (Cuddles) Sakal, Erich Ziegler, Max Ehrlich, Camilla Spira. The list goes on. How then, did this remarkable talent fall so quickly into obscurity?

Although many talented artists from this era fell through the proverbial cracks of history, it is my opinion that Rosen was far too important a player within it simply to be lost to time and be allowed to disappear from the roster of music and musicians that was so carefully orchestrated by the National Socialist (Nazi) Party during the late 1930s and into the 1940s. Rosen's life and work is a story that must be told if for no other reason than to allow the hundreds of musical works he spent his short lifetime composing to be appreciated for what they are—catchy, creative snapshots into a time that came and went much too quickly. Rosen's surviving music is as relevant today as it was during the first decades of the 20th century. It allows listeners to briefly leave their concerns, pressures, and troubles behind, and—for just a fleeting moment—be transported to a time when creativity was king, when formalities were set aside, and when all humanity was allowed to "let their hair down" and simply enjoy the message and music that was Willy Rosen.

This book is a work of creative nonfiction. While nearly everyone is known, in some cases a character was created—although always based on the types of people known at the time—or a character's name had to be made up because some names simply never appeared in the transcripts of events, such as interrogations that happened but by whom is not known. The dialogue, though invented, is very much based on the careful study of people's careers, their personalities, and their history of collaborations and friendships over time. This information is the result of over three years translating and reading over 1,000 pages of documents from the Camp Westerbork Memorial Center in Hooghalen, The Netherlands which includes many personal writings by Willy, interrogations and interviews of Westerbork inmates during the war and postwar, as well as interviews by inmates of Theresienstadt, Willy's performance notes and newspaper reviews, phone books, Gestapo documents from Berlin and Magdeburg, and secondary sources by individuals such as Silvia Grohs, Heintje Davids, Erich Ziegler, Kurt Robitschek, Hans Margules and many others included within the life story of Willy Rosen. A brief Bibliography is included following the Epilogue.

Annotation by month and year is utilized when general events occurred, with full dates used to indicate historically documented events, either from well-known facts or from researched records. The epilogue includes information on the research conducted and what happened to the people in Rosen's life by the war's end.

I hope that you are as inspired by Willy Rosen's life as I have been. My goal is to have his reclaimed story added to those the Third Reich tried to destroy.

Dr. Casey J. Hayes, Franklin College, Indiana

1

1917, Eastern Front, 23 Years of Age

"Keep your head down!" Willy heard someone shout.

The crushing sounds of bombs kept coming, making his ears and head ring violently.

If I could only rest for a second, he thought.

BOOM.

Will it ever stop? Sleep. Sleep. Can't. His thoughts were too jumbled. *Too much noise.*

BOOM.

Everything hurts... and the noise... Where am I? Sleep... The noise was a thunderous hammer. *Everything hurts.* He heard someone say, "Carry that one off. No use wasting the space. Where is the medic? Medic?"

The noise... the screams. I can't tell...

And then, nothing.

1906, 12 Years of Age

"You leave first!" commanded Moritz.

"No, you," whispered Willy, too frightened to speak any louder in case a teacher overheard.

"Fine, I hate school, don't you, Willy?"

Although school never bothered him, and he certainly never told Moritz that it did, he nodded. Moritz was always dragging a reluctant Willy into predicaments. Even now, he found himself racing toward the broad canyon of Wilhelmstrasse. "Why are we leaving school?" Willy asked, a little out of breath.

"Why would we stay?" Moritz was far less the student but had a worldliness that Willy envied.

"Fair enough, but if Mutti and Pappa find out, that's it. No piano for a month." He couldn't think of a worse punishment.

"You spend too much time on that thing. Where do you think playing the piano will get you?"

"Where do you think skipping school will get you?" Willy said.

Instead of answering, Moritz took off, with Willy right behind. Moritz lived at Breiterweg 130/131, and Willy lived at 147, so they would have to first maneuver past Moritz's house. His family lived above his father's drapery business, so the fear was being seen by Moritz's mother through the large display windows of the shop.

Willy followed, still reluctantly, as he knew that the next obstacle would be his house. They walked quickly—being careful not to run —past Willy's home and didn't stop until they reached the cinema.

"What's playing today?" Willy asked, still out of breath.

Moritz looked at his friend with disbelief. "Who cares?" he snipped. "Anything is better than Herr Otterbein droning on about the Napoleonic Wars."

Of course, Willy thought, even though the fear of losing piano lessons for a month hung in the back of his head. They arrived at the theater and came to an abrupt halt at the ticket window.

"Do you have any money?" Moritz asked.

"Why is it always me who has to pay?" Willy grumbled as he shoved his week's allowance under the glass in exchange for a pair of tickets. Once inside, they found their seats and settled in for the show.

"Don't you just love it when you're somewhere you aren't

supposed to be?" Moritz asked, as if they didn't have a care in the world.

"I'm not sure yet. What if someone sees us?" Willy responded. Without waiting for an answer, he noticed something was missing from the movie. *Wouldn't it be better if there were music to accompany it?* He also thought a nature film was not the most exciting way to spend an afternoon. "This is boring! *Beekeeping in the Obersteiermark?* And there's no music."

Moritz dismissed his complaints. "If you want to go, go. School's out in 25 minutes anyway, then we can wander out and be home at our usual time. Voilà."

Voilà? Well, the decision had already been made, so now it really was best to just wait it out. The movie was bad, but at least the seat was comfortable.

Amalie Rosenbaum was a formidable woman who took nothing lightly. She had already figured out that something was up when her son came home a little earlier than expected.

"Herr Otterbein let class out early, did he?"

Willy stopped dead in his tracks. "Why? What did I do?" Although quick with his peers, he was no match for his mother.

"Aha! Just what I thought. You were running with the Michaelis boy again, weren't you? Wait until your father hears this one. And where are your sisters?"

Willy knew the repercussions of his father knowing that he and Moritz were in trouble, again. Arthur Rosenbaum was a close friend of Moritz's father, supplying the material to make into draperies.

"Mutti, don't tell Pappa! He'll make me miss my piano lessons, and he'll tell Moritz's dad and I'll have one less friend. Lucie and Edith aren't even home yet. Why aren't they in trouble?"

"Not my concern, Willy. You must always deal with the consequences of your actions." His mother's words would prove apocryphal at several points throughout his lifetime. "Anyway, your father is with Edith at her voice lesson. He'll be home soon enough."

"Please, Mutti, I promise I will never do it again. We just ran out after lunch and went to the cinema. The movie wasn't even good— there was no music at all."

"Regardless, you will have to pay for your lapse in judgment. I have no concern for the fate of the Michaelis boy."

Willy seemed desperate.

Looking at her son, she rethought her decision.

Willy tried to focus, but his brain couldn't process anything. *Too much noise... I can't think... My head hurts.* He heard a different voice now. "We need a tourniquet over here, quickly! Nurse, grab that cot and help me!"

Sleep would solve everything. At that moment a hand touched his forehead, and he heard, "Corporal, you must rest. Your fever has yet to break."

"Where am I?" He tried to focus, but nothing was coming into view.

"A *Feldlazaret* outside Grodno. You're at the Eastern Front."

"A field hospital?" The last thing he remembered was being in the woods. "What happened? My head..."

"Your fever is still quite high. The bullets went through cleanly, but you were on the field too long. Infection has taken hold."

"Bullets?" Willy remembered walking through the woods, admiring what at that moment had been a quiet, picturesque scene. After that, he remembered nothing. "What about the rest of my division?"

"Scattered here and there. We found some, mostly in pieces. You and about a dozen others were delivered rather intact."

Jolted by this response, Willy could still only concentrate on the pain in his skull.

"Sleep," he was told.

He opened his eyes after what seemed like only a few minutes. *Am I awake? Yes. I'm awake, and my head doesn't feel as bad. Where am I?* He tried to clear his mind, then he heard a voice whisper: "Corporal, keep still. We're under attack."

"Under attack? By whom?"

4

"Russians. Some are resisting, but most have backed well past Slonim. They're angry."

Of course they're angry. We're in their country.

The ground shook.

"I don't feel so good," he said, but he heard nothing in response. *My head will surely start aching again. Sleep will help.*

"Corporal," the doctor yelled at him. "We must move. Get up!"

Willy tried to stand but found his legs uncooperative.

"Move it, Corporal!"

"I'm trying. Help me."

The doctor lifted Willy off the bed and pulled him toward the tent opening. Once outside, he told him, "Run, and keep running until you can't run anymore!"

Barefoot and wearing only a bloodied rag of a hospital wrap, Willy stumbled into the woods on wobbly legs.

BOOOOM.

The ground shook, and he fell on dense foliage. He heard someone scream, and then... nothing.

1910, 16 Years of Age

"Grab the other end of the fabric," Moritz called out above the roar of a half-dozen sewing machines. "Hold it steady. See? If you walk with the fabric while it's being fed into the machine then the stitch won't bunch up."

"This is not how I pictured my career path."

"Funny," Moritz said. He was a little angry that his companion wasn't grateful for this opportunity.

"Why am I even here? Is God punishing me? I would argue that this is my hell on earth. Why else would I be coddling a piece of fabric instead of playing the piano?"

"Shut up and pull," said Moritz, resentful that his friend thought so little of his work. "Remember, you may need this skill later. You never know."

Willy wondered if it were the job or the location that bothered him the most. "I'm not saying that this is the absolute worst thing a man can do, but can it be done somewhere else other than Magdeburg? I bet I could tolerate this if I were in Berlin."

"Careful what you wish for. Vati could make that happen."

He had forgotten that Moritz's uncle ran an offshoot of the family business in Berlin. "Can he? Moritz, can you talk to him for me?"

"Talk to him yourself," Moritz snapped.

Excitement at the prospect of living in Berlin grew inside Willy. "Honestly, Moritz," he pleaded, "I wouldn't mind any job if it were in Berlin. The music scene there alone—"

"Fine," said Moritz. "I'll speak to my father. If he gets approval from my uncle, I doubt they'd mind whether you did your apprenticeship here or in Berlin. What about your parents though? You're a momma's boy. You can't be away from home for more than a few days."

Willy wouldn't give him the satisfaction of agreeing with him. The thought of Berlin was running through his head: the people, the cars, the trains, the music. Oh, the music. *My head hurts at the idea of it.*

Willy heard what seemed to be a thousand screams. He was too afraid to even look around. *If I don't move, nothing can happen to me, right?*

"Look over that way," he heard someone call out. "Find as many as you can and load them into the truck. The sooner we can get them relocated the better."

A huskier voice asked, "What about the dead ones? Leave 'em or bury 'em?"

"Bury 'em? With what? Our bare hands?" the first voice answered sarcastically. "Just find the live ones and get them into the truck."

Willy's mind was clearing. He had to get out of these woods. He stood up but had to brace himself against a small tree to not topple back over.

"Over there!" he heard the huskier voice yell.

Someone was running toward Willy.

He put his hands up over his head and called out, "Don't shoot!

Don't shoot!" As the person grew nearer, Willy felt his legs give way. When he fell, he struck his head against the tree. The last thing he remembered was hearing, "We got a live one! Grab his feet!"

Willy opened his eyes to see a grey-lined tarp surrounding a series of metal tubes. Holes in the tarp allowed small streams of light to illuminate what appeared to be other men. He heard sounds... wimpers, cries, indistinct mumblings and the constant, almost metric pulse of wheels driving over deeply worn dirt. As he strained to make out the details of the body next to him, the brakes squealed to a halt and a voice resonated from behind him.

"Wake up. We're here. Get out," the driver shouted at the men.

Willy struggled to climb out of the largest truck bed he had ever seen. "Where am I?" he asked.

"Krakow. Still behind enemy lines, but safe enough for you to stay in one place."

"Where am I going?"

"Follow the others. They'll find you a bed. Once you're settled in, you'll get food."

Willy obeyed. He was one of dozens of gown-clad bodies shuffling into a gray short-rise cinder block building. There was a large red cross painted on each side of its edifice.

"You over there. Name?" demanded a person sitting at a desk.

"Rosenbaum, Willy."

"Rank?"

"Corporal."

"Sorry, Corporal, you're an NCO, and noncommissioned officers go over there. Only commissioned officers at this end of the hospital."

"No problem. I just want to sleep."

Once settled in his bed among the other NCOs, which was still an improvement over the accommodations of the general soldiers, Willy was given his first meal in days.

"What is this?" he asked, unsure of what he was looking at.

"Whatever it is, you will eat it," the nurse said.

After dinner, he laid his head against the pillow and looked around. Rows of men, or rather the shells of men, with all types of

Although he had been trained to play the classics, he had quickly developed a taste for the *Schlager* music that reflected the sociopolitical climate of the time, and, as a young man of a modernizing world, he was becoming a keen commentator. He worked at Kleider von der Stange und Gros during the day and then worked throughout the night composing catchy tunes with even catchier lyrics. The nights, although long, filled his soul. The days, not so much.

Willy would ask of anyone within earshot, "What time is lunch?"

"Really, Willy? Already?" a coworker would chirp from a nearby working table.

"I'm tired and I'm hungry."

"It's ten o'clock in the morning. You have a while to go."

"Can I move the clock forward? Would anyone notice? Would anyone care?" Willy would call back.

The conversation always came to a close when Karl Böhn, the foreman and overseer of the apprentices, yelled in his direction, "I would care!"

"Damn, caught!" Willy would retort, cracking himself up.

"More sleeping and less composing!"

"Yes, Karl. I promise. Tonight, I'll sleep and wake refreshed and ready to work. But for now, can I move the clock forward?" Willy ignored the look on Karl's face. "Better yet, if you let me sleep now, I promise to come to work earlier tomorrow."

I wonder if it works? Willy asked himself about the decrepit-looking piano in the rear of the officers' quarter room.

"Keep walking, Corporal," the male nurse told him.

"Yes, sir."

Willy's recuperation was steady but it was not fast enough for him. He longed for any semblance of normalcy. After a little while, he asked about the old piano. "Sir? Does that piano work?"

"Not sure, Corporal. Haven't heard it played since I've been here. Now, more walking and less talking."

"Nurse, is that Corporal Willy Rosenbaum with you?" an officer asked.

"Yes, sir."

The officer looked good, much healthier than the average officer in the middle of a war zone. The officer's hand raised into a salute. "Corporal Rosenbaum, it is my duty as a representative of the German State to award you the Iron Cross, Second Class. Your country thanks you for your sacrifice and shall remain forever in your debt for as long as you shall live."

Surprised, Willy managed an awkward salute.

After lowering his arm, the officer placed the medal around his neck.

This is the proudest moment of my life, Willy thought. *How proud Papa and Mutti would be. And Edith and Lucie. Even Moritz.*

The officer turned around quickly and left as unobtrusively as he had arrived.

There was something about receiving the Iron Cross that legitimized his injuries and made them more tolerable. There was a degree of honor, and of time and pain not wasted. The medal helped a little to overcome the uselessness Willy felt. No, there was no ceremony, no laud, no fuss, but it didn't matter. It was a simple presentation from one soldier to another in recognition of the price he had paid for his country. For some reason, the Iron Cross made that quite clear. Willy's head was throbbing.

The nurse shook his hand and said, "Congratulations, Corporal."

"Thank you," Willy choked out, trying to keep back the tears.

"Now, you must keep walking."

"May I return to my bed? I'm feeling a bit tired now."

"Of course," said the nurse.

———

Karl saw a check in Willy's hand. "What's that you got there? You moonlighting on me?"

"My first royalty check. See? All that work at night payed off! That's my song everyone is singing."

"I would like to have a soldier.
I would like to have a soldier.
Made of tin or lead, I wouldn't care!"

"Right," Karl said, getting back to business. "Now, grab the other end of that bolt and carry it down to the pressing room."

Willy was grateful for the work and knew that he couldn't live on a single royalty check. He quickly reached for the fabric and went down the three flights to the pressing room. On his way back he was met by Karl who had a small green envelope in his hand. "This is for you."

"What is it?" Willy asked but he already knew the answer. The telltale green envelope was from the Prussian government.

"I think you know, son," Karl said, handing him the notice.

Willy opened the envelope and read its contents. He knew others who had been called up, and after all, he was certainly not in a civilian job necessary for the continuation of a smooth and cohesive society. "It's my turn, I guess."

"When do you go?"

"Next Wednesday. Can I leave early on Friday to go back to Magdeburg? I would like to see my family before I have to report."

"Not a problem. Can I do anything to help?"

"No, thanks though. Karl, would you mind if I left early today? My head really hurts."

"Sure, Willy. No problem."

"Feeling better, Corporal?"

"Much better, thank you, sir."

Willy managed to raise himself off his bed slightly by grabbing the iron railing, but then collapsed back onto the mattress.

"Best not move too quickly, Corporal. You have plenty of time."

Time was exactly what Willy felt he didn't have. But what he would do with this moment in time, however, had to be more than simply lying in bed.

"The piano in the back of the officers' hall. Does it work?"

"It wouldn't be hard to find out."

Willy watched as his caretaker walked past the rows of iron beds and out of sight. He closed his eyes because he could feel a headache coming on. *Maybe the light is just too much*, but then he heard the sound of a badly neglected piano through the nearly empty barrack. He sprang as close to attention as he could while lying down.

It works! Willy thought, afraid that if he said it out loud it would no longer be true. He made a more diligent effort to stand on his own, and then slowly maneuvered through the room by leaning on each bedframe he passed for stability. When he arrived at the entrance of the officers' hall, the nurse took note of him standing feebly. "Corporal, careful. Your strength is not—"

"Please, help me to the piano."

The nurse could see how determined his patient was, but they had barely got to the doorway before his patient collapsed onto him.

"Please, please, don't take me back. Bring me to the piano," Willy pleaded.

Sensing the importance of the request, the nurse placed him on the piano stool. Even in his weakened state, Willy immediately adjusted the height of the stool to suit his diminutive frame. Like a wound-up cymbal-playing tin monkey, Willy played without having to think. His hands were unsteady and the piano dreadfully out of tune, but he played *Nelli Walc*, his first published composition. He began slowly but within a few bars the song was up to tempo. Willy's fingers were manipulating the ivory keys, and he felt the tension leave his neck and his shoulders drop and relax. There was also a nearly simultaneous jerking of his body that pushed him backward off the stool.

He was caught by the nurse. "That's enough for now, Corporal." The nurse lifted Willy's left arm and placed it over his own shoulder. With one quick pull, he had the patient on his feet.

"That felt great," Willy said cheerily. "Can we do that again later?"

Seeing the change in his mental condition, the nurse agreed. "I'll come back for you after dinner. It's easier to bring you to the piano than to bring the piano to you."

"Thank you, sir." Willy's pitch was quite a bit higher from excitement.

It had been over a year since he had done even the smallest performance for his family before he had left for training. He remembered his mother sending him off with a hug so tight that Willy was sure his hat would fly off. His father shook his hand firmly but did not say very much. Lucie, his older sister, kissed him lightly on the cheek, telling him that she would think of him every day. Edith, his younger sister, on the other hand, had always looked down on her brother for his taste in music. She was training to be an opera singer, so considered anyone involved with popular music to be beneath her. Willy may be going off to war, but that didn't change her opinion of him.

He wondered how they were. Before he could finish his thought, Willy fell into a deep sleep.

2

Kapelle Rosen was a small three-member ensemble Willy Rosenbaum created to entertain in officers' recreation halls throughout the Eastern front, playing some popular music but mostly music that he had written. As his popularity along the front grew, so did his need to come up with more and better performance ideas—not simply for the Kapelle Rosen but also for other, and more unique, forms of entertainment. He expanded the ensemble with a "front troupe" of singers, ventriloquists, magicians, and even drag queens who would entertain the troops prior to the evening's main event. This was a complete vaudeville show, with himself as the star. After nearly a year of recovery, he was returning to what he loved: playing piano and performing his songs. Not being able to send him back to the battlefield, the German military realized that he could entertain the men in the field hospitals at the front filled with physically and emotionally damaged men. These soldiers had given everything for their country. Now, the country determined, Willy would be the best they could give them to aid in their recovery.

Waiting behind the makeshift stage curtain, made out of a sheet suspended over a cord, Willy took deep breaths. He wasn't nervous; he was excited. Finally, he heard, "Gentlemen, I give you Kapelle Rosen!" Willy, along with a violinist and a cellist, entered the stage of the officers' recreation hall outside of Lublin, Poland. And with that, the show began.

Willy organized each act as the show was going on. "Where's Charlie, the ventriloquist?"

Someone shouted back, "He's in the can!"

"Where's Blighty Betty? Is she ready?"

"He's ready, if that's what you mean, Willy."

A voice reminiscent of a raspy Otto Reutter sang out as if to announce the arrival of the Grand Duchess. "*Fabelhaft!* Hey, fabulous! Out you go!"

Willy gave Blighty Betty a gentle shove. As she awkwardly tottered in her high heels to the stage, he hopped behind the piano and began the introduction. "Tonight, Kapelle Rosen and Feldlazarett Lubin proudly present Blighty Betty, the English Lass of German Lieder."

As he looked out over the rows of officers, Willy found it difficult to contain his emotions. This was certainly among the proudest moments of his recent memory; he was entertaining men who were in such need for normalcy, for a semblance of anything that was ordinary. His highlight of the evening came when it was his turn to sing and accompany himself on piano. "The next number is one you may have heard on the streets of Berlin, either before you were called up or while you were on leave. Text and music by me! If you know it, please sing along, for as you will hear, I am no Richard Tauber!" After singing the introduction and first verse, the officers joined in as he sang the refrain:

"I would like to have a soldier.

I would like to have a soldier.

Made of tin or lead, I wouldn't care!"

As the last of the soldiers filed out of the hall, Willy thought, *Another lovely evening. This is what I do best, and wouldn't I want to give my country and comrades my best?*

The show toured the front for five months, visiting field hospitals and the occasional officers' recreational hall. By 1919, Willy recognized that with the end of the war he had to figure out the where, what, and how of the coming months. Returning to Magdeburg was out of the question. There was only one place that could provide the opportunities for which he had prepared himself: Berlin.

1919

"Karl," he shouted as loud as he could. "It's me! I'm back."

"For what?" snarked Karl, as he gestured for Willy to come into his office and take a seat.

"I need a job."

"Why? All you wanted to do was play music."

"Yes, but music won't get me by until I find my way into the new cabaret scene. Can I have my old job back, please?"

"It's all different now," Karl explained. "Most of the prewar jobs have been filled by women. The wives of the enlisted. Even the managerial staff is made up of women."

"There must be something here for me. I have to have a job if I intend to rent a place. Can you call Herr Michaelis?"

Karl had forgotten Willy's connection to the owner of the company. "Never mind that. I'm sure there's something here for you. Tell you what. You go and find a place to live and I'll see you Monday morning. Do not be late and do not expect me to turn the clock forward."

"I promise. Thanks."

Willy jumped out of the chair and made his way down the hall and onto the street. When he'd left Berlin for the war in 1915, it was still an industrial town. The new Berlin—the Berlin of postwar Germany—was different. There was a sense of newness to the city.

The women were visibly altered: their hair and skirts were noticeably shorter, and there was a brashness to them. Kaiser Bill's war brought out a new side of women.

There was a feeling of both modernism and melancholy. Chrome-trimmed automobiles drove down the wide boulevards of central Berlin past lame beggars who were the refugees of trench warfare, seemingly forgotten by Willy's beloved Germany. As he strolled, he noticed the sign in a window of Pankstrasse 39, advertising an apartment for rent: Number 4. Although not his first choice, it wasn't that far from his job, and the new railstation on Gesundbrunnen was no more than a five-minute walk away. He only had his military payout of approximately 54 Marks which would not be enough to rent a room in any of the fancy districts anyway.

When he saw the two-room apartment, Willy knew that he had quite possibly found a place of his own. It was small but it had a bed, and room for a piano, so what else would he need? Knowing that he would work at Kleider during the day and on his musical career in the evening made the size and location of the apartment all that much less of an issue. "I'll take it," he told the woman showing him the place.

"Where's the show at?" Willy asked Friedrich, eager to get the details finalized.

Charlie Wiegenstein, a ventriloquist from the days of the front troupe, desperately needed money. Friedrich Börsc, another old friend from the troupe, was organizing a benefit concert for him.

"It's on Invalidenstrasse. Know where that is?" Friedrich asked.

"It's not far from where I live. What time?"

"Eight o'clock. Do you know what you're going to do?"

"I'll play and sing something. You know, like during the war," Willy said, presuming that was all that was expected.

Willy needed to clear his head, so rather than go home he headed up Pankstrasse towards Prinzenallee. That's when he caught sight of the movie theater. An idea was glimmering. What if, instead of showing a film with music, he simply played the music that should

18

have gone with the film? How would that appear to the audience? A man at a piano reciting to a nonexistent silent film? What would that sound like? The idea was growing. He could play the piano as he described the scenes of an imaginary nature film. *I could say, 'A beehive seen from the right. A beehive seen from the left.' And the big finish would be, 'A slice of honey!' It will either be the best thing I have ever done or the worst. There's little room for anything in between.*

Over the coming days before the benefit he was convinced that he had latched onto something quite new and special, but had no idea what to call it. Maybe a cinema parody? After all, there was no actual movie.

When the time had come for his portion of the evening, Willy cheerfully announced, "*Text und Musik von Mir!*" before performing both his published and new works. When the enthusiastic applause died down, he played the soft and lyrical introduction to *Was Blumen träumen* and started his narration to a nonexistent film. To the delight of his audience, he recited one imaginary scene after the other in this new Dadaesque experience. At the end, the audience leapt to their feet with thunderous applause. Willy stood next to the piano taking his bow. As he stood there, he knew he had developed two distinct and important personal trademarks: this new cinema parody and *Text und Musik von Mir!* That phrase would become his calling card. In a few years, everyone would know it meant Willy Rosen.

"Hey, Willy, wait up." It was Friedrich. "You're not going to believe this, but guess what we've been asked to do?" He was out of breath from running, so he doubled over and grasped his thighs with both hands. "Do you remember Alexander Kirschmann? The magician from our front troupe? We've been asked to do another benefit concert for him. Seems word about the concert for Charlie got around fast. Alexander doesn't have a job and was seen panhandling outside the Brandenburg Gate. What do you say? We could do it exactly as before, and be sure to do your parody thing."

"Of course," Willy said, more than happy to help out another former soldier. "After all, the country isn't helping us, so we'll have to help each other. Where is the next performance?"

"At the Café an Wilhelmsaue. It's a good space and free for any war benefit. It's at eight o'clock next Friday."

"Anything for Alex, Friedrich. And anything for Germany."

The evening was set up exactly as it had been at Charlie's benefit, starting with cocktails. But before he took to the stage, Willy felt a new sensation. He felt himself at a different level of performance, and he knew from the reaction of the audience after each number that they knew it too. At the end of the parody, the audience leapt to their feet and demanded more. Two encores later he walked off the stage transformed. The combination of pride for his country and well-honed showmanship that particular night had turned him from a good performer into something different. He now felt in control of his entire artistic performance. He was finally an *Alleinunterhaltungskünstler*, the versatile, solo entertainment artist he always wanted to be. Now, he was a different man and a different performer to the one who had walked onto the stage.

"Willy, want to go for a drink?" It was Charlie, the ventriloquist.

"Sure. Did you have a good time?"

"Can't remember a better one. Oh, right, yes, I can. Last month when you did this for me. Thanks again, Willy. That performance changed my life."

"It changed mine as well," Willy said. "Only it took this evening to realize it."

Willy was grateful for Saturdays, knowing that he didn't have to rush out of bed. As he slowly came to life, he noticed that at some point after he got home, a note had been slipped under his door. He picked up the small envelope and saw the name Wreschinsky on the back. *Impossible*, he thought, tearing open the note. Siegbert Wreschinsky was the power behind the small but very popular cabaret Schwarzer Kater owned by Peter Sachse. Willy wondered what the manager of The Black Cat could possibly want with him.

The contents of the letter shocked and delighted him to his core.

Wreschinsky noted that his son-in-law had attended the benefit for Alex and had been extremely impressed, in particular with the cleverness of Willy's cinema parody. He was inviting Willy to his office first thing Monday morning. *For all good things comes a reward,* he thought.

On Monday, Willy was out of bed in a flash, quickly dressed, and took the train to the small Schwarzer Kater, making sure to arrive a little early. After a few minutes, he was shown into the office of artistic director Wreschinsky who was in charge of hiring (and firing) all of the artistic talent. He could hardly contain his excitement.

"Herr Rosen, come in please. Take a seat."

"It's a pleasure to meet you, sir. Please, call me Willy."

"Ah, yes, *Herr Text und Musik von Mir!* Very clever. My son-in-law attended Friday evening's benefit concert at Wilmersdorf and immediately called me after the show. He could talk of nothing but your act. The uniqueness of what he referred to as a cinema parody. I have no idea what that is, but if it is anything at all like his description, it's something that I think would play very well here at Schwarzer Kater, along with, of course, you performing your songs at the piano. How about a six-month contract? You would perform only here within the Berlin city limits, but are allowed to perform anywhere in the provinces."

"Six-month contract?" Willy was stunned. This was unheard of—most contracts were day to day or at most week to week. Nevertheless, he played one more card. "I would accept, but I would like to be able to perform my cinema parodies elsewhere within Berlin. Not my songs, but just my parodies."

Willy noticed that Wreschinsky wasn't quite sold yet on the whole concept, so he sweetened the offer. "What if I say, at every performance outside of your cabaret, something like, 'Willy Rosen, as a guest, courtesy of the Schwarzer Kater, Berlin'?"

Wreschinsky liked this idea. He could allow his client to practice his parodies outside of the cabaret and at every performance the Schwarzer Kater would get free publicity. "Done," Wreschinsky conceded. "Let's shake on it. I'll see you tonight."

Along with three cabaret shows a week at night, Willy performed his parodies in cinemas around Berlin. They were so popular with the matinee crowds that he'd often do three of them a week, making him a household name.

It was now 1920, and in the short time since the end of his performances for the military, Willy Rosen had grown as a performer and as a brand. When his contract with the Schwarzer Kater was up, he received many offers to perform around Berlin. He accepted an invitation by Harry Waldau to be the headliner at his cabaret, Die Spinne. It was at The Spider that Willy's life would change forever by a fateful meeting with an up-and-coming cabaret entrepreneur named Kurt Robitschek. In Kurt, Willy found his champion. His musical career as a composer and performer, as well as his personal life, would never be the same.

3

February 1920

Kurt Robitschek was a rather large man with a sharp jaw, anchoring multiple chins. He was an entertainer, composer, lyricist, and a businessman with a keen eye for talent in the Weimar cabaret scene. Kurt was amazed by Willy's ability to captivate his audience with a dramatic flair that he had never seen before. *Text und Musik von Mir!* That phrase resonated in his head as he watched the audience respond to Willy's every nuance, from his nasal and clearly untrained, yet captivating, voice to his frumpy, almost disheveled appearance. These qualities were made even more amusing by the pair of large round spectacles nestled at the end of his nose. He was not your average cabaret performer. No, he was much more. His persona came from a confidence and a sense of knowing that he was exactly where he should be at that moment. Kurt thought about this throughout Willy's performance. As the final round of applause died out, he made his way backstage to the cramped dressing cubicles that housed The Black Cat's stars *du jour*. He had to meet this man, and he had a specific reason why. "Herr Rosen?"

"Yes?" Not yet used to his own developing notoriety, Willy was star-struck. "Aren't you Kurt Robitschek? The lyricist?"

"Guilty as charged, young man. I caught your performance. Are you really the person that you appear to be on stage, or is it all an act?"

"If you're asking if I am a great actor, I'm not. What you saw up on that stage is me."

"The voice? The clothes? The glasses? The—?"

"Yep. All me. How can I help you?"

"I have this cabaret gig in Vienna, a gig that lasts for a couple of months. It requires a troupe of performers to give a revue each evening in several venues throughout the city. I'm looking for some new, unique entertaining acts, or rather people, as I can work out any of the kinks in an amateur."

Willy looked at him in protest.

"Which you obviously are not," Kurt said quickly.

"What I'm looking for is someone exactly like yourself who will come to Vienna and help me to put together a performing troupe. Of course, you would be a performer as well, as would I, but we would be the drivers behind all of it. Vienna's not Berlin, so it will take finesse. The Viennese are so..." Kurt paused, not finding the right word.

"Stuffy?" Willy asked, although he had no personal experience with the city at all.

"Exactly, but your act is perfect. It's not risqué, it has music and a storyline, and more importantly, it's as unique as you are. If I were you, I wouldn't change a thing."

Willy took in Kurt's words. "Good, because I wouldn't even know where to begin to do that."

"So what do you think?"

"Absolutely. What are the terms?"

After they shook hands Kurt said, "Let's have a drink because this may take some time." He added, "And we leave in a week."

A week later in the evening, Willy followed Kurt onto the train platform carrying only a shoulder bag and a small battered suitcase.

Kurt asked, "How can you fit all of your clothes into that one suitcase?"

"The suitcase is for my music. What you see on my back is about it as far as my clothes go. I don't need much. A piano, pencil, paper and something to wear while I write."

"Well, that's a good thing because that's about all I see."

"I'm a modest man, except when it comes to music."

"Good. We've work to do in Vienna. Did I tell you Trude Hesterberg will be singing with us?" Kurt's voice trailed off as the two stepped onto the train headed to the Austrian capital.

"How many hours?" Willy asked the porter.

"Nine on a good day, 11 if we have any issues."

Finding Kurt in his seat Willy announced, "Ten hours or so to Vienna."

"I know. I do this regularly. Haven't you ever been? Are you sure you're a real musician?"

"Just leave me alone. Wake me when we get there."

"Sure. Sleep well, my prince. Hey, did I tell you about Trude Hesterberg?"

"Good night, Kurt."

When Willy awoke, he looked out the window to see nothing but a blinding rain. *So, this is lovely Vienna.* Once on the platform, the pair walked through the arched hallways onto the street and into a waiting cab.

"The Grand Hotel, please," Kurt instructed the driver.

"The Grand? Are you kidding me? I can't afford the Grand!" said Willy.

"No? Well I can, and that's where we're staying. This is my city. I know people, and the right ones can get me rooms for free at the Grand." Kurt seemed to have the situation well under control. "Willy, relax. This is a big venture with big players. It's important that we stay at the Grand. I need to impress some people, and to ask top talent to join us. If I put them up at the Grand, it will be harder for them to say no."

"Who else? Other than Trude, I mean."

"Szöke Sakall, Curt and Ilse Bois, Max Ehrlich. Will they do?"

"Are you kidding me? Yeah, I think they'll do. What's the plan?"

"Well, if we can get these guys, our troupe will be the hottest thing this side of the Danube. Hell, on both sides of the Danube. We can only do this if we have the names to attract, so..."

Willy understood in that moment that it was not enough to have talent, you had to be a name that draws recognition. "So why me, Kurt? I don't have a name."

"You don't have a name yet. This is how we get your name out there. You already have a clever moniker, you have a unique look, and your tagline is something that is easily associated with you. That's a great calling card. Even if someone doesn't remember your name at this point in your career, they'll remember your line. You have talent, and I think with the right people around you, doors will open for both of us. I'm not being heroic here. There's a benefit for me as well. Your talent, along with even a few other well-known names, can bring me to a place where I can go back to Berlin big enough to form my own cabaret."

Willy was impressed. And he couldn't believe his luck. *Of all the people Kurt could have picked to start this venture with, he picked me.* His head throbbed with the pressure he felt from this level of trust. Kurt believed in him so much that he would include him in the climb up the cabaret ladder. "I won't disappoint you. At least I hope I won't."

"Just do what you do, Willy. That's all I need from you."

The cab stopped in front of a magnificent structure on Kärntner Ring. Getting out of the car, Willy looked up at the ornate Historicist building with both disbelief and awe. *This is a far cry from Pankstrasse,* he thought. Walking into the lobby of the Grand Hotel opened his eyes to the magnitude of his new friend's notoriety in Vienna.

"Herr Robitschek, welcome back to the Grand," the doorman said formally.

"Thank you, Heinz."

As they walked to the front desk, Willy noticed just how out of step he was with the current fashions. These men were dressed in beautifully tailored silk-lined coats, and there was a coiffed nature to every inch of their look.

Kurt could sense Willy's insecurity. "Remember. Don't change a thing, and that means your suit as well. Let your talent exude through your clothes."

Willy listened but couldn't help feeling uncomfortable.

At the desk the front manager said, "Welcome, Herr Robitschek. Your rooms are ready," making a quick gesture toward a group of waiting bellmen. Two of them immediately jumped forward taking Kurt's multiple suitcases, and a third reached for the case in Willy's hand.

"Thank you, but I'll take this myself."

"Let him have it, Willy. It's his job. I promise, your music will not be stolen between the lobby and the fourth floor," Kurt joked, but saw his companion still clinging tightly to his case. The look on Kurt's face forced Willy to begrudgingly loosen his grip. "You're going to have to get used to this."

Willy wondered about that. Berlin, compared with Vienna, felt like it had an inferiority complex. He was worried that the Viennese would be more sophisticated than the people who came night after night to the Schwarzer Kater or Die Spinne. *Will they like my act?*

Again, Kurt could sense Willy's uneasiness. "Relax. Get some sleep. We have a big day tomorrow. I got the tip."

What was initially a two-month stay in Vienna was now in its sixth month. Surely, if the Viennese loved them, so too would the Germans when they returned to Berlin.

"Listen to that! They love it!" Kurt was so proud of the troupe, as well he should be. "You're up, Willy!"

Willy bounced to the front of the stage with his flair for the dramatic in top form. Showing his huge toothy smile, he took a bow and leapt to the grand piano. He raised his left hand, fingers together but thumb extended up, and gleefully exclaimed, "*Text und Musik von Mir!*" The audience burst into applause in anticipation of the performance.

The songs, whether they were exclusively his or written with others, had a unique sense of humor. A Rosen song offered a witty commentary on current social trends through a lens of pedestrian observation. Willy would see an issue worthy of commentary and, through his lyrics and catchy melodies, offer a humorous resolution.

He also understood the importance of incorporating the dance craze of the moment, setting his songs to the foxtrot, the rhumba, the two-step, or the tango to facilitate adaptation by dance orchestras.

Willy became more famous and his music more popular with every new publication. In Vienna he met Will Meisel, the powerful music publisher and owner of Meisel Music Verlag in Berlin. Will caught one of Willy's performances during a trip to find an office for a Viennese branch of his publishing business. Upon his return to Berlin, Meisel became a champion of Willy's music.

September 1920

After one evening's performance, Kurt and Willy went for a drink at the Metropole. Kurt seemed a bit more anxious than usual. "I have some news," he said, but could hardly get the words out of his mouth. "We've been asked to bring the troupe to Budapest. It would be a six-month engagement, like this one." He could tell Willy was cautious, but also excited. "We'd have to talk to everyone else, of course. I realize that six months is a long time as it is, let alone asking them for another six months away from Berlin."

Willy was already missing Berlin and barely remembered the inside of his apartment. *Boy, I bet my piano's out of tune by now.*

"Well, what do you think?" Kurt asked, realizing that Willy had left the conversation.

"I think it's a great opportunity. I don't know Budapest, though. Will they like us? What are the audiences like?"

"Budapest is like Vienna, but a lot less stuffy. And everyone speaks German. Willy, we have a name now, and the cabarets are coming to us. They know us through our reputation and trust that audiences will come. This is what we've been working for, and now it's coming true. If we can build an international name, our return to Berlin will be like Napoleon returning to Paris," Kurt said, gaining energy as he spoke to be persuasive, but he really didn't have to.

"I'm with you. Budapest it is. Let's see what the others think. But I know Szöke would love to go to Berlin for a visit first."

"Yeah, I think you're right," Kurt said. "A change of scenery will be good for all of us, but let's have a bit of home first, even though we won't be going to Magdeburg."

"That's okay. Best we stick to Budapest. We'll have to keep a close eye on Szöke, though."

"Leave that to me." Changing the subject, he asked Willy, "Hey, do you think Ilse Bois likes me?"

After their six-month run in Budapest, Kurt Robitschek and Willy Rosen returned to Berlin where they found a very different artistic environment. The carefree Berlin was replaced by a city that seemed on the edge of chaos. The only economic sector to thrive in this environment was the entertainment industry. Berliners, eager to leave the stress of their day behind, flocked to the cabarets and cinemas of the city.

An aftereffect of the government's need to focus on its own political and financial survival was the loosening of societal norms due, in large part, to its inability to contain them. Vice was ignored, which allowed for industries of "pleasure" to expand in the large urban areas of the country, particularly Berlin. Hedonistic pursuits drew flocks of tourists from across the globe to Berlin to experience this new age of the Weimar Roaring Twenties. This opened the floodgates for new and vibrant music that would encapsulate the energetic Berlin society and enthrall the likes of Josephine Baker, Duke Ellington, and Christopher Isherwood. They stood at the gates of the golden age of Weimar Germany, and their timing couldn't have been better.

January 1923

Willy greeted New Year's Day with plans for a new tour with Kurt, this time focusing on the northern areas of Germany as well as Denmark, the Netherlands, Belgium, and then a return to Germany.

What a gritty city, he thought as the train pulled into the station in Düsseldorf. He remembered his arrival in Vienna, which seemed almost a lifetime ago. Rainy, yes, but a pristine beauty of a city so very different from the industrial grime he saw outside his window.

As if reading his mind Kurt chimed in. "This could be the worst city we play. It might have been a mistake to come here. It seems pretty impoverished."

Willy, no matter how he felt, came to the defense of the poor town as they climbed into a cab. "Every German city is impoverished now, Kurt. If we only performed in cities that were void of slums, we wouldn't have a stage to sing on. Anyway, you can only find those places in Switzerland now, and there's only so much of cheese, clocks, and chocolate that a man can take."

"Königsallee 11, please," Kurt told the driver.

The city didn't look a lot better from inside the cab. The rise in unemployment and the devaluation of the Reichsmark had visible effects on the town. Shuttered windows hid empty stores, and no one was on the streets.

"Are you sure we're still in Germany?" Willy asked, looking around at what seemed to be a foreign city far outside the pale of the Republic.

"Remember, the Ruhr area is now occupied by the French, and most Germans want nothing to do with them." Hearing his own words, Kurt added, "You know, I don't think we have to worry. They'll want to come out for some good German cabaret and entertainment."

"Why are there French troops in Germany? They did this to us, you know. I was there, on the Eastern front. Germany was not the only aggressor in this war. We didn't even start it. Yet, the Americans and their Allies insist on us taking all the blame and funding all war reparations out of our coffers. How are we as a nation to survive this?" Willy wasn't looking to Kurt for answers but as a sounding board for his anger.

Kurt agreed but was in no mood for a political discussion, and looked hard at him. "Willy, look. I understand how you feel, and I sympathize with your patriotism. Just remember, nothing turns an audience off like political rhetoric."

"I know, but it's wrong and we have a platform. Wouldn't it help to lift the spirits of the audience if they knew we were on their side?"

"They know we're on their side. It's why we're here. They won't be coming to hear political speech. They want to forget, not be lectured to. They look to us to lift them out of their misery, to help them forget even if it's only for a few hours. Promise me. No politics."

"I promise, Kurt."

The cab turned sharply onto Königsallee and into what appeared to be another world. Gone were the shuttered windows and lonely sidewalks. Königsallee reminded Willy of old Berlin, of Vienna, and of any number of grand cities and streets that he had come to know through Kurt. The cab pulled up in front of a massive Imperial building with a glass portico under which stood an impressively outfitted doorman.

"Another expensive hotel? I'm not paying for this one when I would rather be staying at the Bahnhof Hotel," Willy said, not pleased by Kurt's insistence on high-end hotels.

"I got this, Willy. I just can't do the station hotel. Anyway, your impression of Düsseldorf will undoubtedly change after a night here."

"Got it. Düsseldorf's not a dump." He stopped himself, understanding that his political mood and roiled feelings had to change before the performance. "Let's get our bags up to the room and get over to the cabaret. We have some people to cheer up." Willy picked up his suitcase, tucked his music bag under his arm, and made his way up the sleek marble steps of the hotel.

4

January 1923

Looking out over the audience at Düsseldorf's Apollo Theater, Willy glanced toward the kitchen and noticed one person in particular. She was smiling. *That's a beautiful smile!* He studied the woman until he was convinced he had memorized her face. He wondered why she stood out among so many others awaiting their performance. Sure, she was pretty with blonde hair, but it was that smile. *She's certainly out of my league... Probably married anyway.*

"Willy, you're on," Kurt prodded, just loud enough to break the reverie.

"Okay, I'm ready."

Willy sprinted across the stage to the piano, and with his usual bow of his left hand over his head, he enthusiastically announced, *"Text und Musik von Mir!"* This instantly jolted the audience to an even higher state of energy and anticipation. He wondered what the blonde woman by the kitchen was thinking.

He started with one of his most popular songs, *Die Mädels von Berlin* (The Girls of Berlin). He kept his head slightly turned to see any reaction the blonde woman was having to the music. With her striking blonde hair she was not difficult to spot. With the refrain, he could see her lips mouthing the words with him. Willy was so delighted that he performed the remainder of the set as if just for her. He glanced at her as often as he could—looking up from the keyboard, between songs, and during applause. The darkness over the audience helped to highlight her blonde hair against the glow from the kitchen. Finished, he quickly bowed and left the stage, intent on going to the kitchen area to find her. Through the back hallway, he turned toward the main room. He was face-to-face with this evening's distraction. "Excuse me! I'm... I'm so sorry," he said, overcome by her beauty.

"Sorry for what?"

"I'm not quite sure, but I bet I'll figure it out at some point." He was not experienced talking with anyone outside of the performance world, and certainly not someone this attractive.

"Herr Rosen, I'm Elsbeth Hoffman. I thoroughly enjoyed your performance this evening. Brilliant."

Willy spoke to lots of women, such as Camilla Spira, Ilse Bois, Trude Hesterberg, but they were performers. This one was different. He reached out and shook her hand, not thinking that they were past the point of introduction. "I'm Willy Rosen. Pleased to meet you, Fraülein Hoffman." No sooner were the words out of his mouth that he wanted to put them back. "Idiot," Willy muttered under his breath.

"Excuse me?" Elsbeth asked, unsure of what she just heard.

"I'm sorry. I was calling myself an idiot."

"Hardly, Herr Rosen. I am rarely in the presence of brilliant men, and you are brilliant."

Willy could hear the sincerity in her voice. He took a breath, and then asked bravely, "Would you like to go for a drink, Elsbeth?"

"I would love to, Herr Rosen."

"Please, call me Willy." Feeling excited but awkward, and not knowing what else to say, he blurted out, "And, by the way, I'm Jewish."

March 1923

"You must get a new suit for this. You cannot be married in that same old tattered tweed of yours," Elsbeth warned. A new suit, even for the wedding, was pushing him out of his comfort zone, and she knew this.

Willy retorted as she walked toward the room door, "Fine. Better still, why don't you go down and pick one out for me?"

"Not on your life," Elsbeth called from the doorway. "But I will come with you."

"You know me, don't you, my dear?"

"Yes, I know you. And I love you. Now, March 10 is three days away. We leave Düsseldorf for our honeymoon the day after. By the first of April you'll be back in time to go to Berlin."

"And, my dear, we will be traveling together for the first time. It was so generous for Kurt to pay for our honeymoon in the Netherlands. I hope you like Scheveningen. It's one of my favorite places to visit."

"If you love it, I'll love it," Elsbeth replied, taking his hand.

The two left the hotel and made their way toward the tailor's shop two blocks away.

"You know," Willy said, "when I was in Berlin, I made my living by working for an off-the-rack clothing manufacturer."

"Which is why your suit never fits properly. No off-the-rack clothes for our wedding day."

March 10 was a glorious day for Willy and Elsbeth. After the ceremony, they took the train from Düsseldorf to The Hague, and after a short cab ride to the coast, settled in at the Grand Hotel in Scheveningen. The hotel was befitting of its name, shaming even its Viennese counterpart. The massive domed roof covered a marble-and-plaster atrium that was three stories high, and the interior had balconies which seemed from below to wrap each floor. Within minutes of settling into their room, Willy heard music echoing through the cavernous lobby.

"I think it's Louis Davids. I thought he might be playing here. Let's go and see, and I'll introduce you," he said buoyantly, taking Elsbeth's hand and pulling her off the bed and onto her feet.

"We just got here! Can't we rest for even a minute?"

"You'll love Louis. He is one of the funniest men I've ever met. And his sister is almost as funny as he is. Louis is a musician too."

The music emanating from the cigar room stopped, and there was applause. Not long after, out came a slight figure of a man with a sharp jawline. He had deep-set dark eyes that were barely visible under the lowered boater that covered a thick mop of black hair.

"Willy Rosen, what on earth are you doing here? A bit off your track, eh?" Louis asked, vigorously shaking his hand.

"Careful there, Louis, I'm a married man now," Willy exclaimed, loud enough for everyone in the lobby to hear.

"Unbelievable! Who would take you on? Is she blind, deaf, and dumb?"

"I believe you would be referring to me and, while possibly dumb, I can positively say that I am neither blind nor deaf. It's a pleasure, Mr. Davids. Willy speaks very highly of you."

Willy and Elsbeth let Louis go on about the latest events of his life without interrupting him. "Tell me," Louis finally said. "What's up in your world? Why are you here in Scheveningen? Aren't you more an Amsterdam kind of performer? And where is Kurt? I hear the two of you are inseparable these days."

"Elsbeth and I are here on our honeymoon. I figured a couple of weeks by the sea would do us both good."

"Good choice, Scheveningen. And the Grand is undoubtedly the finest hotel on the coast. You must be doing well."

"We are doing well, Louis, but Scheveningen and the Grand are both Kurt's doing. It is kind of a wedding present to Elsbeth and me." Willy noticed Elsbeth fidgeting.

"Darling, why don't you go to the bar and order us a drink? We'll be there in a few minutes. Louis, do you care to join us?"

"Not on your life. Shame on any man that comes between a husband and his wife on their honeymoon. We can catch up some other time, I'm sure."

"You're a wise man, Herr Davids," Elsbeth said. "I can see why my husband is so fond of you."

"I'm glad you see it. I'm constantly amazed that anyone would be fond of me," Louis said, and he smiled and tipped the edge of his boater. "Willy, where did you find such a charmer? And a Jewish one at that."

"I'm not Jewish, but I'll take that as a compliment."

Louis paused a moment and then said, "I'm glad to hear it doesn't matter, Frau Rosen. From what I'm hearing in Rotterdam, there are some people in Germany to whom it would matter a great deal."

"Yes, the news of the Brownshirts has traveled to Düsseldorf as well. Let them stay in Munich where they belong and not bother the rest of us," Elsbeth said fiercely.

"Let's hope that is the case. Make a toast for me and for the eradication of hate everywhere."

"Certainly, Herr Davids. Good day."

Willy, not one to stay abreast of the news, stood dumbfounded at the conversation between Elsbeth and Louis. He had never heard anything about the Brownshirts or Munich or issues over interfaith marriage. Willy took Elsbeth's arm and they strolled to the outdoor bar for that long-overdue cocktail. There was something extremely peaceful about having a drink with your wife, with ocean waves and the shouts of children playing in the sand filling the air around you.

"So much for a bit of peace and quiet," Elsbeth said, having a different opinion about the noise.

"It doesn't bother me. I love children, and I love the sea, and I love you. What could possibly be better?" He watched Elsbeth's face light up with her beautiful smile, that same smile that caught his eye when he was performing in Düsseldorf. But that same smile faded quickly as Elsbeth focused her attention on her glass.

"What's wrong, my dear? Is it the Brownshirts? Is this something I should know about?"

"No, it's nothing."

Willy learned that his new wife was not a good liar.

"Let's not forget to toast to the eradication of all hate," Elsbeth said, raising her glass.

"Yes! To the eradication of hate."

As the glasses clinked, though, he felt a shiver go up his back. He glanced at Elsbeth only to see her look down at the table.

On April 1, 1923, the train pulled into Amsterdam Central Station, and Kurt was waiting to greet the couple. The tour had to continue— Kurt had scheduled performances in Amsterdam, Antwerp, Luxembourg, Zurich, Hamburg, Copenhagen, and Prague. The married couple did not return to Berlin until the spring of 1924.

Spring 1924

"So, Willy, are you familiar with the old cabaret Die Rakete (The Rocket)? You know, on Kantstrasse at the corner of Joachimsthalerstrasse? I just bought it! I didn't want to say anything at the time I was negotiating. You never know, it may not have materialized. However, I'm signing the paperwork this evening. By this time tomorrow, I will be the owner of my own club. And I need you there. I need you to be my headliner. I have an idea to make Die Rakete a different kind of club, one that primarily offers comedy in any form. Song, parody, scenes. You name it, and it will be funny. People need humor. Look around. This is not the same Berlin."

Willy paid some closer attention to the people outside the station. No one was smiling. The streets were absolutely filthy with beggars everywhere. When they got around the corner, he saw a long line of people waiting for food. He also saw a shop window with a sign reading "Out of Bread," and another sign reading "Milk 1,000,500 Reichsmark."

"One million and five hundred Reichsmarks for a liter of milk?" Willy couldn't contain his shock. "What's going on, Kurt?" He glanced over at Elsbeth, who wore an equal look of surprise and disgust at the sight of their city. "Well, if there was ever a time when the people of Berlin needed a good laugh it's now, eh?"

"And Die Rakete will be just the place to give it to them," Kurt replied. "Let's talk in a day or so, okay?"

"Sure, Kurt. Anytime." Willy let go of Elsbeth's hand, and lifted his left hand into his familiar bowing position. As Kurt walked away, Willy hailed a cab to take them to his apartment.

When they entered Pankstrasse 39, there was a feeling of both the Occident and Orient. *This is home, yes, but not for Elsbeth*, Willy thought, as he opened the door to Apartment 4.

"Oh my," Elsbeth exclaimed, as the two were greeted by a strong stench of dead mice and rotted houseplants.

"Elsbeth, we'll go out and find a new apartment first thing in the morning. We won't even unpack."

"Maybe so, but we do have to clean this place, or there will be no sleeping tonight. Now, where's your mop and bucket?"

"Thank you, my dear. I love you."

"Don't talk. Clean."

November 1924

"Do you really think we should be writing a show about this?" Willy asked with trepidation.

Paul Morgan said, "Why not? Those guys in Munich are getting out of control, and someone has to make Berlin aware of what's happening." Paul was a Jewish actor-cum-comedian, famous for his work in the film industry. By 1924, he had already appeared in half a dozen silent films and had had an active cabaret career. Paul was one of three partners, along with Kurt and Max Hansen, in the new cabaret renamed Kabarett der Komiker to better indicate what the audience should expect: cabaret and comics.

"Elsbeth and I heard about these guys from Louis Davids in Holland. They don't sound like a group that would take parody lightly. Are we really going to have them dressed in brown shirts?" He was nervous about choosing such a subject for their inaugural performance. "Louis said that they don't like Jews. That they're spreading all kinds of lies. Basically, they're blaming everything bad on us."

"All the more reason to do this. People don't want to be taught about something as if they were sitting in a schoolroom. They want to be taught in as easy and pleasant a way as possible. And what's more pleasant than comedy? *Quo Vadis?* will use the themes of ancient Rome but place the action in direct comparison to what's happening in Munich. I fear that brawl in the beer hall last week is just the beginning."

"And that Hitler is not a good man. He seems to be the one behind it all. At least he's in prison," Kurt said, not really trusting his own words. "In any event, *Quo Vadis?* will be clever, witty, and drenched in humor. If people make the connection between the Roman Legionary and the Brownshirts, well, all the better for them."

Changing the subject, Paul asked, "Willy, how's the music coming along?" Of course, he already knew the answer.

"It's all done. Come rehearsal on Monday, we should be able to move quickly through the songs and ensemble numbers. The orchestra will be a different beast, but that's only because I won't see them until production week."

"Okay, then," Paul said. "Opening day for Kabarett der Komiker is December 1. That's only three weeks away, so let's keep our eyes on the prize."

"There's a prize? Splendid... Can it be more money in my paycheck?" Willy quipped.

5

The opening night in December 1924 of the new Kabarett der Komiker, or KaDeKo as it was called by the public, went as smoothly as any of the performers could have hoped. "Wonderful," declared the popular yet tough Berlin theater critic Max Herrmann-Neisse, making it an even bigger draw than everyone expected.

January 1925

For a solid month *Quo Vadis?* played to a packed house night after night. The parody made the work's political sentiment vibrant and purposeful. Willy, preferring to keep work and life out of trouble, was still concerned that this was not a subtle statement and was going to make some people mad, very mad indeed.

January 4, 1925 was a snowy, blustery day. Willy went into the theater to meet Paul and Kurt to start work on KaDeKo's next show.

"We don't need to keep doing stage plays like this, do we?" Kurt asked, annoyed with the same theatrical work night after night. "We need to start doing what we intended to do. Acts by the greatest comic names in Germany and Europe."

Paul assured him, "We will, Kurt. Let's just see how long this plays out. Who have you been in contact with for the next show? Do we have any firm commitments yet?"

"Well, we have Trude Hesterberg."

"Really?" Willy always kidded Kurt about his obsession with Trude.

"Hey, don't laugh. She is one of the biggest comic stars of the stage now. Having her is a real bonus. I mean, she won't be a steady performer, but she'll show up when she can. And Max Adalbert has signed on."

"I love Max," Paul said.

"Yup, he's the best," Kurt agreed. "We also have a firm commitment from Ilse Bois."

"Well, I would hope so. She is your wife, after all," Willy joked.

Kurt was quite content with the lineup he was putting together. "These are big names, gentlemen. And we will always attract—" but he was interrupted by several sharp bangs on the side door of the theater. Before he could open it, a piece of paper was slid underneath. He picked up the note and read it.

"Well," said Kurt, holding the note above his head, "we have the first of what will probably be many warnings to shut down *Quo Vadis?* Honestly, I am surprised it took this long for the news to reach Munich."

"The news didn't have to reach Munich," Paul replied. "There are National Socialists here in Berlin. They go out at night and look for trouble; there were a couple in the audience a few nights ago. I saw them. I figured at that point it was just a matter of time."

"What do we do?" asked Willy, shaken by the news.

Paul's attitude remained unaltered. "We do nothing. We were planning the exit for *Quo Vadis?* anyway. Let's just keep to the schedule and get the comedy acts up and running."

The early to mid-1920s were a fertile, creative period for Willy Rosen. He collaborated with the well-known composer and lyricist Kurt Schwabach in 1922 on a trio of songs that became big hits, entitled *Mit uns ist aus, mein Schatz!*, *Per Sofort*, and *Was man zu zweien macht.*

In 1924, they wrote three *Musikal Lustspiel*—two- or three-act short musical comedies—set to Willy's music and Kurt's lyrics. Willy performed at matinee performances of a *Lustspiel* during the days and at the KaDeKo in the evenings, and he filled in what little other time he had with his cinema parodies and songs as break numbers in the largest movie houses in Berlin.

With all this success Willy was a huge asset for the KaDeKo, leaving the others to wonder where it would be without him. All his outside work, however, didn't come without some hurdles.

"Really, Willy? We need you this afternoon to go through the dance number of the girls' act. As it is, attendance at our matinee performances is down, due in part to people going to see your parodies. I'm not asking that you give up your cinema performances. I'm only asking that you don't perform them within a 15-kilometer radius of the KaDeKo. You have to give this to us."

"Fifteen kilometers? How am I supposed to get there and back within an hour?"

"You'll need a fast car," Kurt joked, trying to reduce the tension. As much as he hated to do this, he had no choice. He hoped that Willy would understand.

Willy took a moment to respond, "I can do it. I promise that I can."

"What about Elsbeth? Where did you move to again?"

"Cicerostrasse. She likes it there, and it's a lot closer to the action." Willy preferred it too.

"And probably no rats!"

"No rats, I swear. The apartment is almost in good enough shape to invite you over."

"You know, I didn't care when you lived on Pankstrasse. It was more an Ilse issue. You know women."

"I'm learning quickly," Willy admitted. "I'm doing most of my writing at home... with Kurt Schwabach."

"What are you and Schwabach working on now?"

"Well, we're focusing on a few new songs."

"Schwabach's a clever man."

Willy agreed. "I actually prefer his lyrics to my own. However, it causes a problem on stage because my tagline doesn't work when I perform a song with his lyrics. I have to give him the credit!"

"Which is exactly what I would expect from you. No one can claim that you're not generous in your recognition. It's one of your finest qualities."

"I thought the way I dress is one of my finest qualities," Willy said, trying to sound insulted but not succeeding. Elsbeth's influence had him looking every bit the star now; he wore white tie and tails when performing, and was polished from head to foot.

"I would say that Elsbeth is your finest quality."

Paul came out from behind the curtain, hearing the last bit of the conversation. "That's certainly true."

"So, who do we have?" Willy asked, getting back to KaDeKo business.

"Next week's lineup is big. We have Szöke Sakall coming in for the next two weeks. He'll do his lamp routine, no doubt."

"Yeah, but the audience loves it," Kurt said.

"We have Claire Waldoff. Very popular with the lesbian crowd."

"They do love her! And hey, I'll be there. Don't forget me."

"We could never forget you, Willy. You wouldn't let us," said Kurt, laughing.

January 1926

The new year began with Willy's first offer to be in a movie, the documentary *Der sprechende Film*. This project, however, troubled the *Meistersingerquartett* of the KaDeKo, Kurt Robitschek, Paul Morgan, Max Hansen, and now Max Adalbert.

"I don't know why you are so upset," Willy said. "It's all about the voice, gentlemen, and it's my voice they want!"

"Well, I guess you're right, because it can't be your looks," Max Hansen said.

Willy wasn't joking though. "Really guys, this could be something big for me. It's my first break into the movie business. Who knows where it'll go from here?"

"It's great news," Kurt said honestly, even though it increased his concerns over Willy's availability. "Remember, the more famous you become, the more money we make."

When Willy started putting some music into his bag, Paul asked, "Where are you off to now?"

"Dinner. I have to eat. Look at me, wasting away to nothing."

The five broke into laughter because Willy's increasing fame brought with it an increasing waistline as well.

"Maybe one day I'll be thin enough to stand in for Louis Davids."

"I wouldn't wish for any such luck, Willy. That man is dangerously thin."

"I'll bet it would be easier to buy clothes," and with that Willy picked up his bag and left for home.

Willy walked toward the taxi station on Kantstrasse as quickly as he could, but a bright red cover in the window of a bookshop caught his attention. He stopped dead in his tracks: *Mein Kampf*, by Adolf Hitler. Its prominent position indicated that it was very popular. *Wasn't Hitler in prison?* Willy thought as he crossed toward the Tiergarten. Flustered and agitated, he hopped into a cab.

"Where to?" the driver asked.

"Cicerostrasse 55, please." Willy couldn't get the book cover out of his head. *How did a man in prison write a book that was now published? Who would even publish a book by a man like that?* He asked the driver whether he had ever heard of Hitler.

"Adolf Hitler? Yes, sir. He's quite something, isn't he?"

Willy couldn't tell if the cabbie approved of Hitler or not, so he kept on questioning. "I thought he was in prison for that fight in the Munich Beer Hall in '23. Wasn't he sentenced to five years?"

"Out in nine months. So much for the German justice system," the cabbie responded.

"What do you think about him? I noticed he has a book out."

"Came out last year. Haven't read it, don't intend to. I don't much care for his language. He seems to be mad at everyone, particularly at the Jews. I have a lot of Jewish friends, so he's no friend of mine. What about you? Are you a member of the Heil Hitler club?"

"No, not a fan, either. But then again, I'm Jewish. I heard about him years ago. I wish he'd just go away."

"Not likely. Lots of drivers, factory workers, and laborers are following his every word. The book's a best seller. No, he just got started, so it seems."

Willy was in a cloud of thought, but he was jerked into reality by the sharp stop of the car.

"Cicerostrasse 55. That'll be 30 Reichsmarks 20." Willy reached into the pocket of his coat and pulled out a 50 Reichsmark. "Keep the change. Thanks for the talk. Very enlightening."

"You take care, okay? Keep your head down for a while. Maybe it'll all pass quietly."

With that, Willy got out of the car, but his mind was still racing. "How am I supposed to keep my head down?" he asked out loud.

6

The year 1927 had been a banner one. Willy Rosen completed the lyrics to his fifth *Lustspiel* and made 11 recordings—all but two for the prestigious Odeon label—and published 22 songs. Most were with Will Meisel's company, Drei Masken Verlag. Of these, Willy wrote both the text and the music for 12. The other ten were a mix of collaborations with Kurt Robitschek, Kurt Schwabach, and others. He was now as much a power player in the Weimar cabaret as any of his idols, but dwarfed all of them when it came to the quality and quantity of his creative output. He was the most versatile, most published, and among the most recognized performers in all of Weimar Germany. This was especially true in his hometown.

March 1927

"Willy, a letter arrived from Hermann Beims of Magdeburg. Who is he?" Elsbeth asked, extending the small envelope toward her husband.

"He's the mayor. What could he possibly want with me?" When Willy read the letter, he looked at Elsbeth with an enormous smile. "It appears that there will be a German theater exhibition in

Magdeburg this year. Mayor Beims has invited me to perform at the opening celebration on May 28."

"A theater exhibition? What is that?"

"Representatives from every stage industry gather there: curtain manufacturers, lighting companies, costume companies, and the like. I would imagine Kurt, the two Maxes, and Paul would go to see the latest developments."

"What do they want from you?"

Willy read the mayor's invitation again. "I would be the opening act at the Press Ball; I'd play concerts in the new exhibition hall and throughout the event." His excitement was ballooning with each word. "There's nothing like returning to your hometown and being treated like a star. Mutti, Pappa, and Lucie could come. And, of course, you will be at my side the entire time." He wondered what Moritz would think of this.

"What about Edith? Have you heard from her lately?"

"No. She's in Wiesbaden working with Arnold Schönberg. He's written a monodrama with her in the lead role. She's rather impressive." Willy was happy for his little sister, even if she didn't approve of his popular music or return the feeling.

Since they had married quickly and without his family present, Elsbeth added, "Well, even so, it'll be nice to meet the rest of your family."

May 1927

The exhibition was everything that Willy hoped it would be. For his performance, he walked over to a piano that was in the center of the new floating stage and opened with his trademark. He played his popular foxtrots, rhumbas, and tangos for the audience to dance to. For the next several days, he was the main guest for every special occasion at the exhibition hall. He was even crowned the Prince of the Circus by the Circus King before sitting at the piano in the band pit to conduct his march *Das Macht Uns Keiner Nach!* (*Nobody Does That!*) while 12 elephants were paraded around the center ring.

Looking into the audience, Willy could see Elsbeth next to Lucie, and his parents directly behind them. He couldn't help but think of the time when he received the Iron Cross in the hospital outside of Krakow. He thought that had been the most meaningful event in his life. *But maybe this was it. My homecoming as a celebrity with my wife and family.* As he played selections from his Menage Dances, he could hardly see the keyboard through his tears.

After the circus was over, Willy made his way through the throngs of humanity leaving the seating areas. *I feel like a fish swimming upstream!* Through a clearing, he glanced up to see his Elsbeth in deep conversation with Amalie, who was next to a rather detached Arthur Rosenbaum, who appeared not the least interested in their conversation. Willy maneuvered quickly into place, and gave his mother and Elsbeth a light kiss on the cheek before he interjected a new conversation.

"Mother, what did you think of the show?" Before she could answer, Willy noticed a sharp glance directed at him from Elsbeth. "I'm sorry! Mother, this is Elsbeth; Elsbeth, my mother, Amalie. I know you two have met, but I should have done this properly and much sooner. Please forgive me!"

Elsbeth began to speak, but was cut off by an eager Amalie. "No need for apologies, Willy. She's lovely. I'm sure we will have plenty of time to catch up when you both return for a visit. And please...call me Mother." Nodding her head toward her husband, she continued. "Maybe you'll be able to inspire Arthur to speak rather than smoke!" Willy turned toward his father, noting an awkwardness in his body language. "Father, what did you think? Did you like it?" Arthur tapped the ash from the end of his cigar and turned toward his son with a characteristically serious look on his face, which promptly turned into an enormous smile.

"Son, I couldn't be prouder of you. I don't know what I have done to deserve such talented children. You, Edith...even Lucie in her own way have found their way in this world." He grabbed Willy's hand and shook it vigorously, careful not to disturb the cigar between his lips. As he shook, he pulled Willy closer to whisper in his ear. "Elsbeth is not only witty and smart, but completely devoted to you, son. You were all she could talk about during the show. Your mother and I are both so proud of you." Willy turned slightly away to hide his watering eyes.

"Thank you, Father."

When they finished, Willy and Elsbeth said their goodbyes to the family and headed for the train back to Berlin. It was a trip of only a couple of hours, but Willy knew he had to rest.

"Do you mind if I take just a brief nap? I promise that we can chat —" Before he could finish his sentence, Willy had fallen into a deep sleep.

Elsbeth thought about this past year. Willy had written some of his most popular and successful songs to date. His compositions *Fräulein Lo* (Miss Lo), *Ein neues Hütchen und neue Schuh – Marie wie geht das zu* (A new hat and new shoes – Marie, what's up with you?), *Frau Maier tanzt Tango* (Mrs. Maier dances the tango), *In Halensee nicht weit von Lunapark* (In Halensee, not far from Lunapark), *Was soll Ich bloß machen?* (For crying out loud, what should I do?) and her personal favorite *Wenn das Wörtchen 'Wenn' nicht wär* (If the tiny word 'if' didn't exist) were playing on the radio and in record stores across Germany. Additionally, he was performing every day and every night at cinemas, at small performance spaces for children, and at the KaDeKo. She knew that her husband was an extraordinary man. Apart from a husband, he was a performer, composer, lyricist, and singer. She considered herself a lucky lady. The train's rhythmic thudding on the tracks and gentle rolling helped Elsbeth join her husband in a sound sleep.

July 1928

"And *Die Goldene Geige* for 1928 is awarded to... Willy Rosen!"

"Willy, you've won!" Elsbeth blurted out joyously, squeezing his arm.

"The Golden Violin. This is unbelievable!" Willy shouted, springing from his chair. Crossing the stage, he nearly tripped over his own feet. The audience broke into laughter when he said, "You need to get that fixed. Someone could be hurt!" Reaching the podium, he shook the hand of the presenter and told the audience, "I would like to thank my wife, Elsbeth, for always supporting me during long days and even longer nights. And my publisher, Will Meisel, who will seemingly publish everything I throw at him. It's his marketing genius that has helped my music sales top the charts these past few years. I would also like to thank my collaborators in song: Kurt Robitschek, Kurt Schwabach, and everyone at the KaDeKo. Without them, I would be just another man searching for his dream. Thank you all very much." Willy returned to his seat, intoxicated with happiness.

Elsbeth wrapped both arms around his neck and tenderly kissed him on the lips. "Well done, my love."

"It can't get any better than this, can it?" Willy said.

September 1928

"Who wants to do the honors?" Kurt Robitschek asked, holding out the scissors to anyone who wished to cut the ribbon.

"I'll do it, thank you," Max Hansen said. After cutting the ribbon, he announced grandly, "Gentlemen, welcome to the new KaDeKo!"

The new *Kabarett der Komiker* was magnificent. Moving from the 450-seat space into a brand new one with 950 seats in the WOGA complex on Lehniner Platz was a fresh start.

"This is the kind of space we have needed for years. No more renting out other theaters when we have big shows," Kurt said, exhilarated with their accomplishment.

Max Adalbert reached for the bottle of champagne sitting in the doorway. "Who wants to christen the place?"

"And waste good champagne? Not on your life. Go get some glasses," Kurt said, laughing, as Willy retreated into the theater and returned with a small stack of paper cups.

"To comedy," said Kurt. "May we always live in a country that laughs."

"To comedy," the others cheered, raising their cups first to the gods of comedy and then to their lips.

"Truly, gentlemen, life is good," Willy reflected, eyeing his empty cup.

And it continued to be good throughout the remainder of 1928 and most of 1929.

October 1929

"Have you seen the papers today?" Willy shouted as he entered the theater. "The American stock market collapsed!"

"Why would we care about that? We're Germany," Max Adalbert said.

"The entire German economy is tied into the American stock market. Remember the Dawes Plan? The American economy is our economy!" said Kurt, who had plenty of friends in New York City. "I'll make some calls right now and see just how bad things are." Kurt left the room as the remaining three contemplated the day's headline.

"They're calling it Black Tuesday. How did they not see it coming?" Paul wondered.

"More importantly, what's it going to do to us?" asked Max, now understanding the consequences.

Kurt ran into the room. "It's bad, guys. We can expect a big hit at some point."

"There is a flip side to all of this," Paul added. "When times get bad, people look to comedy for relief. They'll need to laugh. We've seen this before. People were paying one million Reichsmark for half a loaf of bread, but we still saw record audiences. I knew people who would give up dinner to save their money for a show. We're not programmed to give up everything, even in hard times. And laughter isn't even a luxury. It's a necessity."

Willy nodded. "When Kurt and I were in Düsseldorf, we saw a city shuttered up tightly. However, our performances were packed every night. And I met Elsbeth. See? You never know what good things can come out of a bad situation."

"I get your point. The only way we'll truly know is by waiting it out and seeing what comes. Better yet, who comes," Kurt said, and he gestured toward the 950 seats. "That is my concern. We have to fill this space at every performance."

"We will, Kurt. You'll see," Willy said, as he walked over to the piano to rehearse.

One by one, the others went about their business, now clouded by the uncertainty of Wall Street.

By January 1930, the German economy was in a downward spiral. With their heightened anxiety, people needed to laugh, so they kept the cabarets in Berlin running at a fevered pitch day and night. Cinema revenues were at an all-time high, fueled by the output of high-quality films by the UFA and over 250 other film companies in Berlin alone. Brothels and opium dens opened throughout Berlin, to which authorities turned a blind eye. The constant threat of workers' strikes stoked by the daily rhetoric of the National Socialist Party— now the Nazi Party—kept local police occupied. The Brownshirts became the *Sturmabteilung* (SA), and the even more threatening Blackshirts were the *Schutzstaffel* (SS). Both groups terrorized the country, but no place more than Berlin.

To the Nazis, Berlin was a modern-day Sodom and Gomorrah that threatened the moral fiber of the entire country. Hitler and his party, based in Roman Catholic Munich, viewed such vice as weakness rather than escape. Jews, he felt, were not only the cause of vice but also profited from it, making their work criminal in the eyes of the Nazi Party. All of this played out on a daily basis in front of Willy and his fellow performers, most of whom were Jewish.

April 1930

"Remember, that we are Germans first. They won't turn on their own people. I earned the Iron Cross. Surely that demands respect, even from the likes of them," Willy said with a confidence that seemed to calm the others. "Elsbeth heard the talk, and it seems to be made by only a few individuals. The newspapers are blowing this completely out of proportion."

"I agree with Willy," Paul said. "Look at our receipts. We've only become more popular in the past six months. The economy is bad, but things here are good."

Kurt agreed. He knew they were right about the receipts and the business. KaDeKo was enormously popular. Night after night, the theater was packed with patrons eager to leave their day behind. When he was alone with Willy, he changed the topic. "When do you go to Scala?"

"Tonight, at seven o'clock." Willy was up for the Hit Song Competition again, and was hoping for a repeat of winning The Golden Violin. "Would you like to come? Kurt Schwabach and Elsbeth will be there as well. We could go out afterward."

"Sure, I'd like that," Kurt said.

That evening, Willy picked up his second "Die Goldene Geige" for *Wenn Du einmal dein Herz verschenkst* (Once you give your heart away), making him the first two-time winner in the history of the *Schlagerwettbewerben.*

On their way out of the awards ceremony, Elsbeth asked, "Where to now? I'm hungry. How about the Wintergarten?"

"Sounds good," Kurt Schwabach said, and he turned toward Friedrichstrasse, leading the group as he spoke. "So, I want you all to hear it from me first. I'm going to have to lay low for a bit."

Willy couldn't believe what he was hearing.

"Do you remember that song I wrote back in '20 or '21 with Mischa Spoliansky? *Das Lila Lied* (The Lavender Song)? Kurt Schwabach said.

"I've played it. It is wildly popular with the homosexuals," declared Willy.

"Well, that's the issue," he explained. "I dedicated the song to Dr. Magnus Hirschfeld, but Hirschfeld and all issues surrounding sexuality are now taboo. Hitler's goons are looking for anyone associated with Hirschfeld to harass them. I'm starting to hear things, and I don't like it. I've even heard that Paul O'Montis is being heckled during his performances because he's homosexual."

"Poor Paul. He's an amazing performer," Kurt Robitschek said.

Schwabach was serious. "What I'm saying to all of you, is to watch out."

Willy was adamant. "I don't care. I'm a Jew and I hear things as well. Let's just say that we all have to look over our shoulder from time to time."

"Everyone except Elsbeth," Schwabach said.

"As long as I'm married to a Jew, I consider myself a Jew."

"But the truth is, you're not, Elsbeth. And if things get worse, you may be glad that you're not," Schwabach said, his voice almost angry.

Rather than make the conversation worse, she did not react. "Here we are," she said. "The Wintergarten awaits us, gentlemen. Who's going to get the door for me?"

"Honestly, my dear. Do you really expect them to open the door for a lady?" Willy always found a way to interject humor when it was most needed. "I am the gentleman here."

"Lordy, I need a drink. Shall we?" said Schwabach, bolting for the bar.

August 1931

Kurt Robitschek was in his office at the KaDeKo when he told Willy about being nominated for yet another award, in the *12-O'Clock Sheet*.

"What's the *12-O'Clock Sheet*?" Willy asked.

"It's one of the popular newspapers that comes out at noon, get it? The *12-O'Clock Sheet*?" Kurt could be so condescending. "I would guess, with my educated palette, that you will prevail, Herr Rosen."

"Thanks, Kurt, but don't jinx me. Us. I wonder if Schwabach knows. It's his text. I've got to call him," Willy said, but before he could pick up the receiver, the phone on the desk rang. "I bet that's Schwabach."

Kurt stayed to hear Willy's half of the conversation. "I know. I just saw it, too. Who knew? Congratulations?! Right, so much for keeping a low profile."

It was a short call, and as Willy hung up his smile faded a bit. "I forgot about Schwabach wanting to keep a low profile because of the whole Nazi thing."

"Tell him to start writing shitty lyrics, and then he won't have to worry about it," Kurt joked.

Willy's mind wandered for a little. The only conversation they'd ever had about Hitler and the Nazis was that night on the way to the Wintergarten.

"What if I call the newspaper and ask them to pull our name from the contest?"

"What do you think would happen? The paper's printed. It's out there. The next edition of the *12-O'Clock Sheet* comes out on Monday, when they announce the winner. At this point, you may as well hope that you win. At least that way you both are getting something out of it, right?"

Willy was truly worried for Schwabach. "I guess so, but of all the songs I wrote this year, why this song? Out of the 48 songs I had published in 1931, Schwabach wrote the lyrics for five. What are the odds?"

"I'd say about one in ten."

"Wise guy. Anyway, I had a lot of things put out into the public this year, and a song I did with Schwabach gets on the front page of a noon paper?"

On Monday, it was announced that Willy and Kurt Schwabach had won the contest. Kurt was relieved that the award was presented at the newspaper's office, making his concern of drawing unwanted attention "much ado about nothing."

October 1931

Willy noticed Paul was rather quiet. "What's up, Paul? You're usually tossing insults by this time."

"The Nazis won 18.3 percent. That's the percentage of the Reichstag that belongs to the Nazis."

"That was over six months ago." Willy looked straight at him. "What are we supposed to do? Just remember, if 18.3 percent of the Reichstag are Nazis, that means that 81.7 percent of the Reichstag are not Nazis. Now, I have to practice my parody for this afternoon. Either of you want to go to the cinema with me?"

Max broke out into more laughter, saying, "Not us! Thanks, but we've seen all your parodies at least a dozen times."

Noticing the bag at Willy's feet, Paul asked, "Where are you off to now? Looks like you're going somewhere."

"Elsbeth and I are going to Magdeburg to legally change my name to Willy Rosen. It's time to make it official. I haven't referred to myself as Rosenbaum since I was in the war. So, next time you see me gentlemen, I will officially be Willy Rosen and not Willy Rosenbaum."

"With everything going on, it may be better that way," Max said. "Think about it. Rosenbaum. It screams J-E-W! Rosen, not so much. The Nazis will like Rosen much better and it will be harder for them to decide if you really are Jewish or not. Take my name. Adalbert. Could be Jewish, could be Goy. They'll have to dig deeper to find out. If your name is a 'Baum,' you have an issue. So, Mandelbaum, Kirschbaum, Rosenbaum. You should just put a sign around your neck that reads, 'Here is Willy Rosenbaum, Jew.'"

Willy was mortified. "You don't think that's why I'm doing this, do you? I'm not afraid of being a Jew. I just want the legality of my name cleared up, if for no other reason than for Elsbeth. She's doesn't like that I'm known as Willy Rosen but she's Elsbeth Rosenbaum. When I change my name legally, we'll both be Rosen. Mr. and Mrs. Rosen. Understand?"

"I understand why you're doing it," Max said, "I just wanted you to be aware of the word on the street when it comes to Jews changing their family name. Just... just be careful. And tell Elsbeth I said hi, will you?"

"Thanks, I will." Willy picked up his bag and, after giving Max a troubled look, left to catch a cab to his apartment.

7

December 1931

Kurt and Willy were getting ready to leave KaDeKo for the day. Last night's sales did not look good, and Kurt had a disturbing explanation.

"Look at these numbers. We're not even close. Why do you think we missed our mark?" It was a Saturday night, and the day after Christmas. "By all indications we should have had record takings. Only half of the seats were occupied, and to see you, Claire Waldoff, and Sig Arno perform. Any one of the three should have filled the house, but not now. Let's break it down, okay?"

"Sure, Kurt." Willy wasn't sure he wanted to know, but understood that Kurt needed the support.

"You, Claire, and Sig. Three Jews performing. Claire is a lesbian; Sig is the hottest film comic in the country. We should have at least drawn a large Jewish crowd, and an even bigger percentage of lesbian and homosexuals. And with Sig, the upper-income crowd. But nothing." Kurt was agitated, and becoming more so with each passing second. "We filled one-third of the seats. I don't know if we'll be able to survive this."

Trying to make light of Kurt's premonition, Willy told him,

"Elsbeth was in the crowd and said that even though it was a small audience they were extremely appreciative. That should count for something."

Kurt, his face flushed red, swiped the papers off the desk. "Are you getting this? We're filling one-third of our seats. That's 300 of 950. The box office is becoming a seismograph of political earthquakes. It's the Nazis, Willy. They're killing us!"

Willy finally figured out that Kurt was worried over more than just box receipts. "What are we supposed to do? Maybe 1932 will be better."

"It's not getting better, Willy. It's getting worse. I don't want to be the harbinger of doom here, but if you can't see that things are changing for us... for Jews, for homosexuals, for cabaret, for Berlin... then you need to open up your eyes to what's happening around you. This is all Hitler. His rhetoric is driving us not only off our stages but also out of our homes, our cities, our country."

Kurt's emotions were getting the better of him, and he couldn't keep his tears from welling up. "At first, I thought that the economy was the reason why Berliners have no money. But that's not the truth, is it? The truth is that Berliners are afraid to come out to see Jewish or lesbian performers, afraid that they'll be labeled and harassed by Hitler's thugs. Willy, you have to wake up and see just how bad this is, and that it is only going to get worse for us. It's not just about KaDeKo. It's about Jews." Kurt wiped his face dry with his palm.

"We'll be okay, I promise," Willy said. "Listen, we'll take less money. We'll do what we have to do in order to keep the theater going. People will come, you'll see. It may have absolutely nothing to do with the Nazis."

"Maybe you're right. I sure hope you are." Kurt knew that Willy's optimism was becoming a potentially dangerous hindrance. "But just in case you're wrong, I would recommend that you make plans for where you're going to go if we're all forced to leave Germany."

"Leave Germany? Are you crazy? I'm a German. I have no intention of leaving Germany."

"Have a plan, Willy. You must have a plan if we all need to go."

"Why? Do you?"

Kurt's silence answered Willy's question.

"I'm not going anywhere," Willy spat out. "There will always be a place for the heroes of the war regardless of whether or not they are Jewish. We are Germans first." He was cemented in his steadfast belief that Germany would never turn on its war heroes. It would become his gravest mistake. Willy looked hard at Kurt. "I have to go home. It'll get better, you'll see. 1932."

"I sure hope so. For all of our sakes."

Willy published hit song after hit song in spring 1932 including *Kleine Elisabeth* and *Schenk mir rote Rosen* and the songs for the film "Holzapfel weiß alles". The presidential election on April 10, 1932, brought shocking results to the entire Republic, but nowhere in the Reich was it more unnerving than in the large cities of Berlin, Hamburg, and Leipzig. The Independent General Paul von Hindenburg had been reelected as president of the German Republic during a second run-off election, but Adolf Hitler and his Nazi Party came in second. The Social Democrats, and the Communist Party lagged behind. With no party winning a clear majority and no two parties willing to work together, Chancellor von Papen was forced to declare new Reichstag elections for November 1932. Hitler and his Nazi Party were nearing the end of their slow but consistent rise to power. It would soon be a tidal wave.

Spring 1932

Elsbeth was surprised how Willy seemed to take everything in his stride. At one point, she asked, "Aren't you the least bit concerned about how the elections may affect KaDeKo or your other performances? You never speak about the Nazis to anyone but me. How does Kurt Schwabach feel?"

"He's living in complete fear."

"Do you think perhaps that he may be justified? What does Robitschek think?"

"He's also concerned. The audiences are way down at the theater. I've heard him talking about leaving Berlin and going on tour. Maybe going up to Holland for a while. I even heard talk about America.

Right now, though, he's trying to keep KaDeKo afloat and off the Nazi radar."

Elsbeth worried that Willy wasn't looking at this clearly. "People are afraid to go out at night. If you appear wealthy and the slightest bit Jewish, you're harassed by the SS or SA thugs. Who wants to put up with that? I fear it's only a matter of time, my love, until the KaDeKo is finished."

Willy never wanted to hear about this, but even he knew that each performance had a smaller and smaller audience. He was KaDeKo's biggest—and now only—star. And the problem wasn't just there; no cabaret in Berlin could attract talent or audiences. Willy had heard about gangs of Nazis hanging outside Berlin's gay mecca, the El Dorado, harassing anyone going in or coming out of the club. The El Dorado was where Marlene Dietrich and Claire Waldoff had headlined almost weekly in 1930. Two years later, and the club was at the point of shutting its doors.

He let out a long sigh. "I don't want to think about it, let alone admit it, but I agree. What are we supposed to do, though? These are our friends, and this is our life. Am I supposed to watch my career wither away?"

Elsbeth had finally navigated the conversation to the point she could talk to her husband and know he'd listen. "Willy, my love, I am not saying that you need to sit by and watch as your... as our lives change. But I do believe that we need to have a plan. If things continue to get worse, where can we go? To Magdeburg? I don't think so. If we're seeing it here in Berlin, they're seeing it in Magdeburg too. We have to have some place to go should it get worse for us here in Berlin."

"Worse?" said Willy despondently. *How could it get worse?*

November 6, 1932

Paul and Kurt were going over the KaDeKo numbers from the past weekend's performances. Neither had been sleeping much, and this afternoon's audit had them even more shaken.

"They're blocking people from coming in," Paul said, adamant that he had seen SA troopers stopping people even as they were walking toward the theater. "We've seen it coming now for a year, and it's here. The Nazis are keeping our audience away." They had discussed the bullying tactics of the Nazis more than once.

Kurt said, "I know. We barely get 300 people for a performance now. We can't keep the theater open like this. It's too big a space, and the rent's being raised after the first of the year. What a way to ring in 1933."

"Who do we have for next month?"

"Willy, Max Adalbert, and Max Ehrlich have agreed to come back. We can use Ehrlich again. He's a big calling card, particularly for the visiting Viennese. They love him." Kurt sounded relieved, realizing that the coming month may not be as dark as they were expecting. "We could call it 'Willy and the Two Maxes.' What do you think?"

"It's awful. The only one who will love it is Willy. The Maxes would be fighting about which one was better for the draw."

"Yeah, let's just leave it for now," Kurt agreed.

"Are you going straight home?"

"I was planning to stop at the Wintergarten for a drink. Want to join me?" He needed to get to some sense of normalcy, regardless of what the future might be for his beloved KaDeKo.

There was a moment of silence. "Don't you know what day it is?" Paul asked nervously, which made Kurt tense up.

"Well, I know it's not Hanukkah."

"It's November 6. Election day. Remember?"

"Ah, no, I forgot all about it," Kurt responded, stuffing paperwork into his briefcase. "I'm going straight home."

"You're not going to vote?" Paul asked, shocked that his friend wouldn't jump at the chance to cast a vote against the Nazis. "I am! If they beat me up, at least I will have cast my vote. Come on, there's safety in numbers."

"So, where can we quickly round up 100 Jews?" Kurt asked, not really joking.

On the way to the KaDeKo, Willy stopped to pick up a newspaper. Yesterday's elections were all anyone could talk about, so he had to know the exact results. His face brightened a bit, even though he was cautious not to smile in public. He read that the Nazi Party lost 34 seats in the Reichstag to the communists. While he was still hopeful about his Germany, he could no longer ignore the politics of the moment. *From now on, it's a waiting game*, Willy thought, as he tucked the paper under his arm. When he arrived, he heard Kurt in the back. Willy said loudly, "It's freezing in here! Don't you pay the bills?"

Kurt came out front, seething with anger. "Damn pipes have frozen up and I can't get anyone out here to fix them. I'm telling you, something's up. I took my shower here this morning, and then I went out to pick up the new shoes for the dance number. How can pipes freeze in a few hours unless someone intentionally leaves all the doors open? This was deliberate. I've been calling plumbers to come fix the pipes, but no one is available. Too busy, they say. They're available, but they're just not coming because we're Jews. We've been sabotaged, and no one will help us."

Willy had an idea. "Move the spotlight into the kitchen. You know how much heat that thing puts out. Point it right at the pipe. It'll be thawed in no time. Are all the doors closed?"

"Hell, yes. I don't want anyone else coming in here. We won't have any heat until that pipe thaws out."

"Okay," Willy said, as calmly as possible. "Let's go get something to eat and I can talk to you about this *Lustspiel* I've been working on."

The two arrived at the café, and sat down at a table. Willy continued, "We're going to do something that's not been done before, at least by me. We're going to do two openings at the same time. One in Amsterdam and one in Berlin."

"What? How are you going to pull that one off? Same cast for both productions?" Kurt was intrigued by Willy's plan.

"Yep. I'm planning a June opening for both. I'm working with the Stadsschouwburg in Amsterdam and the Theater an der Behrenstrasse in Berlin." A waiter took their order, and Willy continued. "The way it looks right now, the premiere in Amsterdam will be next June 17, and we'll run through June 24. We'll load the production back up, pull into Berlin on the morning of the June 26, rehearse for two days, and open the Berlin premiere on the evening of June 28. What do you think? Amazing, eh?"

"Amazing? Yes. Exhausting? Yes. You know what the best thing will be about the Dutch opening as opposed to the one in Berlin? The Dutch press. They love the Jews. You'll get publicity about the opening in Amsterdam. That's much more than I can say about the Berlin papers, with the notable exception of the *Jüden-Blätter.*"

Willy was aware that notices announcing performances by Jewish composers, lyricists, comedians—or any Jew in the entertainment field—were becoming less and less common. With a lull in the conversation, the two noticed that the usually bustling restaurant was nearly empty. There was a young woman and man sitting at a table in the far corner with their faces buried in the latest copy of the trendy *12-O'Clock Sheet,* and a man sitting by himself at the bar.

"Doesn't this seem a bit odd, Kurt? Lunchtime on a Monday? The day after a big election?"

Kurt looked around nervously only to see two SA troopers walking past the large picture window. "A bit too odd. And there are Nazis outside. These Nazis make me crazy. I forget what I'm doing, what I'm talking about, where I'm going..." His voice trailed off, trying to watch the troopers with his peripheral vision.

"I understand, but you can't let the fear of the unknown cripple you. We have too much going on right now. The New Year's Eve party at the KaDeKo will be here before you know it." Trying to get Kurt's attention back into the café, Willy asked, "Who do we have scheduled?"

"Coincidentally, it's a Jewish lineup. Erich Ziegler is going to perform. Max Ehrlich will be there, and he'll help draw them in. Claire is singing. If you can call that singing. Oh, and you. We should do something special at the stroke of midnight, right?"

"Of course," Willy agreed. He thought a moment, then added, "As long as we have heat."

"Speaking of heat, we better get back to the theater. We may just burn the place down if we don't check on that spotlight."

Willy arched his back over his chair and called out to the waiter. "Excuse me. Can you cancel our order? We have to get back to work."

"Certainly, sir," the waiter said.

As they stood up from the table, Willy heard the waiter mutter, "Jews."

January 30, 1933

Willy had fallen asleep in his overstuffed chair and covered by his favorite afghan while he and Elsbeth were listening to the radio after dinner. He was startled awake when Elsbeth said loudly, "Willy, wake up!"

"What? What's the matter?" He tried to clear his head as quickly as possible.

"Hitler has just been named Chancellor of Germany by President Hindenburg," she said, her tone sharp. "They announced it on the radio."

"What? What happened to Papen?"

"He's now Vice Chancellor. Hitler has been given instructions to form a government. Willy, this is bad." Elsbeth was shaking with both fear and rage.

Willy, the cobwebs from his slumber now gone, had to consider all of the meaning wrapped within this moment. The Nazis were in charge of everything now. Yes, Hindenburg was still president, but Hitler—that loud-mouthed, brazen hate-monger—would figure out a way to get around him. Hindenburg was old. Hitler was young and powerful, and had armies of loyal followers all reciting the same hate speech he had been spewing for the past several years.

His mind turned toward the KaDeKo. "Kurt is going to lose his mind. You know how he is."

"I know, my love."

Neither had any idea what to say to each other. After several minutes of silence, Elsbeth suggested, as she usually did in such circumstances, "Things will look better in the morning. Let's go to bed."

"I just want to think here for a bit. You go on. I'll be in shortly." Willy stood up to kiss her goodnight. He watched her leave the room, and with a heavy heart sat back down. He was shaken to his core. This was not his Germany. He'd heard all the talk, but he was fine because it wasn't happening to him or anyone he knew. He heard himself say, "But it is happening to us." He realized that he had just verbalized his worst fear. "It's happening to us. But what that is, who knows? It won't be good, and things will change. What did that taxi driver tell me all those years ago? Keep my head down? Well, where can we hide and keep our heads down?"

He reached for the photo from his wedding day, and he stared deeply into the eyes of the man looking innocently back at him. "Why didn't you listen? Why were you so involved in your music that you didn't look up, that you couldn't see what was happening? Why didn't you listen to anyone?" A profound wave of sadness overcame him, and he returned the framed picture to the table and turned off the table lamp. He sat in the darkness of his living room, with the only light coming from a gap in the curtains. Willy shook his head. "Poor Kurt," he whispered.

8

Willy was correct about one thing—Kurt took the news about the appointment of Adolf Hitler rather hard, and for good reason. Within three days, Hitler pulled Germany out of the League of Nations. Leaving the League didn't raise that many eyebrows among most Germans, and actually solidified Hitler's position with his base. However, it was the radio speech that the new Chancellor gave concerning the creation of *Lebensraum* for a master race that scared Kurt and his Jewish friends.

Willy called out to Elsbeth, who was in the kitchen, "Living space for a master race. I'm certain that a master race does not include the Jews."

Elsbeth entered the living room with a midday newspaper. "No, and if that isn't enough to concern us, this will," she said, handing the paper to her husband. "Read the headline."

Across the banner was REICHSTAG BURNS. COMMUNISTS SUSPECTED. "Well, at least they're not blaming it on the Jews," Willy said. "Why would this necessarily concern us?"

"Read on," Elsbeth told him.

The article spoke of Hitler's preparation for a decree that would consolidate all powers under the office of the President, allowed under Article 48 of the Weimar Constitution. Willy stopped reading. "But Hitler's not the President. Hindenburg is. I think this is a good thing because it will keep Hitler's hand out of it."

Elsbeth shook her head at his ability to always see a hopeful side, even when there was no hope. "Hindenburg has no power. It's already in Hitler's hands. Look here," she added, pointing to an article at the bottom of the page. "Hitler has just made a decree which takes away our civil liberties because of the Reichstag Fire!"

"Where is he going with all of this? Hitler now has only Hindenburg between himself and absolute power. Surely, they won't allow that to happen. Would they?"

"Think about who 'they' are. They are the Reichstag, and the Reichstag is under Hitler's control. Hindenburg will fold to the pressure because he's too old to fight back."

Willy knew she was right but couldn't wrap his head around the consequences. "Well, what are we supposed to do? Sit here and wait for the country to be handed to Hitler on a silver platter?"

April 1933

Over dinner in their apartment, Willy said, "Things are going from bad to worse at the cabaret, my dear. Kurt's beside himself. He's even talking about using the cabaret flier *Die Frechheit* to put out some kind of preemptive announcement supporting the new government. He wants to try and fend off a raid or a closure. Or something. He doesn't even know what, but he thinks he must do something. My gut tells me that would be a mistake."

"Is he hoping to get on their good side? There is no good side to them. Look around. Do you see any of our Jewish friends walking the streets? No. They are all afraid to be seen, to be detained, arrested. The word is out, and that word is hide." Elsbeth was worried for her husband more every day. "Willy, you have to keep a low profile."

"You mean I have to keep my head down? I was told that years ago. Hell, I don't even know how to keep my head down. I'm onstage every day and every night. How is that going to facilitate a low profile? We need money, now more than ever. I doubt we'll be able to trust the banks for too much longer. I don't know. Maybe Kurt's announcement would keep things from getting too bad for us."

"Who is us? For you and me? For Jews?"

"I only wish I knew, but let's start with you, me, and the KaDeKo, okay? When we get to the theater tonight, we'll talk to Kurt. Of all of us, he's the one who's been taking the news the hardest. I just hope he doesn't do something irrational."

"You mean like publishing some announcement so everyone will think that all is well in Germany? No. I don't think he would do something like that."

Willy took looked deeply into her eyes. "Do you?"

It wasn't long after Willy arrived at the theater when Paul burst in waving a piece of white paper above his head. He recognized the nameplate for *Die Frechheit*, and the look on Paul's face was a mixture of anger and terror. Willy instantly stopped rehearsal and ran to Paul before he could get onto the stage. Paul shoved the pamphlet into his hand.

"Oh my God. He didn't. Oh, Paul, he didn't," Willy said.

To our Friends in New York, London and Paris!

Many hundreds of copies of our Programs are being sent to Managers, Artists, Newspapers and Magazines in Foreign Countries. By that medium we therefore wish to convey our sincere greetings to all our friends abroad in these days of the Great German National Revolution. At the same time, telling them that:

All the news spread about atrocities and excesses against Jewish Citizens, Jewish enterprises and Jewish Artists are common lies from beginning to end. Wherever irrelevant encroachments of provocatory elements who have nothing to do with the great movement have taken place, the German Government of the National Revolution has re-established order with the utmost dispatch. The National Revolution in Germany has been made by Men of Honor in the service of a great idea. Never has a world-historical act been carried out as pure and without slaughter as the experience of the recent weeks in Germany.

Perhaps, in the course of the general reconstruction of the empire and the consolidation of national ideas, many a single fate will have to go under. Perhaps an important construction law will also meet the artistic director of the "Kabaretts der Komiker." But nothing will obliterate the greatness of admiration for men and ideas which every nation, profession and race would wish for as guides and goals.

In the following weeks, when we welcome artists and friends from abroad to our home, they will be proclaimers and reporters of peace and order in their homeland, which will increase the magnitude of Germany's national uprising above all the events of the last century.

– Kurt Robitschek

When Willy was done, Paul looked at him. "He's lost his mind. What are we supposed to do now?"

"So much for keeping a low profile. We're going to have to stay away from KaDeKo for a couple of days. Get Kurt to close it up, say there's a plumbing issue. We're going to have to find out his true intentions." Willy started to walk back to the stage but turned around to Paul. "Don't show this to anyone else but Hansen and Adalbert. Keep it under your hat until we can get to Kurt, okay?"

"Okay, Willy." Paul folded up the pamphlet and shoved it into his coat pocket.

They looked at each other but didn't know what else to say.

By the time Kurt arrived at the KaDeKo, Paul, Willy, Max Hansen and Max Adalbert had had plenty of time to stew.

"Why? Why would you do this? What were you thinking?" Willy asked, trying to understand why one of his best friends, whom he thought he knew inside and out, would crumble to the Nazis.

"What did you expect me to do?" Kurt replied. "What choice did I have? Have you read Hitler's latest?"

The four shook their heads.

"Well, with the Law for the Restoration of the Professional Civil Service, Jews are out! If you are a Jew or communist, or anyone perceived to be against the new government, you are out of a job and not likely to get a new one," Kurt's words tumbled out of his mouth, and his face was as red as a Nazi armband.

Every bit as agitated as Kurt, Paul shouted at him, "Maybe, but we're not civil servants!"

"Yes, we are. Anyone with a connection to the public, that serves the public in any capacity, is considered a civil servant. Musicians working for the city and state opera houses, concert halls, museums... all will lose their jobs because of an Aryan clause. There's even going to be a separate Jewish Arts Council of some sort, where Jews can only perform for other Jews in theaters and spaces approved by the Nazis. We have to appear to be with them. Don't you understand that's the only hope we have of being left alone?"

"Well, you played your cards poorly, Kurt," Willy said. "If we weren't on the Nazi radar before, we certainly are now. Not all attention is good attention and this is not good attention."

They looked at each other uncomfortably. Paul finally broke the silence, saying, "In the meantime, Willy, you have some premieres to take care of, so let's leave you to it."

They attempted to get back to business as usual, but it simply wasn't possible. Every day there were further restrictions on Jews and Jewish performances.

In May 1933, the former director of the Berlin Municipal Opera, Kurt Singer, and a young production assistant, Kurt Baumann, drafted a proposal to present to the new Prussian Minister of the Interior Hermann Göring. This proposal asked the government to allow the formation of a culture league of German Jews. This would allow the thousands of recently unemployed Jews artists—musicians, actors, dressers, costumers, designers, writers—the ability to perform for Jewish-only audiences.

After weeks of internal arguing among many of Berlin's

prominent Jews, the proposal was sent to Göring, who agreed to it—much to the shock of many, particularly Joseph Goebbels, the new Reich Minister of Propaganda. The league was started in 1933 under the *Jüdischer Kulturbund*, or Jewish Cultural League. The agreement with Göring allowed for the league to organize and perform under three conditions. The first was that it had to be staffed only by Jewish artists and financed by the all-Jewish audiences through a monthly fee. The second was that only the Jewish press was allowed to report on events, further isolating Jewish activities. The third was that Kulturbund programs had to be submitted to Prussian Theater Commissioner Hans Hinkel for approval before each production.

The leaders of the league quickly organized into many departments. The *Kulturbund* would oversee all Jewish performances in Berlin, and as 1933 went on, in every major city in the Reich. Cabaret ownership, as well as performances, by Jews could only take place under the umbrella of the *Kulturbund*. This, of course, meant Kurt Robitschek and his partners no longer ran KaDeKo, and their performers could perform only under the constant scrutiny of the Nazi Regime.

Kurt was not one for being told what to do. "I have to get out of Berlin," he decided. "But to where?"

June 26, 1933

Willy hadn't seen or heard much from Kurt since their argument over the flier, and their subsequent conversation about the new *Kulturbund*. One thing was certain now: his letter had created much more damage than remedy. Throughout the Berlin cabaret community, Kurt's name and reputation was diminished, and he was being called a sell-out to the Nazis. The truth, however, was that things were bad, no matter what Kurt had done.

The fear that Jews felt in Germany was indescribable. It was never more apparent to Willy, having just returned from Amsterdam where there was no social tension. Performers were free to do what they wanted. Louis Davids had told him that there was a high demand for German performers, particularly since the rise of Hitler.

"Willy, I'm not comfortable going back to Berlin," said Elsbeth in their darkened sleeping room. "It's keeping me awake."

"What has you so bothered... the book burning?"

"Yes, of course. Those books were by Jewish authors... dealt with Jewish issues. I even heard that they raided Magnus Hirschfeld's office. Who are these monsters?"

"Elsbeth, Berlin is our home. Germany is our home. I tell you, we're safe. Even with the new civil servant laws, front-line soldiers like me are exempt. They would never harass a recipient of the Iron Cross." There was that unshakable belief again. "I think we should focus on the opening in Berlin. After that, let's go out to dinner with Kurt to see where his mind is at. I've heard he has the cabaret open again under the purview of the Kulturbund. There's a modest increase in attendance so that should please him."

Elsbeth agreed. "If Kurt is doing better, then I'll feel better. We'll use Kurt's emotional state as a barometer for how things have been going in Berlin since we've been in Amsterdam."

September 28, 1933

"How long has *Chauffeur* been playing in Berlin, Willy?"

Kurt had invited Willy to the Wintergarten to catch up. It'd been quite a while since they'd seen each other.

"I can't believe it, but it's been three months." Willy was thankful that his show was still playing in both cities. "What's new with you?"

"It's been hell. I have to get out of here. And you know things are only going to get worse. I'm going to Vienna. I'm leaving Berlin for good, and I want you to come with me." Kurt's look showed unwavering determination—he was going, with or without Willy. "What do you have left here? You have a performance going on that will undoubtedly be forced to close. Then what'll you do? I'm selling the old KaDeKo space to Hans Schindler. He's in the good graces of the Reich, being a non-Jew, and he believes he can keep it going."

Willy let his mind wander to the New Year's Eve party again, when all of them—Kurt, Paul, Max Hansen, Max Adalbert, and his beloved Elsbeth—watched acts, laughed, hugged, and toasted to a

1933 that would be the best year to date. "Funny how fate works, isn't it, Kurt?"

"Funny? I would say... sad. Unfair."

"Vienna? Can we stay at the Grand Hotel again?" Willy asked, trying to lighten the mood.

"Not on your life. We have to save everything we earn and spend as little as possible, just in case the Austrians end up bowing to German pressure and we have to leave there too. Our best bet will be to convince as many Jewish performers as we can to go with us. We'll form a troupe again, just like before."

"Die Prominenten!" Willy exclaimed. "What better than to call a troupe of celebrities than what they actually are? Just the name Theater of Celebrities itself will be the draw as well as our calling card."

"Clever. That's very clever. So now the big question. When do you think Elsbeth will let you leave?"

October 1933

Willy had agreed to go with Kurt, but he found himself deeply anguished on the train trip to Vienna, as Elsbeth thought it wiser for her to stay in their apartment. She knew that, once vacated, a Jewish apartment was confiscated and turned over to a non-Jew. With Willy's parents still in Magdeburg, she knew that her place was in Berlin.

In Vienna, Kurt and Willy shared a room at the small Bahnhof Hotel, where travelers arriving from the train station stayed. "So much for having a hotel room that impresses people," Kurt said, as if he knew what Willy was thinking. "But this time if anyone joins us, it will be for the same reason that we are doing this. To be able to perform wherever we want and use whatever material we want, with no Hitler or Göring."

Kurt seemed emboldened by their move, even though they were in Vienna less than two hours. Willy, on the other hand, was lonely and depressed. He missed Berlin, he missed Germany, and most of all he missed his wife. "What now, Kurt?"

"We have to get the word out. Once it does, they'll be coming to us, I guarantee you." Kurt exuded such an air of confidence.

Maybe this will be a good thing, Willy thought.

Within 20 minutes of arriving at the hotel room, Kurt called Szöke Sakall, Max Ehrlich, and Rosy Barsony, who he knew were seeking refuge in Vienna. They jumped at the opportunity to join the Kabarett der Prominenten. Within three weeks, the Cabaret of the Celebrities was the most popular cabaret troupe in Austria, filled with famous stars looking to escape Germany, including Siegfried Arno, Franz Engel, Oskar Karlweis, Otto Wallburg, Trude Berliner, and Rita Georg.

The Kabarett der Prominenten toured Austria, Hungary, Czechoslovakia, and Switzerland, and anywhere else where they had artistic freedom. During the tour, Willy became close friends with the famous actor-comedian Max Ehrlich, also a Berliner and someone who spoke frequently of going back to Germany. They spent hours reliving the days of Berlin cabaret when there were pure, artistic creations, many spontaneous and unplanned. They longed for the work of true genius night after night.

December 1933

After a performance in Basel, Kurt, Max, and Willy headed for the Café Lucht. Shortly after sitting down, Willy said, "I've got to get home... to Germany." He sounded as desperate as either man had ever heard him.

Max agreed. "I'm going, too, as soon as possible. When this tour returns to Vienna, I'm going back to Berlin. Things back home aren't as bad as they were. At least that's what I've heard."

"I know. Elsbeth says the city's calming down, but only because of the Nazi troops. She says they are on every street corner at all hours of the day. She says I wouldn't recognize the city... how clean and progressive things are." Willy noticed the shocked look on Max's face, and quickly added, "Out of fear, Max."

Max looked relieved, wondering for a moment if Willy's wife admired the work of these thugs.

"I'll never go back to Berlin. I'll go anywhere else, but not back to Germany. If you two are thinking seriously of going back, count me out," Kurt said defiantly. Neither Willy nor Max was surprised at his reaction.

"Where will you go, Kurt? We only have a few weeks left of the tour. Are you staying in Vienna?" Max asked.

"I'm going to Prague. I'm going home. I doubt that the Nazis will bother me there. If they do, I'm off to New York."

"Seriously?" Willy said. "What would you do in New York? I would have no idea where to even start to reinvent myself in America."

"Germans are flocking to America. Hollywood, New York, Chicago. There's so much to offer and best of all, no Nazis," Kurt explained.

"If I had to leave Europe, I would go to Cuba."

"Why Cuba?"

"The weather and the women," Willy responded with a grin.

It reminded Kurt of the old days when the only worry they had was where to have dinner.

Willy turned to Max and continued the earlier conversation. "What will you do in Berlin?"

As sure as Kurt had made plans, so had Max, who said, "Cabaret. It's what I do and it's what the Jews need. Seems there's so little to laugh about these days."

"Maybe I could write some music for you when you get established back, eh, Max?"

Kurt looked straight at Willy. "Right back into the days of *Text und Musik von Mir!*"

"And I'd get to see Elsbeth," Willy said. "I'm concerned about the Nazis, though."

"Willy, you can't go back to Berlin permanently. You just can't. I know Elsbeth is there, but you're going to have to consider finding another home."

Max worried even less than Willy about the Nazis. "If you like, you could just write the stuff. I'll take care of the rest. Me? I'm not one to hide. I just can't continue to keep my head down and do nothing."

There was that phrase again. Keep your head down. Willy was not going to escape hearing this. "Where should I go? What country is truly safe? Switzerland?"

"You enjoyed Zurich when you were there, so why not? It's clean and safe. And if you can establish a permanent address, you may be able to apply for a work visa. That's much more difficult, but maybe Zurich would be a good place to make a home."

Willy knew that Kurt was looking out for him, but the idea of making a permanent home somewhere without Elsbeth, and not in Berlin, was nearly unthinkable. He took a long time to respond. "Okay, I'll go to Switzerland. But I'm not going to stay away from Berlin. I'll come back, if only to see Elsbeth or bring you music, Max. When I'm there, I'll keep my head down and stay in the apartment. You won't see much of me, but it'll be better than staying away from Berlin altogether."

Kurt looked at the pair with some admiration, but was resolved that he would not face the forces wreaking havoc upon the Jews of Germany. "I'll miss you, Willy. A lot. We've been through times, haven't we?"

Willy looked at Kurt, not believing what he was hearing. "It doesn't mean we'll never see each other again. Does it?"

Kurt looked down into his coffee cup. He glanced at Willy long enough to notice his friend's eyes watering. "Doesn't it?"

9

Willy spent much of 1934 and 1935 performing abroad, primarily in Vienna and Zurich, both of which held an ever-increasing German ex-pat community of wealthy Jews seeking a place familiar and safe from the increasing Nazi threat. Between gigs, he would return to Berlin, where the formation of the *Jüdischer Kulturbund* moved at a snail's pace. He had no choice but to keep performing on foreign soil, and the constant traveling took a physical and emotional toll. When he was home in Berlin, exhaustion kept him from spending quality time with friends and his beloved Elsbeth.

May 1935

The phone rang, nearly knocking Willy out of his chair. *How long has it been since anyone's called?*

"Brabant 612," Elsbeth answered, and then listened to an animated voice on the other end of the line. "Hold on, I'll get him," and said to Willy, "It's Max Ehrlich. Something about a revue."

Willy and Max had a brief conversation, after which Willy hung up, put on his coat, and told Elsbeth he was leaving for a bit.

"Does he want you to write for him?" Elsbeth always worried

when Willy went out, yet she knew that he couldn't stay in their small apartment, as much as she wanted him to.

"Yes, he does. I'm going to meet him at Café an Nestorstrasse. He has some news about the Nazis and cabaret I should know. You know I have another appointment, so I'll get both things done today. I'll be back in a bit." Willy kissed his wife, put on his hat, and left.

Walking up the steps to the café, Willy could see Max through the large window. He looked just as he had one year earlier; no, actually he looked better. Rested. He must have enjoyed performing his revues in Holland. As soon as he was inside, Willy extended both arms to hug his friend by the shoulders, telling him, "You look great."

"Nice to see you too," Max said. He was never one to give a compliment if he hadn't received one first. "You're looking well. How was Switzerland? How's Elsbeth?"

"Zurich isn't Berlin, but it's safer and I can perform there. Elsbeth is doing well. She doesn't like my going out, but it's necessary."

"It is, Willy. So the Nazis, or I should say Hermann Göring, is missing his favorite entertainment and wants it back."

Because he knew what was meant, Willy laughed before saying, "You mean the young men he's seeing day-to-day have too many clothes on?"

"Good one," Max said. "Use that. No, don't use that. As a matter of fact, just forget that one altogether. Anyway, he's letting Jews open a few cabarets around Berlin. Nothing like the KaDeKo, but it would still be cabaret." Max was clearly elated at the news. Willy was skeptical.

"Where would these cabarets take place?"

"Most *Kleinkunstbühne* will be small artistic spaces, where the Nazis would allow Jews to perform. I told you back in Basel that as long as there is a stage, I feel I owe it to our community, the Jewish community, to make them laugh." After studying Willy's face, he added, "Let's do something together. We'll do a revue and premiere it at the Café Leon. We'll call it *Kunterbunt*. Colorful. You'd write the songs, I'd do the comedy and act as a sort of emcee. What do you think?"

Willy was intrigued, and he so missed performing and the

camaraderie among cabaret artists. *"Kunterbunt* it is," he said. "How many songs do you need, and when do you need them by?"

Max was delighted. "Welcome back, Willy," he said, picking up the check. "It's the least I can do."

"Thank you," Willy responded while checking his watch. "I have to go, but let's reconnect soon, okay? I have to get to my recording session."

Jews weren't allowed to make records, so Max was confused. Keeping his voice low too, he asked, "What? Where are you recording? You know it's against the law, right?"

Raising his index finger to his lips, Willy leaned in and said in a hushed voice, "Yes, I know. Lukraphon Records has set up a primitive recording studio in the basement of an old synagogue." He made sure that no one was eavesdropping. "I'm recording some songs there. Hopefully, they'll make it out onto the airwaves. Call it a bootleg recording, but it's better than nothing." He was resolute in his decision to record, even against Nazi policy.

"You know best. Just promise you won't get picked up and taken away before you finish my music," Max said. "You take care, and keep your head down while you're doing this."

Willy was beginning to hate the phrase. On his way home from the recording session, Willy felt his step was lighter and his mind was clearer. He was making music again. And the prospect of performing new songs on a cabaret stage added to his renewed sense of self-worth.

September 1935

After a brief morning outing, Willy unlocked the door of his apartment and overheard Elsbeth on the phone saying something about Nuremberg Laws. By the time he walked into the living room, she was sobbing and collapsed in a chair.

"Why are you crying? And what are these Nuremberg Laws?" Willy was both trying to figure out the politics of the moment and comfort his wife.

"The laws now say that relationships between Jews and non-Jews are forbidden," Elsbeth explained, but she could barely get out the words through her heaving breaths.

Willy pulled her tightly into his chest. "It'll be all right, my dear. I'm certain that they don't mean couples already married." He was again showing his naivety.

"It specifically says all relationships, current and future. What are we going to do?"

What he said next would be critical, so he took a few seconds to think by first drying her cheeks with his handkerchief and then looking unwaveringly into her eyes. As much as they wanted to make Berlin their home, they weren't willing to stay if they couldn't be married.

"I'm going to work on a plan to get us both out of here. I'll ask around, but I suspect that some of our friends have already begun to figure out an exit strategy." Willy found himself remarkably calm. "It's September. I've agreed to write a revue with Max that's will open in December, so over the next four months, we'll figure out something. By the time we reach New Year's Day, we can welcome 1936 with a solid strategy. What do you think?"

He had finally calmed Elsbeth, who was breathing normally. She wiped the last of her tears away. "In the meantime, my love, you can't stay here. We can't be seen together. It's going to have to look as if we got a divorce, a separation or something. Go on tour to Zurich. Write your revue there. You mustn't stay here in Berlin."

"I know... I'll work it out with Max." Willy kissed Elsbeth. "I'll always be with you, even if I'm not physically here. You know that, right?"

"I do. Willy, know that I love you very much."

"So, why don't we go out to dinner, my dear. Let's get out of this apartment. And I need to look at a stage at Café Leon."

Elsbeth looked surprised. "Café Leon?" she asked.

"Long story. I'll tell you as we walk. I'm hungry. Aren't you?"

One reason for the Reich to allow the return of Berlin's Jewish cabaret scene was the 1936 Olympics. With hundreds of thousands of tourists from around the globe visiting the German capital, Hermann Göring, as the Prussian Minister of the Interior, knew that there had to be other things for visitors to do, and entertainment would play a key role in keeping them occupied at night. Göring's other reason involved propaganda concerning the restrictions placed on German Jews. He recognized that if Germany's most famous Jewish performers were seen in their element by the scrutinizing eyes of the world, then even the harshest critics of Jewish treatment outside the Reich would soften their rhetoric.

October 1935

The two men had agreed to meet up at Café Leon, which is where Max explained to Willy why Jews were suddenly allowed to perform again outside of their limited spaces.

Trusting Max's assessment of the situation, Willy nodded his consent. Max then leaned in so closely to his ear that Willy could feel his breath. "Once we re-establish ourselves on the German stage and build our brand internationally, we leave. Willy, this must be part of a bigger plan to get out of Germany while we're smiling and laughing and keeping the tourists happy. The authorities will only be concerned with what we do on stage, not off. We need to make plans."

"I don't have a plan, yet. I know that Kurt and Ilse went to Prague, but what's your plan? Does Szöke have a plan? Am I the only one without one?"

"Shhhh, not so loud," Max hissed. "You never know who's listening." He leaned in even a bit closer. "Aren't you still working out of Switzerland?"

Willy whispered, "Zurich. Yes. Why?"

"Zurich is perfect! Since you work in Switzerland, you have a better chance of getting a work visa to stay permanently. You have to apply immediately. With any luck, by the time the Olympics are over, and Jews are forced back into the shadows, you and Elsbeth will have a permanent place to stay. Swiss neutrality would guarantee that."

Had Max figured this out beforehand? Had he developed a plan for Willy and Elsbeth to get out of Germany safely and together?

"You're famous enough that the Swiss should recognize the importance of your work. But you're also famous enough that the German authorities wouldn't want you to be seen running away. It could be perceived as a black mark on the cultural life of the Third Reich."

Willy was frustrated by this addendum to the plan. "So, what you're saying is, I'm damned if I do and I'm damned if I don't, correct?"

"That would be an accurate assessment, I think," Max said. "The question is, will the Swiss bow to the pressure of the Reich? There's no way to find out unless you do it. However, if the Swiss turn you down, you'll have to leave Berlin immediately. Plan A will have failed, and you'll be on the Reich's radar as someone of prominence attempting to leave. You'll need a Plan B, too."

"Plan A, Plan B? How did you get this far, and I'm only now thinking about how to create any plan?" His voice got louder again.

"Softly, Willy. If you don't mind my saying, you've been hiding behind your Iron Cross. Make a Plan A, a Plan B, even Plans C and D if you need to. But you must have a plan to save yourself. In a worst-case scenario, Elsbeth will be fine. She has no Jewish blood even though she's married to a Jew. She's safe. Well, as safe as any non-Jew is in Berlin these days."

Max could see the terror on Willy's face; his eyes were enormous, and his bottom lip quivered. Max had to act quickly to keep things looking normal. "Listen, if things with the Swiss go poorly, then you'll come with me. You and I will go to Holland. Amsterdam first, then we can do the summer season at the Grand Hotel in Scheveningen. How does that sound?"

Willy was mortified at the state of things. He had only just talked to Elsbeth about leaving, even though she'd been worried for quite a long time.

"Thanks, Max. Thanks for everything. I owe you so much. I'll get our applications prepared for the Swiss and keep my fingers crossed. If that doesn't happen, then it's the Grand," Willy said. Perhaps with the help of his friend, he had come up with a way out of Germany. "Now, what are we looking to do for *Kunterbunt*?"

December 1935

Max and Willy's revue *Colorful* opened on December 3rd, not far from where the large KaDeKo continued to give cabaret performances by and for the non-Jewish population of Berlin. Their revue opened as the city and country prepared for the Olympic Games to start on August 1, 1936. For the Jews of Berlin, the Olympics meant a brief respite from fear. With the eyes of the world on Berlin, even Hitler would be hesitant to show animosity toward the Jewish community.

Willy immediately started on his Plan A by returning to Zurich to live and applying for a Swiss work visa. To bolster his application, he founded a small performing company based in Zurich that traveled to all the major Swiss cities. He continued traveling back and forth to Berlin to write songs and lyrics for the second of their joint revues, which was set to open on February 4, 1936—just as the first masses of foreign visitors were to descend upon the city.

After a performance close to the end of the run of the revue, Max invited Willy to his apartment to discuss the coming months. Being an "employee" of the Reich via the *Kulturbund*, Max and his wife, Charlotte, were allowed to stay in their apartment. At least there was that benefit.

With a drink in his hand, Willy asked, "What are your plans, Max, after this revue closes? What'll you do for the summer?"

"I'm staying here in Berlin. Are you off to Scheveningen?" Max looked as if he were a lost puppy, ready to beg Willy to stay with him.

"Yes, I'm off for the season. However, if you'll have me, I'll keep writing the revues for you. I can go back and forth to deliver the material, and even help rehearse. Elsbeth won't leave Berlin until our plans are in place for fear of losing the apartment. So, I'll need to be here on and off throughout the summer."

"Wonderful," Max said, with a tremendous smile that lit up his eyes. "Have you heard from the Swiss yet?"

"No, but I should hear something anytime now. I just hope that it's sooner rather than later. The more occupied the Nazis are with the Olympics, the less focused they may be on the visa applications," Willy said, although he knew the Reich had dozens of resources to scrutinize the applications of every Jew in the country. Not wanting to think about the Reich, the Swiss, and his visa, he changed the topic. "Is your revue ready for music yet? If so, I can start to work on it right away. I assume I'm in the cast?"

Max nodded his approval before polishing off the remains of his cocktail.

Summer 1936

"The Swiss denied us, Max. I just found out the other day. I'm applying for Cuban visas now. I hear that they're easier to get."

"Easier, yes, but still not easy. Have you applied yet?"

"I stopped by the Cuban Embassy and picked up our paperwork on my way here. I'll fill it out on the train back to Amsterdam. Elsbeth would rather go to Brazil where my sister Lucie and brother-in-law, Rudolf, are, but Cuba seems to be the easiest plan. It may be Plan B, but at least it's a plan."

Changing the subject to something lighter, Max said, "Well, the Kulturbund has asked us to coordinate another performance, so I thought about another revue to run during March or April 1937. Is Meisel still on board to publish?"

"I believe so. I sure hope that doesn't change. I'm meeting with him tomorrow before I go back to Zurich. I'll keep you posted. For now, I'm off to dinner with Elsbeth."

"Well, be careful and keep your head down," Max said, knowing full well the effect that phrase had on his dear friend.

Willy smiled. "And you keep your head down as well. After all, you're the one living in the lion's den."

"Thanks for the reminder."

The following day, as Willy climbed the stairs to the offices of Meisel Musik Verlag, he overheard a loud and angry conversation. When he got to the office door, he recognized one of the voices as

Will's. The other voice was unknown, and much calmer. The door flew open, and an outraged Will shoved out a Nazi Brownshirt.

"You may come back when you learn how to speak to me properly," Will said aggressively. The fearlessness that he was showing to a soldier of the Reich amazed Willy.

"Just know, Herr Meisel, that we will be watching everything that you publish. Let this small discrepancy be a warning. If you continue to publish works by Jews, you will be shut down by the orders of Göring himself." With that, the Brownshirt brushed past Willy and down the stairs.

"What the hell was that all about?" asked Willy.

"What do you think? It's a mess here. Do you know they won't even let me release a new edition of Mendelssohn's *Songs Without Words*? Unbelievable. He's Jewish, they say. Well, he converted, and he's been dead for almost 90 years. What are they afraid of?" Will retreated into the sanctuary of his office.

Willy followed, dreading the conversation about to take place, considering what he had just witnessed.

"I'm sorry," Will said, looking at his friend. "I'm sorry you had to see that."

"It's all right. It must be hard."

"It is hard. They scrutinize everything. Every song published, every edition released. 'Why do we need another edition of that Jew's music?'" he said, gesturing out into the hallway. "Can you believe that?" Will was livid.

"So, where does that leave me?" *If he can't publish Mendelssohn, he certainly can't publish Rosen.*

"Better than Mendelssohn! I can publish what you've given me. The people are clamoring for it. Even the Nazis realize that there still must be popular music published, and your songs were approved before they went to the stage. Believe it or not, it's easier to get a Rosen song published than a Mahler or a Bruckner."

Willy breathed a bit easier. So far, he only had the revue numbers and a few songs published in 1936. It was not a profitable year in publications. Performances, yes. Publications, not so much. "Will you be able to publish the revues we have slated for spring?" Willy felt a bit more confident asking.

"Yes, we just need to get them out as soon as possible. Many of my composers are leaving Germany, which makes for too few compositions to publish. Of course, there's no end to the amount of Aryan drivel that comes across my desk," he said, gesturing at three particularly tall stacks of manuscripts. He promptly shoved all three into the carefully placed trash bin next to his desk.

Willy was astonished once more at the brazen action of his publisher. He wondered why he wasn't as strong. "Thanks, Will. I'm very grateful. You know that, right?"

"I do. Just get me those songs as soon as you can. I'll get them in print right away."

March 1937

Bitte Einsteigen, Max and Willy's third revue for the Kulturbund was billed as *"Eine Reise in 23 Stationen von Willy Rosen und Max Ehrlich"* (A Journey in 23 Stations by Willy Rosen and Max Ehrlich) and premiered at the *Kleinkunstbühne Loganhaus an Kleinstraße* on March 28, 1937 where it played until it was relocated to the *Kleinkunstbühne Brüdervereinshaus an Kurfürstenstraße* for its final two performances on May 29 and 30. Since it was a sanctioned performance, the crowds were enthusiastically large and exclusively Jewish. "Why would they only let us perform twice?" Willy asked, frustrated that there was audience enough for another two-month run.

"We don't get to ask those questions. All we can do is nod, thank them, and hopefully be granted another opportunity to perform. This was a great revue, so who knows? Maybe we'll get another chance to put it on." Max thought that they might be allowed to run it the following month.

"I'll tell you what. It's going to play again, because I'm taking it to Holland. This is it for me. I'll help you in any way I can, but I'm out of here. At least in Holland, Jews can do what they please," Willy said, having already made the decision to remount the revue in a friendlier location. Since being denied a work visa in Switzerland, he'd spent the past few months in Amsterdam doing performances at the Stadsschouwburg. His Plan A for now was to stay in Holland. "I have to go. Elsbeth's waiting outside. Want to go to dinner? We're just going up the street. Nothing fancy before I head for the train station."

"No thanks. I'm going to stay here and clean things up a bit. Best to keep my mind occupied. See you soon?" Willy was puzzled by Max's question, since they had earlier discussed plans for another revue in Berlin.

"Of course, my friend."

As Willy and Elsbeth walked to dinner he noticed she was quieter than usual for a closing night. There were no questions about what the next revue would be, or when it would go up. Nothing. "What's wrong, my dear? The show was good, wasn't it? I know it's always sad when it ends, but there'll be another," he said, prodding her to talk.

"Will there be? Where? Not in Berlin," Elsbeth said. Although it had been her idea for Willy to leave Berlin, his absences always frightened her.

"Elsbeth, I'll return as often as I can. I promise. Remember, you'll be in Amsterdam on June 15, so we'll see each other in a couple of weeks." Willy was trying anything to ease the tension, but he knew where this conversation was going.

"It's not that. But Berlin... Germany. It can never be your home again... our home again. It will always be somewhere else. This week, Holland. Next week, who knows?"

"We'll get through this, I promise. As long as there are trains, we'll get through this. You could always come with me. We could give up the apartment in Berlin."

"No, we can't give up the apartment as long as your parents are in Germany. If I leave, we're breaking our ties completely, and we can't do that to them. If things get too bad in Magdeburg, they can come and stay with me."

Willy grew sentimental at his wife's dedication to his parents. "This is just one fraction of why I love you, Elsbeth. You think of everything."

"And I love you. We'll eat, you'll catch your train, and I'll go home and sleep. Everything will look better in the morning, my love," she said, even though she looked particularly solemn.

Having reached the restaurant, Willy opened the door and, after a kiss on her lips, gently led Elsbeth into the café.

10

May 1937

Willy was excited as he and Siegfried Arno entered the elevator and descended to the lobby of the Grand Hotel in Scheveningen. The hotel would finally have a real cabaret space created in the lower-level catacombs of its massive structure. The Lutine Palace would serve as another popular cabaret space without disturbing performances in the main hall of the hotel.

Sig was a Jewish actor and top draw in German films, but he left Berlin because of Nazi censorship, as did his cohort and film collaborator Otto Wallburg. Both Sig and Otto, film stars with international reputations, would be doing their comic routines as part of the 1937 summer series known as Theater der Prominenten. Willy had originally created the Theater of Celebrities with Kurt Robitschek, but now he was running it by himself.

"Where is Otto?" Sig asked.

"Out on the deck, smoking a cigar and having a drink. Where else?" Willy said, shrugging.

As if on cue, an enormously loud laugh rang through the lobby of the hotel, rattling drink glasses on their tables. Again, the two erupted into laughter.

"Otto, you're here," Sig called from across the wide space, holding his arms open as if to embrace him from where he stood.

"As if we didn't know," Willy said, attempting to control his laughter.

Sig and Otto enjoyed a happy reunion until Willy said, "Hey, guys, let me show you the Lutine Palace."

They walked to the east wing of the hotel where a small gilded elevator stood alone in a marble wall. After the short elevator ride, the trio emerged: The walls of the Lutine Palace were painted in shades of blue, green, and turquoise, with colorful fish and sea creatures in plaster relief. Tables held small seashell-shaped candle holders set in the center of tablecloths that matched the walls. Sconces of bronze seashells let out just enough pinpoints of light to add to the aquatic ambiance.

Sig and Otto looked around in disbelief, then at each other. In perfect unison they said, "It's small."

"It is small," Willy agreed. "Narrow and long, like a bike track. But think of it this way. All the more intimate an experience for our audience."

Sig and Otto were elated with the prospect of a summer of consistent employment, as both actors had been censored by the Reich and were desperate for work. News of the Theater der Prominenten had traveled quickly and had attracted the pair.

"This is great. We appreciate the work," Sig said, biting his lip.

"Don't thank me, Sig. We all need each other during these times. Right, Otto?" The two had lost track of their friend. Willy said louder, "Otto?"

"What?" Otto came out from behind the stage curtain, leaving the tell-tale trail of cigar smoke.

Willy said, "Let's go back upstairs. I could use a drink. Hey, did you notice they named the cigar room after Louis Davids? I want a room named after me one day."

"Careful what you wish for, Willy," said Otto, taking a long puff on his cigar. "Louis can't smoke anymore. Asthma, it seems."

"That's a lesson for you to learn, Otto," said Sig, as the three headed for the bar.

May 15, 1937

Opening night for *Bitte Einsteigen* went well, and the newspaper *Het Vaderland* published its review the following day. Willy read the review to his cohorts over breakfast. " 'The Lutine Palace's room is too small for a revue and too long for a cabaret! Rather, the conglomeration by Willy Rosen is a handsome piece of craftsmanship. The cast have the means to make such a firework of jokes and sentiments a success.' That's a good review."

"I think it went well, but boy, that space is tight," Sig said, making a point of the obvious. "The lights are right on top of you, aren't they?"

Willy brought the conversation back around to the performance. "Look at it this way. We'll only get more comfortable as we perform. The next revue opens in a couple weeks."

"No rest for the weary, eh?" Otto intoned as he lit up another cigar.

"Why don't you smoke that out on the veranda?" Willy asked.

Otto looked at the two of them, not sure if he should be insulted, and decided that wasn't a bad idea.

After Otto was out of earshot, Willy said, "Listen, Sig, next month is Otto's 25th year in the industry. I thought it would be nice to have a special performance honoring him. Ask as many of his old actor friends to come as we can locate."

"That'll be quite a task. They're scattered all over the world now. Most of his non-Jewish friends are still in Germany. The others? If they're not here in Holland, they're most likely in America. Or who knows where." Sig mulled the thought over in his head, and got excited. "I know who to ask. I'll call Anny Ondra in Berlin. She'll be the best person to round up the German contingency and invite them here. What day are you thinking of?"

"July 10, a Saturday, so most of the people could get here on Friday night. It would be a complete surprise."

"He'll love it, Willy. I'll call Anny and let her know what we're planning."

"Tell her I said hi, okay? And tell her I look forward to seeing her and her husband, so they both better come."

"I'll tell her. Better watch Otto. He's making his way toward the buffet again."

"That man will cost this hotel a fortune in cigars, food, and liquor. At least he's funny," Willy said, walking toward the buffet line.

June 16, 1937

The reviews for *Hinter den Kulissen* were as positive as they were for its predecessor, *Bitte, Einsteigen*. The following morning, the *Haagsche Courant* referred to the opening of the second revue of the Theater der Prominenten as a "Baptism where joy and laughter were everywhere in the air!"

Willy, in particular, was thrilled with the reference to of one of his numbers, sung my Sig Arno.

"Willy Rosen, author of the text and music, garnered the lion's share of success. The new song *Wir richten uns eine Wohnung ein* (We set up a flat) will soon become very popular. There was no spectator, as there was no one in the entire audience who did not leave the Lutine Palace quietly singing."

"Nice job, Willy. It's great that they liked the songs so much," Sig said, and he was especially pleased because he got to perform them.

"I heard from Anny this morning. She's on board and will spend the next few days contacting our old buddies around Berlin. Max and she will arrive on Monday, July 5 under the guise of a vacation. With that, there's no way Otto would suspect others arriving as well. He'll be completely occupied with the show during the day and entertaining Anny and Max in the evening. It couldn't have worked out better."

"I'm so glad that they can come. They're a wonderful couple. I only hope that Max doesn't cause a media uproar by being here."

Sig looked surprised. "Any attention Max and Anny get will only work in favor of the revue. I think it's perfect."

"You're right. It's fabulous planning. I can't wait to see Otto's face when he enters the room on Saturday afternoon."

"Listen. I gotta run." Sig said.

Willy found himself alone with his thoughts. Anny was one of the most recognized German film stars of the Republic and, because she wasn't Jewish, she still had her star status. As big a celebrity as she was, however, her husband of four years was even bigger. But then again, she was married to the heavy-weight boxing champion of the world Max Schmeling.

Back in Berlin, Anny, Max, Willy, Max Ehrlich, and others would frequently have dinner after the movie studio shut down for the weekend, sharing stories of Anny and Willy's rising fame and Max's latest conquests in the boxing ring. Ehrlich's newest jokes would keep the table in a constant state of laughter.

Willy slipped into melancholia, yearning not just for his past life but also for Elsbeth, whose dedication to his parents kept her in a life of near solitude in Berlin. After a few minutes of burning loneliness, Willy went to the concierge's desk. "Can I get an international line? Berlin. Brabant 612. Thank you."

The concierge dialed, and handed him the phone.

After several rings, he heard, "Brabant 612. Hello?" Elsbeth's voice grew higher, instinctively knowing who was on the other end.

"Hello, my dear! How are you?" Willy could hardly get the words out.

"Willy! My love! How are you? What have you been doing? I miss you. When are you coming back for a visit?" Elsbeth spoke quickly, grasping for contact with her husband.

"I'll do you one better, my dear. Why don't you pack your bags and come to Scheveningen? Anny Ondra and Max Schmeling are arriving on Monday, July 5. Why don't you call her and arrange to travel with them? You can stay for the week or the month. The longer, the better. You need to get out of there, and I need to see you."

"Oh, that'd be wonderful. Goodness, that only gives me a week to get things ready. I'll ask Dieter to check on the apartment while I'm gone, and I'll call Anny right away to organize my train ticket."

"Who is Dieter?" Willy asked, searching his brain for a reference.

She was surprised that he'd forgotten their neighbor's son so soon. "Do you remember the boy who lives below our unit? Mrs. Schaeffer's son? That's Dieter."

"But he's just a boy, barely ten years old."

"Ten? Willy, he's nearly 16 and is extremely responsible. He's a good boy. I'll ask him to occasionally check the door to make sure no one has broken in."

"Broken in? Elsbeth, what are you not telling me? Have things been that bad in Berlin for you? If so, you must tell me!"

"No, my love. Nothing has happened to me. However, there are reports. I hear things. Some non-Jewish women married to Jews have come home to find that someone has broken into their apartment. Nothing's ever taken. The hoodlums seem to want only to scare them. They tear up a few things and leave the apartment a mess, that's all. I'd feel better if Dieter would keep an eye on the place while I'm gone. Is that okay?"

Not wanting to show his anger and frustration with the state of affairs in Berlin, he said, "Of course. You just call Anny and let her help you with a ticket."

"I'll call her right now. You take care, and I'll see you next week." She didn't want the call to end. "I love you, Willy. Don't ever forget that."

"How could I, my dear? I'll never let you stop telling me." He became serious, and added, "I love you too."

After he hung up, Willy couldn't stop worrying about Elsbeth. He left the concierge desk to find Sig in the cigar room. "Sig, there may be problems for Elsbeth back in Berlin. I'm having her come here with Anny and Max. I asked her to call Anny to help with coordinating the travel so they could come together. Would you do me a favor? Call Anny to make sure that if they've already bought their tickets, that they get one for Elsbeth as well? I'll pay them when they get here."

"Sure, I better call her right away." Sig immediately walked to the concierge's desk.

Meanwhile, Elsbeth called Mrs. Schaeffer to ask if Dieter could come upstairs to see her. She then went to the bedroom wardrobe, pulled her suitcase from the top shelf, and laid it on the bed. *What should I bring?* She sorted through her blouses and shirts, selecting the ones she felt would be most appropriate for a summer week by the sea. Folding her swimsuit, she heard a loud bang on the apartment door. She went to answer it before another bang could echo through the apartment.

"Hello, Frau Rosen, my mother said you wanted to see me."

"Yes. Hello, Dieter. Come in." Elsbeth showed her young neighbor to a chair. "I'll be going out of town for a week. There have been a lot of apartments broken into lately, so I would like you to keep an eye on my place while I'm gone. I'll pay you five Marks for the week to come up and check everything is in its place. Would you do that?"

"Absolutely, Frau Rosen. For five Marks? I can certainly do that."

"Here's my key. Please put it somewhere your mother can get to it as well, just in case."

"In case of what, Frau Rosen?"

"Never mind. Just make sure that you check the apartment every day. If anything looks wrong, tell your mother right away so that she can call me at my hotel."

"Yes, Frau Rosen."

Elsbeth gave Dieter her key, five Marks, and a piece of paper with the name of the hotel. After walking him to the door, she took his arm to stop him. "Dieter, don't tell anyone what you're doing. Only talk about this to your mother. It's important that no one knows I'm gone. Remember. Only your mother."

He nodded and started to walk downstairs to his apartment.

"Thank you, Dieter." Elsbeth instinctively knew what she had to do next. She immediately locked her door and headed for the hall closet where she took out two large leather-strapped satchels and pulled them into the bedroom. She then flung open the wooden wardrobe holding Willy's remaining clothes. There'd be no choice; she'd donate them to the poor just to get them out of the apartment. She should have removed her husband's things by now anyway. With her being gone for a week she worried about the stories she'd heard, and she couldn't risk anyone finding them. It was yet one more rip in their lives, and she had delayed this task perhaps longer than she should have, but there could be no indications that Willy lived there.

Within the hour, she had the last of his clothes and personal items packed neatly into the luggage set. She looked at what appeared to her to be an empty apartment. She checked the table next to Willy's favorite chair where his pipe would be... nothing. Pictures of the two of them in Düsseldorf, at their wedding ceremony, of their travels together... all gone. If this was going to work, all traces of her beloved husband would have to disappear. The apartment must look as if it were the home of a single woman. She understood that would mean there'd be nothing of her husband's to comfort her. Deep unending waves of sadness overcame her as she reached for the telephone.

"Hello? Can I get a cab at Cicerostrasse 55 please? I'll be ready in ten minutes. Thank you."

July 5, 1937

"Elsbeth, over here," Anny called, standing on her tiptoes and waving from the end of the train. "Max, you get her attention."

Max had no problem getting anyone's attention. At over six feet tall and 200 pounds, he was a formidable man who only had to raise his hand to be seen from the railway platform. "Elsbeth. Down here."

Elsbeth had only met them once during Willy's film career but knew they were both genuinely good people. She understood that some celebrities were snobs, but not Anny and Max. She was happy to be riding with them and to catch up on things.

As Elsbeth made her way to the end of the platform, she noticed a young man in the corner of the baggage area. She muttered to herself, "Is that Dieter? No, it couldn't be."

She reached Anny and Max, and said heartily, "Hello you two, how have you been?" She hugged Anny closely and whispered in her ear, "Thank you, Anny. I don't think I could have made this trip alone."

Anny kissed Elsbeth lightly on her cheek. "It's our pleasure. It will give us all time to get reacquainted. It's lovely in Scheveningen. Have you been?"

"Yes, Willy and I went there for our honeymoon. I was supposed to go last month for the opening of the summer season but have been too concerned about leaving the apartment. Have you heard about the Nazis ransacking Jewish sympathizers' flats?"

Anny pulled Elsbeth a bit closer when they entered their train car. "We've heard everything. We're always concerned that we'll come home to find Nazis in our apartment. Max and I are constantly scrutinized by the authorities. You should know, Elsbeth, since you are traveling with us, if they didn't know you before, they do now. The downside to celebrity is that we are always being watched."

As they walked the narrow hallway to their sleeping car, Max motioned to them to be silent. Once they entered the compartment, Max locked the door behind the trio. He pulled a cigarette case from his coat pocket and offered it to both women, keeping silent until after lighting all three cigarettes. He took a long drag. "Elsbeth, everywhere we go there are informants watching our every move. They know we're sympathetic, but they have no proof," adding rather nonchalantly, "and even if they had proof, they would have to act on it, and they won't do that. Not to me and not to Anny. But they're everywhere. It's difficult to make out who you can trust and who will turn you in, so you keep your cards as close to your chest as you can."

Elsbeth became queasy at the thought that she had inadvertently exposed her husband to any danger. Sensing her concern, Anny attempted to calm her. "Darling, it's the world we're living in. There is little you can do. Even if you never left your apartment, they would find you. You may as well enjoy life while you can. We know that Willy's Jewish. Are you?"

"No," said Elsbeth quietly, as if it were something to be ashamed of. "But as long as I am married to him, I am a Jew."

"Well, that's not how the authorities see it. They know that you are not a Jew. But you are married to one, which is forbidden," Max said.

"That's why I stayed in Berlin. I'm hoping they think we've separated or divorced."

"They know you're not divorced. They may think you've separated, but they would assume it's because of the Nuremberg Laws. Be prepared. If they're convinced that you are still married, they may force you into a divorce." Anny knew her words were difficult for Elsbeth to hear. She reached out and held Elsbeth's hand as she continued, "Max and I know several couples in your same situation. Sometimes I think it would be better if you were both Jewish and on the run together."

"On the run?" Elsbeth had never thought of it that way. She had let herself believe that Willy was only away until things changed.

"I think he is wise not to be in Germany right now. Let's not say he's on the run. Let's say he's where he is able to work freely and without scrutiny, shall we?"

Elsbeth felt better talking about the situation with someone. She had long thought about their being apart and all the reasons behind it, but never had a conversation with anyone other than Willy.

"Thank you, Anny, for being someone I can talk to about this. It's hard to be strong for someone else."

Anny took a while to respond, knowing that what she was about to say would be very difficult for her to hear. "If you want to be strong for Willy, you must convince him to divorce you. As long as you're married, you are in danger."

Elsbeth was horrified. *Did she just hear Anny correctly? Divorce?* "Anny, I can't do that. I love him. There has to be... No, there must be another way," she stammered. "What if we simply announce that we are filing for divorce? Wouldn't that be enough?"

"I'm not sure. These days, you never know how deeply they will look into something. They may not have the time to investigate—" but Elsbeth cut her off.

"I know. But they may." After several long moments, she added quietly, "I'll speak with Willy in Scheveningen."

"The apartment's up on the second floor, Herr Oberst. Unit 4." Dieter was glad that the officers arrived when his mother wasn't at home. If she had been there, she would have made up something, anything, to get them to leave. Dieter, however, had his own motives for keeping secrets from his mother. "I'll be promoted in the Hitler Youth, right? By helping you?"

"Of course, Dieter. Just let us into the apartment. Your mother will be very proud of you."

He knew his mother wouldn't be proud at all, but it didn't matter. Dieter brought the officers up to the Rosen apartment, unlocked the apartment door, and then reset the inside lock so that he could take the key with him.

"Good boy," said the Oberst. "You've done a great service to your country and your Führer. Now, leave us alone."

The officer snapped his heels together as they gave each other the sharp *Heil Hitler* salute. Dieter closed the door behind him as he thought about his mother. He replayed the Oberst's words in this mind. What he was doing couldn't be wrong, could it?

As soon as Dieter was gone, the Oberst said, "Check the wardrobe first. Make sure his clothes are gone. If they are here, so is he."

The Brownshirt quickly walked into the bedroom and flung open the wardrobe. "Nothing here, Herr Oberst."

"Nothing out here as well. Everything is as it should be... but there is still no record of a divorce. The boy said she left on the train with a couple who turned out to be Anny Ondra and Max Schmeling, but she was without her husband. Maybe she was going to meet him somewhere."

"If he's not in Germany, Herr Oberst, then there is little we can do, correct?"

"If she is still married to a Jew, there is plenty we can do. We'll keep an eye on her and see if her husband returns to Berlin. We're done here, Let's go."

The two left, careful not to make noise as they passed Dieter's apartment.

July 10, 1937

"But that isn't the right outfit for the opening number, Willy," Otto said. He couldn't figure out why he was being asked to forgo the gangster outfit and wear a dinner jacket instead.

"We're trying something a little different. I'm thinking that at rehearsal today I'd like to try some new costumes. Oh, and we're not having rehearsal until five o'clock. So until then, why don't you take it easy in your room?"

"You're the boss, Willy. See you then."

As Otto walked to the elevator, Willy saw Anny, Max, and Elsbeth come in from the patio.

"Willy, why don't you join us on the beach?" Max asked. "It's a lovely day. Look at you, all dressed in your tweed suit. Don't you know it's July?"

Max, you don't need to concern yourself with covering up an oddly shaped body, Willy thought. "I wouldn't be seen dead in a swimsuit," Willy proclaimed. "You three enjoy the sun, though. And remember that we need everyone in the cabaret by 4:45 p.m. That should give us enough time to get everyone into place."

As the hour neared, Willy herded the guests into the Lutine Palace to await the entrance of the guest of honor. At 5:10 p.m., when Otto had not yet shown up, he went looking for him. Otto was in the buffet line, a cigar in one hand and a drink in the other.

"Otto," Willy called, tapping his watch.

Otto let out an "Oh, damn," and quickly left his drink on the buffet table. Realizing what he had done, he picked it back up and followed Willy to Lutine Palace. "I'm so sorry. I lost track of time."

"Yes, you lost track of time. And at the buffet, again? Of all days, Otto..."

The two got in the elevator.

Otto looked at Willy, and asked, "Why? What's so special about today?" No sooner had the words come out of his mouth than the elevator opened to a crowd of friends and fans. Otto stopped in his tracks and looked at Willy. "What is this? I don't understand..."

Willy pointed to the poster announcing the 25th anniversary of his film career.

"You did this, didn't you? I love you, Willy. For this and for so many things."

"It's my pleasure, my friend, and I love you, too. Now, go and greet your audience," said Willy and pushed Otto into the room. Otto wiped his eyes dry, and stopped at each table to thank everyone for coming.

Once on stage, Otto took his place in a grand over-stuffed throne, where Anny and Max came out from backstage to place a paper crown upon his head and a scepter made out of rolled-up newspapers. Anny and Max stood on either side of Otto's throne and proclaimed: "All hail King Otto!" With that, the entire theater stood up and rewarded the star with applause deserving of a 25-year film career.

Otto, clearly overwhelmed, thanked everyone repeatedly between puffs on his cigar and sips from his low-ball glass. The evening centered around performances by the cast members of Willy's Theater der Prominenten, with each actor or actress taking their turn in performing a number or two in tribute to their friend.

After Lilly Majus's performance Willy approached the microphone and, to the surprise of many, announced: "Ladies and Gentlemen, I give you Louis Davids!"

As the audience rose to their feet, Otto was very touched. He knew that Louis had asthma; severe asthma, which had ended his performing career only a few months earlier. Otto was only expecting Louis to speak. Rather, he nodded to Willy who, seated at the piano, began to play a familiar introduction while Louis said a few words. "Ladies and Gentlemen, this evening we honor the great actor and my dear friend, Otto Wallburg; the only man I know who can eat, drink and smoke simultaneously... even in his sleep. Otto, would you like to go to the zoo with me?" The audience went into a frenzy, knowing that Louis' hit song *Naar de Artis*, his homage to the Amsterdam Zoo was soon to follow. Knowing that his friend was told by his doctor not to sing, Otto became overwhelmed with emotion. While Louis Davids sang about the comic adventures of animals and humans, Otto Wallburg, comic genius and all-around funny man, was weeping.

After the celebration, Willy, Otto, Sig, Anny, Max, and Elsbeth went into a private dining room for an evening meal. While the entertainment had centered on Otto, the dinner focused on Berlin. Willy, Sig, and Otto, having been away for some time, relied on Elsbeth, Anny, and Max to answer their many questions.

"What's happening in the cabarets?" Willy wanted to know

immediately. "Is Max Ehrlich's revue still playing? We miss Berlin so much. We can't wait to go home."

Anny told them, "Yes, it is. You know, Ehrlich now runs all of the revues."

"You know that Willy writes the music for Ehrlich?" Elsbeth asked Anny, always ready to highlight her husband's work.

"Of course. Max and I are always so proud to see his name. But, Willy, you are wise not to come to Berlin. The authorities harass Max mercilessly, and I fear they would do the same to you. He's always looking over his shoulder." Anny paused to take a sip of her cocktail.

"Most Jews in Berlin are leaving the city for the countryside," Max said, picking up where his wife left off. "They feel if they're not visible, they're safe. The only real way they're safe is to leave Germany completely. There is no place for them now. Hitler is making that very clear. Berlin and all of Germany has abandoned their Jews." Max took a breath to control his emotions.

Willy couldn't listen anymore. He could barely compose his words. "That simply cannot be true. I received the Iron Cross in the war... and my family... we are all Germans by our birthright. It just can't be true that we're no longer welcome in our own country. Please excuse me. I need some air." He walked outside to the veranda, with Elsbeth following him.

"Darling, I must talk to you about something that you won't want to hear." She stroked his damp cheeks. "I have been speaking with Anny and Max on the train about our separation. Willy, we need to file for divorce. At least appear to file for divorce."

"What? Divorce? Elsbeth, no... I can't do it!" Willy collapsed onto the balcony railing. "Why would you even say this? I couldn't go on without you."

Elsbeth knew she had to press on. "Willy, just listen. As long as the German authorities know we're married, they will view us in violation of the Nuremberg Laws. If you announce that you have filed for divorce here in Holland, it will be public knowledge, maybe even written about in the newspapers. Remember... filing for divorce does not mean that we're divorced. It only means that we are in the process of divorcing. The official event would have to take place in Berlin and, as long as you're not in Berlin, the divorce can't be finalized. Understand?"

Willy couldn't believe how thoroughly she had laid out the plan. He looked at his wife. As much as he didn't want to, he understood that this was now the best plan. It was their new Plan A. He pulled her close to him and kissed her passionately. She was the only person he was meant to be with, and the only person who knew him better than he knew himself. He let out a deep breath. "I'll do it. I'll do it after the season's over. I'll file the paperwork there and that'll be it. Nothing can happen until I'm forced to do so in Berlin."

"And you need to heed Anny's warning. You have to stay away from Berlin, now more than ever. If they believe you are there, they could force the finalization."

"I understand, Elsbeth. Can we go up to our room? I'm quite exhausted."

The following morning, the two of them met Max and Anny at the train station. After kissing his wife goodbye, Willy whispered in her ear, "Listen, my dear. Keep in touch with Max and Anny. When they are in Berlin, go out to dinner with them, go to the movies with them. Just know that you will be my excuse to continue to say yes to Ehrlich's revues. If I need to get word to you, I can do so through him." He kissed his wife again, and after helping her into the train car, took Anny and Max each by the hand, saying softly, "Please keep an eye on my Elsbeth. I know she comes across as strong, but she's a great actress in her own right. I would be so grateful."

Anny kissed him on the cheek. "Of course. When we're in Berlin, we will make sure to call and visit her. Don't worry, she won't be alone. And Willy, Elsbeth is much stronger than you know."

Willy nodded, remembering the conversation from the previous night.

Max helped Anny into the train car and turned back to Willy. "Know that we will do anything." With those final words, Max joined the waiting pair.

Summer 1937

During their final week at the Lutine Palace, Willy was approached by the owners of the Rika Hopper Theater in Amsterdam. They requested that the entire company bring all four revues to Amsterdam to run September through December.

When Willy informed the others, they all breathed easier knowing there were plans for the near future. No one could return to Germany, and no one had any other way to make a living.

"Can I have word with you, Sig?" asked Willy.

"Sure."

The two walked the lobby while Willy told him about the plans to file for divorce. "I'll need to be away a few days before we leave for Amsterdam. Can you hold down the fort while I'm gone?"

"Of course. And I'm so sorry that you and Elsbeth have to go through this."

"So am I Sig. Thanks for the help."

On September 18, Willy filed for divorce from Elsbeth in civil court in The Hague. On his way out of the courthouse he was inconsolable.

11

January 1938

"Willy, are you sure about this?" Sig asked as he helped his friend with his coat and hat. "Don't you think it'll make people upset?" Sig was holding the *Haagsche Courant*, a Dutch newspaper in which Willy had published a notice placed prominently in the entertainment section.

The Willy Rosen Tour

The management of the Willy Rosen tour would like to draw attention to the fact that the members of the company, which now perform in the Stadsschouwburg, are Jewish artists who are "exiled from Germany" and no longer allowed to perform their craft in their homeland, thus starting a tour through Western Europe.

"To read the truth? Yes. It should upset them. I'm upset about it," Willy said vehemently. "And by the way, I have already sent this notice to every city we'll be playing."

Sig was shocked. "Have you forgotten about Elsbeth? Think about what they could do to her back in Berlin. You may be safely tucked away in Holland, but she's back in Germany and alone. And she will have to deal with any consequences by herself."

"Oh my God, what was I thinking? You're right. I'll pull the articles from all the other cities. Amsterdam is already done, and it's too late for The Hague and Rotterdam. Let's just hope that no one with any influence sees them."

"I'll keep my fingers crossed for Elsbeth, but Willy, please talk to me before you do anything like this again, okay?"

"I will. Promise." He took Sig by the shoulders and looked straight at him. "Thank you, my friend. I must call Elsbeth and give her fair warning, just in case." Willy quickly walked to the concierge. "Can I get an international line? Berlin, please."

The phone in the apartment rang so loudly that Elsbeth nearly jumped out of Willy's chair. When she returned from Scheveningen months ago, she suspected that someone had been in the apartment looking for... something. Since then, her nerves remained on heightened alert. She cautiously answered, "Brabant 612. Hello?" Elsbeth heard the distinct electronic noise indicating an international call.

"Willy? Is that you?" Her tone gave away how excited she was to talk to him.

"Yes, my dear, how are you? I miss you terribly," Willy responded in kind. "I'm calling to warn you that there may be issues that arise with the authorities. I wasn't thinking clearly, and I posted a statement in Dutch newspapers informing audiences that we have been expelled from Germany and could no longer perform there. I just wanted to let them know why we were still in Holland and not back in Berlin like every other year. But that means there's a possibility that you could receive a retaliatory visit from the SS. Or worse, have the apartment gone through while you are out one day. Please, be careful and stay close to the apartment. Has everything been okay? How are you doing? Have you checked in with Anny and Max?"

"I haven't seen or heard from them since returning to Berlin, but I'm sure they're busy. Everything here is fine. There's nothing to worry about. Now, hang up because they could be monitoring the phone. I love you. Stay safe, my love." She blew a kiss into the receiver before hanging up. The last thing she wanted was to give the authorities any reason to return to the apartment. If they suspected that Willy might come back to Berlin, they would both be arrested for violating the Nuremberg Laws.

Elsbeth still felt guilty about never telling him of her suspicions. She knew that he would want to come home, but what could he really do, even if he were here? She had determined that what he didn't know kept him safer. Yes, he had published a notice that might cause her problems, and she wondered what might happen. In thinking about that, she had an epiphany: she could wait for the authorities to come to her, or she could live her life. Of course, they'd expect her to be afraid to go out, and that she'd hide in the apartment and do nothing—which is exactly what she had done for the last six months. She could try to control of the situation, or let the Nazis control it. *I can either remain scared, or I can go out and live.*

A new and better course of action was required to save her husband: she would have to act like a single woman. And it would start now. She sprang from Willy's chair and dashed into the bedroom, where she put on her best dress and then examined herself in the mirror. *I need lipstick, powder, and all the things that I haven't used since Scheveningen.* Elsbeth Rosen, to keep the Nazis off her husband's tracks, would return to being Elsbeth Hoffman. A much more visible Elsbeth Hoffman. She'd make sure to be well dressed and attractive to every single man she might meet. *I must look like a single woman and act like a single woman. Please forgive me, my love.* She put on her coat and hat and looked in the mirror again as if to glean one final look at her old life. And with that, she walked out into the evening.

February 8, 1938

"Willy, a letter came today from the Reich's Music Cabinet. Sit down, as this will upset you." Elsbeth was trying to soften the blow, not knowing that he was already prepared. It had simply been a matter of time.

"It's alright. I know what it is. I've been expecting it since I published the notice in the Dutch papers concerning our exile. Removing me is not a surprise."

Willy was remarkably calm as he explained what it meant to be removed. "From this point forward, my dear, my music will not be played on the radio or in live performance outside the *Kulturbund*. Record sales will have to be on the black market, and Will Meisel cannot publish anything for me. I'm sure this was facilitated by the announcement in the *Haagsche Courant*. And, if that's the case, I'm glad I did it. After all, what else can they do to me?" That question made the hairs on Willy's neck stand up as soon as he asked it. He remembered what Sig had told him about the trouble the announcement could cause Elsbeth. Nothing had happened, but now with his removal from the Cabinet, might the Nazi hoodlums watch her even closer? "Elsbeth, you're going to have to take extra care. Between the newspaper and now this, you have to be cautious who you speak to, who you allow close to you in any way. You can't trust your friends. I would only trust Anny and Max, and of course Max Ehrlich. If you should ever need me, get ahold of Ehrlich. He'll know how to reach me. You can't contact me directly. I'm going to need to keep my head down for a while if for no other reason than to keep you safe." He could hear her take a deep inhale of air. Elsbeth didn't want to accept this, yet she knew that Willy was right, at least for the near future. "Elsbeth, I'm so sorry. The only thing they can take away from me now is you, and we can't let that happen."

So, this is it? I'm never to see my husband again? She regained her composure if for no other reason than to not alarm him. "I understand. Don't worry about me. I can take care of myself. If I need to contact you, I'll send a letter through Max. I promise."

Willy was surprised by the strength that he was hearing from his wife. He simply said, "Yes. Max will always know how to find me. And writing is best. Elsbeth?"

"Yes?"

"I love you so very much, my dear."

"I love you too, Willy." She didn't want to let him go, but told him, "Now, hang up. If I need you, I'll contact Max." After another gentle kiss, Elsbeth put down the receiver. She could feel the power grow within her. She was determined more than ever to be strong for them both. Brushing away her tears of both pain and anger, she took her coat and hat from the hall tree. Pulling a cashmere scarf out of her coat pocket, she wrapped it around her neck as she left the apartment to go into the snowy Berlin night as Elsbeth Hoffman.

On Saturday, March 12, 1938 at 5:00 am, Heinrich Himmler and Reinhard Heydrich landed at Vienna's airport and forced the legitimate Austrian government to resign. Hitler called the action an *Anschluss*—a union of Germany and Austria. Vienna had long been a sanctuary for German Jews to avoid the restrictions and ever increasing detention and imprisonment taking place in their homeland. However, Austria was Adolf Hitler's homeland, and his goal was to reunite all German-speaking areas of Western Europe. After March 12, German Jews who had sought refuge in Austria fled to other parts of Europe considered safe or left the continent all together.

Many members of the Theater der Prominenten, including Otto Wallburg and Sig Arno, both based in Vienna, had to find other places of residence. Sig would relocate to Amsterdam during March and April 1938 to perform with the troupe. Otto went to Paris, his absence from the summer season filled by Franz Engel, a Viennese native and actor who fled the Anschluss. Also new was the concert pianist Erich Ziegler, another relocated Viennese; he'd worked briefly with Willy and Kurt Robitschek during the Kabarett der Komiker tour in 1924. Like Max Ehrlich, Erich would play an important part in Willy's future.

The changing face of the Theater der Prominenten reflected the considerable pressure Jewish performers throughout Europe felt to have an exit strategy and a timeline on which to act. For Willy, after his rejection by the Swiss government, the only plan was to stay in Holland. He could have left for Cuba, but did not want to. Even though he had been forewarned, he considered sneaking into Berlin to visit Elsbeth.

June 1938

When Szöke Sakall rejoined the troupe in Holland, Willy was eager to hear any news he might have about their friends. "Do you know how Kurt Robitschek's doing in Prague? Do you think he'll come here?" he asked, excited at the prospect of his old friend joining the troupe.

"No, he's too fearful of Holland. He thinks the Dutch government is too weak to defend itself against German aggression, just like the Austrians. He and Ilse are going to Paris, then America. Between you and me, I'm planning a move to America as well. What about you, Willy?"

"Are you really leaving for America? And Kurt too? I have Cuban visas for me and Elsbeth but I don't want to go there. I only want to go home. Besides, Elsbeth won't abandon my parents."

"Listen to me, Willy. You have no home now. You can't go back to Germany, and now you can't go to Austria. You must wake up because things are not going to get better for us. They are only going to get worse." He could see his words were having no effect. "Fine, you do what you will, but I would recommend that you both go to Cuba, or apply for American visas as soon as possible."

But Willy was adamant in his argument. "I don't even know what I'd do in Cuba or America. More, I'd have to get two visa applications, and the Americans are at their quota. And I just said that Elsbeth won't leave my parents." He was so tired of running. "How did you and Kurt manage it?"

Szöke reminded Willy that he was Hungarian, and Kurt was Czech, and neither country had yet filled their visa quotas. "After we finish the season, I'm going to Budapest and then to Hollywood."

At that moment, Sig Arno entered the cigar room, catching the last part of what Szöke said. He looked at Willy with a forlorn look, adding, "I'm leaving as well."

Willy could hardly speak. "Wow...okay... can I ask you both to stay until October? Max van Gelder at the Leidsepleintheater in Amsterdam asked me to put together a major revue opening in mid-

September to play for four weeks. He's envisioning it as the biggest performance of the season. Can you two do that for me?"

"Sure, I can do that," Szöke said.

"Sorry, I can't," Sig said. "I'm already booked for America. I came in to tell you that I'll be leaving the troupe after we close the second review. If it's alright with you, I've asked Henriëtte Davids to replace me in the third one. She'll be a huge draw for you, and she's a lot funnier than me." Both men looked at Willy, waiting for him to say something.

"Okay, sure, Sig. Thanks, guys," but he couldn't hide the disappointment in his voice.

Sig took Willy's hand in his own. "You and Elsbeth should come to America. If you don't leave now, you may never get another chance."

"What would they want to bother me for? I'm staying." And with nothing else to say, he got up to leave the room.

"Listen to us," Szöke called out after him. "You're not a German anymore, Willy. You're only a Jew."

Willy walked out, slamming the cigar room door as he left.

"What else can we do?" Szöke asked. "And he'd be big in Hollywood."

"That's my intention, Szöke."

"Mine as well, my friend."

October 1938

I love autumn in Berlin, but it'll be breezy, Elsbeth thought as she put on her coat and pinned a hat to her hair. When she checked the angle of the hat in the mirror, she was surprised by the image looking back. *I'm beautiful... no longer the frumpy Hausfrau.* When she created this plan, she knew she'd need some guidance, but it was easier than she'd thought. All she had to do was shed a few tears at the make-up counter about her husband leaving her and how she wanted to feel pretty again and voila! With a final look at herself, she collected a small stack of books and headed to the library.

As she walked up and down the long, wooden aisles that held an endless supply of reading material, she couldn't help but feel like she was being watched. She brushed it off. *Someone is just looking at a beautiful woman picking out a few books.* However, she had the same feeling when she left the library. She took a look behind her and glimpsed someone ducking behind the statue of Artemis under the library portico. *Is that Dieter?*

Her thoughts immediately went back to her departure to Scheveningen last year with Anny and Max and remembered wondering if she had noticed him at the train station as well. *The apartment. Dieter was watching it when it was gone through.* Before she knew it, she spun around and ran up the steps to the statue. She could see someone in the shadows, and pulled out a young blond man in a Hitler Youth uniform. Elsbeth stepped back in disbelief. "Dieter, what in the world—"

Before she could say anything else, he raised his right arm out in the Nazi greeting. "Heil Hitler!"

Elsbeth couldn't believe her eyes and certainly not her ears. Here was her neighbor's son, the boy she had entrusted with her apartment, the boy who saw her coming and going every day and night. She quickly regained her composure. "Dieter, are you following me?" She was careful not to draw any attention to the Nazi regalia or greeting, acting as if it were to be expected of her young neighbor.

"Frau Rosen. I've been worried about you since you're alone. I feel responsible... to look out for you."

Elsbeth knew when she heard a lie. "Thank you, but I don't need anyone watching out for me or worrying about me. I have friends, should I need company. It's neither your place nor your right to follow me. I'm going to speak with your mother about this when I get home." Feeling she had made her point, she walked down the steps again.

He followed her to the sidewalk. "Frau Rosen, it's not your decision."

Elsbeth slowly turned. That voice had aged in mere moments. She looked into his eyes. *These are no longer the eyes of a boy.* He didn't blink or move a muscle; he simply glared at her. Shaken, she walked toward home as quickly as she could. She knew he was following her, studying her. She picked up her pace. Once she was at their building, Elsbeth went straight to her apartment rather than speaking with Dieter's mother. She fumbled to lock the door behind her while still holding the books, and her knees crumpled as she reached the sofa, the books tumbling to the floor. She looked down at her hands; they were shaking uncontrollably. She panicked when she realized how long she'd been out, and searched the apartment for anything that looked out of place. It took the ringing of the phone to bring her back into reality.

It'll be Willy. I can't answer it. They'll be listening. If Dieter's one of them, they'll be listening. Her mind couldn't contain the rush of thoughts. *I've got to get word to him. I can't use the phone. How can I tell him?* "Max Ehrlich," she said out loud, the volume surprising herself. *I've got to send a note to Max. I'll tell him not to let Willy come back to Berlin.* She got out her stationary, and first wrote the address of the *Jüdischer Kulturbund* on the envelope. Then she carefully chose her words:

Dear Max,

I hope this finds you well. I need a favor. Can you send word to Holland that the Roses were beautiful, but I simply cannot accept any more? Please stress that I cannot have Roses sent to my apartment until I say it's alright to do so.

I'm doing quite well, Max, and I hope that you are as well. I only wish I was able to attend one of your performances, but as they are only for Jews, I understand that cannot happen.

Please take care.

Elsbeth

12

November 9, 1938

Elsbeth was jolted awake by screams and sounds of glass shattering in the night. Before she could think, she was putting her coat on over her nightgown and ran down the stairs. When she opened the door of her apartment building she was horrified at what she saw. Mobs of men with flashlights and torches were walking down her block. They were armed with sledgehammers, shovels, and wooden sticks, clearly intent on violence. They bashed in the large window of the repair shop directly on the other side of the street. Elsbeth watched as these men and even some women reached through the broken panes to steal anything they could grab. Meanwhile, two men were painting a large yellow Star of David on the door to the shop, with the word *Jüden* in all capital letters above it.

Instinctively, Elsbeth shouted at the mob and started to run toward them, but she was pulled back into the shadow of doorway. She turned to confront whoever was stopping her. "Dieter? Is that you?" Elsbeth said, shaking with anger.

"You mustn't, Frau Rosen. They'll hurt you." His voice was pointed but calm, and he held onto the sleeve of her coat.

"What's going on? Who's doing this?"

"It's the Jews, Frau Rosen. They're coming for the Jews. There's nothing you can do about it. Don't get involved."

"What have they done to anyone? These are your people doing this, aren't they?"

Dieter looked across the street at the actions of the mob. He knew the shopkeeper and his family, and all of them had been nothing but kind to him. He began to shake his head and his eyes closed for a moment. "They're not my people, Frau Rosen. Not anymore." He pulled Elsbeth into the safety of the building. He looked directly at her. "Go home and lock your door. Don't come out, no matter what you hear. They're going to start taking Jewish men away tomorrow. Make sure Herr Rosen knows that he must never return to Germany."

Elsbeth didn't even know how to respond to his pronouncement. *Was her young neighbor a Nazi? Or was he the boy she knew?*

"Herr Rosen and I are divorced. We've been—"

"No, you're not divorced, and they know it. They're waiting. Waiting and watching for him to come back. If he does, they will know it and they will take him away."

She couldn't contain the panic rising up. "Why are you telling me this? Why are you telling me if you're one of them?"

Dieter looked at Elsbeth with eyes she recognized. He was no longer pretending to be a man. He didn't say a word as they listened to the shouts of the mob, breaking glass, and cheers and applause. He hung his head and slowly started up the stairs to his mother's apartment. He turned around. "Go home, Frau Rosen. Tell your husband what I said." Once he reached his apartment, Dieter glanced back at Elsbeth, and closed the door.

Just before dawn, Max Ehrlich ran down Kommandantenstrasse as quickly as he could, heading for the Kleinkunstbühne. He immediately went backstage and took a can of white paint and a paint brush, and then rushed to the entrance to paint a large Star of David on the door of the theater. Max thought that he could protect the theater if the crazed mob believed someone has already done damage. When he finished, he locked himself in and retreated into the office on the mezzanine level. While waiting, he could hear very faint sounds. Were they sirens? Alarms? He finally made out the sounds: they were shouts and screams. Terrified, he huddled tighter under the desk until he heard someone knocking on the door. Max crawled out from his hiding space and crept down the short staircase to the lobby of the theater.

"Max... it's Elsbeth Rosen. Open the door!" Elsbeth was pounding her fists against the heavy wooden doors, the paint covering her hands.

He quickly opened one door just enough to let her in.

"Max, oh, you're alright, but they're coming... you've got to hide." Elsbeth grabbed him by the hand and ran up the stairs, not even knowing where she was taking him.

"Elsbeth, what are you doing here? Why are you here? These people are crazy!"

"Max, they're starting to take Jewish men away this morning. These mobs have been going through the entire city destroying Jewish businesses and homes."

"I know. That's why I'm here. I had to paint the door to make them think a mob had already come here."

She ran back downstairs, took off her shoe, and used the heel to bash two small windows in the doors. "If there's damage, it's more believable. Let's go!"

The two ran upstairs again, hand in hand.

Max pulled her into the office.

The sounds on the street grew louder, and the noise was unlike anything Max had ever heard. It was already all too familiar to Elsbeth. "The mobs came down my street last night. What's happening is unbelievable. It's—" but the sound made her stop talking.

There was a tremendous blast of broken glass and shouts from the stores across the street. The pair, crammed under a desk in the dark, held onto each other and waited to hear sounds of the theater doors being smashed in. After a few minutes, the noise was dissipating as the crazed horde continued their path of destruction away from the theater.

"Did it work, do you think?" Elsbeth whispered, afraid to speak at a normal volume. Only distant sirens could be heard.

"They're gone," Max said, releasing all the breath that he had been holding. He crawled out first, and held out his hand to Elsbeth, and asked, "What are you doing here?"

"Did you get my message to Willy? Does he know not to come back here? I have to know."

"Yes. We've been writing almost weekly. He asked me to look in on you, but I've been busy. And, really, too scared. I don't want to go outside unless I absolutely have to." He made a sound of agony Elsbeth had never heard before. "I came back from New York for my people, for the Jews of Berlin, to give them some entertainment and maybe hope, but I can't do it anymore. Charlotte and I must join Willy in Holland as soon as we can."

"Of course, take your wife and get out of Berlin as soon as possible." She tried to comfort him as best as she could, knowing that there was no way to comfort such grief. "When you write to Willy next, tell him I love him and will find a way to see him soon."

"You have to get out as well. They'll eventually come for you, too, you know."

She had heard this warning before. "I can't, as long as Willy's parents are in Magdeburg, someone needs to stay here."

Elsbeth could start to make out Max's face in the early morning light. Max smiled and hugged her tightly. "I hope your husband knows what he has in you."

Elsbeth pulled a handkerchief out of her coat pocket and dried his face. "Come home with me. I'll fix us some breakfast and we can catch up on things, okay?"

November 1938

"Willy, there's not much you can do and that's just the way it is. You can't return to Berlin, and phone calls to Jewish numbers are monitored. Patience is your only friend in these matters." Franz was the clown in the revue, but offstage he was an intellectual force: smart, focused, calm, and composed. All things that Willy was not at the moment. "I can't believe Max is still there," Franz added. "At this point, after *Kristallnacht*, there is little that laughter can do to help anyone. But don't you and Max have a revue going up soon?"

"I have no idea what's going on. I haven't heard from him in two weeks." Willy's voice began to raise, along with his frustration.

"Herr Rosen," the concierge said, handing him a letter. "For you."

Willy tore open the envelope. Franz couldn't tell by the expression whether the news was good or bad. Finally, Willy said, "Max is coming here. He wants to do one final revue together as a farewell to the Jews of Berlin. After the revue is over, he's coming to Holland. He wrote that Elsbeth went to the theater to help him during Kristallnacht and that I'm not to return to Berlin under any circumstances." He stopped there, not sharing the news of the rounding up of Jewish men in the city, the authorities knowing that they were not legally divorced, or any of the specifics of the Night of Broken Glass. "Max wants the revue to play for four weeks then move to Holland."

"Excellent news. Max Ehrlich getting out of Berlin and joining us as part of the Theater der Prominenten. What a stroke of luck," Franz said, elated at the update.

Willy though, was forlorn. "No, you don't understand. That leaves Elsbeth with very few friends in Berlin. She won't leave Germany as long as my parents are alive. I have to see her." He stood up from the table, tucking the letter into his pocket as he walked to the elevator.

"Willy, you can't go to Berlin. Don't do anything foolish," Franz warned, following him.

Willy turned to answer his friend. "What's foolish nowadays?" Even he understood this was a terrible plan.

"Don't even think about it. If you stay here and write Max's final revue, perhaps you could meet him somewhere less conspicuous than Berlin, and he could bring Elsbeth with him to see you."

Willy thought for a second, and his eyes brightened. "I've got it. I've got a plan, Franz, and it will allow me to see my wife and my work at the same time."

"Just be careful, Willy. That's all I'm saying."

March 3, 1939

When opening night finally arrived, Max was relieved. He would soon set in motion his plans to leave Germany. He answered a knock on his office door.

His assistant stage manager stood there, flustered and stammering her words.

"What's wrong, Gretchen? Spit it out. I have no patience for anything on an opening night."

"There's someone asking for you downstairs. He says it's urgent."

Leaving the office, the pair looked at the bottom of the stairs to see a familiar pair of bespectacled eyes looking at him.

"Willy!" they cried out, worried that together their voices had just carried throughout the Kleinkunstbühne. The two immediately ran down to greet him, and Max indicated for the trio to whisper.

"What are you doing here? You shouldn't be back here. You know what Elsbeth said. They will be waiting for you."

"I know, Max, but I just had to see my... our... final work to be performed here in Berlin. Can you get word to Elsbeth to come to the theater?" Willy asked Gretchen, who raced back into the office to make the call.

"I know you miss Elsbeth, but this is just reckless. She's warned you that the authorities are keeping an eye out for you. Why do they want you so badly? It doesn't make any sense."

Willy felt it was finally time to him tell the whole story. "They want to force the finalization of our divorce. I filed it in Holland, but it's not legal unless it's filed in a civil court here in Berlin."

"I had no idea. She never told me." He was sympathetic to Elsbeth, and thus couldn't understand why Willy would take such a risk and return to Berlin.

Before he could ask, Gretchen was announcing the night's performance. "Ladies and gentlemen, welcome to the *Jüdischer Kulturbund* Kleinkunstbühne an Kommandantenstrasse, and tonight's performance of *Revue der Revuen* with music and lyrics by Willy Israel Rosen and story by Max Israel Ehrlich. *Revue der Revuen* will be the final show by Max Israel Ehrlich and the *Jüdischer*

Kulturbund, as Herr Ehrlich will be leaving Berlin for the summer season at Scheveningen, Holland."

Now backstage, he took Willy by shoulders. "You stay back here and out of sight." Before Max stepped onto the stage to the cheers and applause of the audience, he whispered to Willy, "All of that applause, that's for you as well, my friend."

"Thank you, Max." He was about to thank Max again when something caught his eye. He turned to see his Elsbeth running toward him across the cluttered backstage.

"Willy, my love!"

They embraced and kissed as if for the first time.

She was so stunned to see her husband that she could barely get out her thoughts. "You can't be here. I love you, but you can't be here. You must go now."

Willy knew she was right, but he had to spend any amount of time with her that he could. "I couldn't do another day without you, my dear. This is my last revue in Berlin, and I haven't seen you since Scheveningen. Let them take me. I'm a happy man right now. Happier than I've been in a year."

Max was deeply cheered by the sight of this reunion. "Hey, you two, I have to go on. You hide back here. You won't be able to see me, but you sure will be able to hear me."

The show was everything one would expect from an audience which adored its idol. Laughter, both sincere and irreverent, flooded the theater and engulfed Max with a cavalcade of memories of past revues, performers and dear friends who came into his life and left for a variety of reasons. However, these were his people. They were the reason he stayed. Now, they were the reason he had to go.

Following the performance, Max said farewell to them both, and hailed the couple a taxi. When the cab pulled up to Cicerostrasse 55, Willy looked at his apartment building as if for the first time. When he got out, he saw the destroyed repair shop across the street, and the large Star of David under the word *Juden.*

Elsbeth paid the driver, took Willy's hand, and pulled him quickly into the building. "Don't mind that, my love. Let's not think about all that. Let's just go upstairs and pretend it's like the old days."

Willy tried to act normal, but his voice was noticeably thin. "Yes, my dear. I don't want anything to spoil the time we have together."

Inside the apartment Elsbeth put on water for tea while Willy took off his heavy coat and collapsed into his favorite chair by his favorite table where his favorite pipe would be.

"Elsbeth, where's my pipe?" he looked around, realizing that there was nothing of him in the apartment.

"I had to make it look as if you were no longer my husband. Everything that was yours is gone. Everything. I couldn't have them finding anything of yours in the apartment."

Elsbeth handed her husband a cup of tea, and told him the stories she'd heard about the authorities breaking into apartments and looking for incriminating evidence or stealing valuables. She had prepared for that before her trip to Scheveningen by ridding the place of anything that could implicate they were still married. She also finally told him that she believed the SS had indeed come into their apartment while she was visiting him. "My love, you also need to know about your parents. Your old home on Breiterweg was Aryanized and given to non-Jews. They, as well as the Michaelis family, were forced to move. They're not far... on Westendstrasse. I visit whenever I can. They're doing as well as can be expected."

He was learning how bad it had been for his wife and family while he was enjoying the luxurious surroundings of the Grand Hotel and dozens of friends. He was overcome. "My Elsbeth, I am so sorry. You've had to deal with so much. Why didn't you tell me?"

"This is exactly why I couldn't. I knew you would come straight back to Berlin where you simply cannot be!" Elsbeth looked at the clock on the mantle, seeing that it was nearly dawn. She realized he would have to stay for the day. "You need to sleep. Go to bed and sleep the day away. As soon as it's dark, you'll get back onto the train for Amsterdam and never return, understand? It'll be okay, I promise. If anything happens here, I'll go to Magdeburg." She pulled Willy up from the chair. "Right now, I just want to be with you." They entered the bedroom wher Elsbeth slipped off her shoes and turned off the lights. The long separation since Scheveningen made their being together that much sweeter.

The morning light came streaming in through a crack in the bedroom curtains, waking Willy to the smell of freshly brewed coffee and toast. He put on Elsbeth's housecoat and joined her in the kitchen. "Good morning, my dear," he said, kissing his wife tenderly on the lips.

"Good morning, my love. Sit down and have some breakfast." As they ate, Elsbeth looked at the train schedule or Saturday, March 4, trying to find the best time for him to return to Amsterdam.

"Saturday trains. They're such a problem," she complained, frustrated with the lack of runs between Berlin and Amsterdam. "There's no night train on the weekends. You'll have to catch the 4:30 p.m. train. I was hoping to avoid going out in the daytime but that's not possible."

"I'm not ready to go. It hasn't even been a day, and I need more than that," he complained, but he was no match for the resolve facing him.

"No, the longer you're in Berlin, the more chance they have of getting to you. You're leaving on the 4:30 p.m. train. You're only putting both of us in harm's way the longer you stay in Berlin."

"You're right. I'm being greedy. I'll be on that train. I promise."

"Thank you, my love. Your being here won't help anyone." Elsbeth took a deep breath and reached for the pot on the stove. "More tea?"

A few hours later after a lovely afternoon, they went to the station. "One ticket to Amsterdam, please," Elsbeth said, buying the ticket so Willy could stay near the coatroom, out of sight of most people in the busy station. "Is the train on time?"

"Yes, it is," said the station master. "It will be leaving from track 3."

"Thank you. Which is track 3?"

The station master pointed to a cluster of trains waiting on what looked to be multiple tracks jumbled together. She didn't see where he was pointing.

"Well, if you could see the tracks, it would help," he admitted. "See those three trains over there? The ones clustered together?"

Elsbeth nodded.

"The center train is on track 3. The other two trains are on track 2 and track 4. Go to the platform over there, the one between tracks 2 and 3."

Elsbeth thanked the man again and went into the station to join Willy in the shadows. She whispered, "You can board right away. The train is on track 3 and leaves in ten minutes." They held hands tightly and avoided the main platform by walking toward the sliver of wood that was the platform for tracks 2 and 3. The jolt of the train starting up on track 2 made Elsbeth jump. Ahead, she saw two men in black coats walking straight at them. "Look down," she told him.

They both lowered their heads and kept walking until one man called out, "Herr Rosen? Willy Rosen?" Willy looked up quickly and saw the two men now running toward them.

"Willy, jump!"

Elsbeth shoved her husband to the edge of the platform and pushed him toward the departing train on track 2. Willy grabbed hold of the siderail and hoisted himself up the steps and into the doorway of the train car. Meanwhile, she ran directly at the two men, shoving them to the ground.

Willy watched the two try to deflect the heels of a determined Elsbeth Rosen.

They both managed to get up, and one man held Elsbeth's arms behind her back while the other placed her wrists in handcuffs and lead her down the platform.

Willy was shocked at what he was seeing. As the train sped away, he collapsed onto the nearest seat, weeping uncontrollably for the fate of his wife. *Why did I come back to Berlin?*

13

Still March 4, 1939

A man approached Willy's seat. "Ticket, please," the porter said.

"What?"

"Your ticket, sir. I need to punch your ticket."

"My ticket. Yes, of course." Willy handed the porter his ticket, and the last thing he saw came rushing back to him.

"Sir, this is the train to Innsbruck. How did you end up here?"

He explained the confusion of the three tracks in Berlin and that he was directed to what he thought was this train.

"I'm terribly sorry, sir. You're not the first passenger to board the wrong train on tracks 2 and 3. When we arrive in Innsbruck, I'll get a ticket reissued for you to Amsterdam. I just need your name."

"Willy Rosen... baum. Wilhelm Rosenbaum."

The porter studied Willy with a look of curiosity.

Damn! Now he knows something's up. What was I thinking?

The porter left and Willy quickly considered the potential consequences of his slip. *What will he do? Can he call someone and say he suspects something? Will they stop the train? Where are we? How long have I been asleep?"* He broke into a heavy sweat.

"Excuse me, porter?"

The young man came back.

"Where are we now? I feel like I've been asleep for hours," he said, trying to sound conversational. "I only remember pulling out of the station at Berlin."

"Oh, we're nearing Salzburg. We'll be in the station within 15 minutes. Then, on to Innsbruck."

Willy sensed the porter was open to friendly conversation. "Will we have any time to depart the train? You know, to buy a newspaper or anything?"

"Unfortunately, no. We are only picking up passengers. No one's allowed to leave."

As the porter left again, he had to think this through. Ten minutes wasn't enough time for anyone to leave the train, barely enough time for anyone to board, and the porter hadn't been out of sight long enough to make a call to anyone. If he got through Salzburg without incident, he'd be safe, at least until Innsbruck. *I'll cross that bridge when I come to it.*

His thoughts went back to Elsbeth, and his last sight of her being led away by the authorities. In his mind, the impression of her being pulled from the platform was burned in his memory. It was his fault. Had he simply heeded the advice of Max and all of his friends, he would never have returned and put Elsbeth in jeopardy. He could feel his anxiety swell up as he pictured her face... frantic, angry and scared. *Where is she?* He was brought back into the moment when the train screeched its arrival into the Salzburg station. Willy waited nervously, examining every man getting onto the train. *Could any of them be Gestapo?* Sooner than he anticipated, the wheels started up along the tracks, and he convinced himself that the eight new passengers were harmless. He sunk back into his seat, exhausted from being on high alert. His closed his eyes for a moment to recover his spent emotions. Instead, the calming thudding of the train lulled him into sleep.

"Herr Rosenbaum?"

Willy bolted awake, his mind again in a state of panic. He saw the smiling face of the porter holding out a new ticket.

"Herr Rosenbaum, your ticket to Amsterdam. Unfortunately, there is no direct train, so you must go through Zurich."

Willy regarded the porter for a moment, and then said heartily, "Thank you. Thank you so much."

"You are welcome, Herr Rosenbaum." The porter started to leave, but stopped to whisper into his passenger's ear, "I didn't think you would want to change trains in Munich, correct?"

Willy's face turned pale. The young man looked genially at him and, placing his hand on his shoulder, he continued, "My favorite song as a child was *Warum hat Bloß das Zebra so viel Stripen*. It still is, Herr Rosen. And *Text und Musik von Mir!*" Willy's jaw dropped as the young man stood up, smiled broadly at the composer, and returned to his duties.

Elsbeth, her wrists handcuffed behind her back, looked around the waiting room. *No. No tears. They'll think it's because I'm scared."* She wasn't scared. Just angry. "What are you charging me with? I demand that I be told the charges against me!"

A door opened down the hallway, and a small-framed man with a sharp jawline and round glasses approached her. "Not to worry, Frau Rosen. I will gladly inform you of the charges."

Elsbeth studied him as he approached. *He doesn't look intimidating. He has a rather nice face.* She noticed that he was handsome despite a slight scar at the hairline over his right ear and, moving her gaze to his eyes realized that he was staring at her with a look that nearly bore a hole through her.

"Yes, Frau Rosen. I will gladly take you through the reasons why you're here." Officer Müller placed a chair squarely in front of Elsbeth and sat down, removing a notebook from his uniform pocket. Elsbeth was determined to return the same stare.

"Frau Rosen, why were you and your husband at the Berlin trainstation this morning? And why did you push him onto the train bound for Innsbruck? I believe he was returning to Amsterdam, was he not?"

She had to accept that Müller had done his homework. "Why do you think? I saw two strange men charging at us, no identification, no attempt to say who they were. They just started running straight at us, so I pushed him onto the Innsbruck train because it was moving. I wanted my husband safely out of the station. That's why." Now she wanted some answers. "Why were you chasing us? What have we done? What has my husband done? He is a German warhero—"

His smirk stopped her. "Your husband is a Jew, Frau Rosen. He's not a German. You, on the other hand, are not a Jew. Your marriage is in direct violation of the Nuremberg Laws. Either you divorce your husband, or you go to prison. It's really quite simple."

She now knew that what Dieter had told her was true; the authorities hadn't been fooled at all. "My husband filed for divorce in The Hague last fall. It will be just a matter of time until it goes through. You have nothing to concern yourself with."

Officer Müller was losing his patience and demeanor. "Frau Rosen, either you file for divorce today, here, where the Reich can finalize the paperwork, or you will be put into protective custody."

She would not be the one to end their marriage. "Do it, put me away. What kind of a human deliberately separates two people who love each other? And only because one is a Jew?" Elsbeth was so outraged that she couldn't help herself and spat at the officer, her spittle landing on target. Without a moment's hesitation, he gave a sharp blow across her face. Elsbeth wasn't sure if she was bleeding, but the intense pain almost made her pass out. She would not give him the satisfaction, though, and forced herself to be alert. "My husband's out of the country now, and there's nothing you can do about it. Put me away because I won't divorce him!"

He raised his arm again, but then changed his mind. Any attempt at pleasantness had disappeared. "Frau Rosen, your husband is in Innsbruck, bound for Amsterdam, no doubt passing through Munich. When his train arrives in Munich, we'll arrest him. Once we have your husband in custody, he'll sign. He won't resist when he knows that you are in our possession."

"Since it's just a matter of time, I am fine waiting for my husband until he arrives. It'll be nice to see him again."

When Officer Müller raised his arm he made sure the metal buttons on his cuff struck her cheekbone.

Elsbeth cried out as the flesh opened on her face.

"We'll see just how brave you are when your husband gets here. You know what the problem with love is, Frau Rosen?"

The second strike was so painful that Elsbeth didn't even hear the question. She was looking down at the floor where small droplets of blood were quickly pooling at her feet.

"The problem with love is it weakens the soul, rendering you helpless to keep your resolutions. We'll see how quickly your story changes once your husband is picked up in Munich." Officer Müller walked back to his office as Elsbeth lost consciousness.

As soon as the train crossed the Swiss border at St. Margrethen, Willy let out a tremendous sigh of relief. He was out of occupied Austria and safely in Switzerland, making his way to Zurich.

He watched the countryside go by and thought of the porter's kindness. He was fortunate his notoriety saved him. Elsbeth, on the other hand, would not be so lucky. He knew that no degree of fame or notoriety would keep her safe. He sent up a prayer. *God, please watch over her. She's not very strong.* He had no idea just how wrong he was.

Elsbeth awoke in a tiny chamber. She instinctively reached up to her cheek, which was still throbbing from the beating. *At least I'm not still handcuffed.* She could feel the dried blood on her face, and looked at her blood-stained clothes and shoes.

Sitting up on the cot, she tried to piece together what she'd been told. She remembered something about Willy in Munich. *Oh, no... Munich was much worse than being in Berlin, and he was heading directly into the lion's den.* By trying to save him, she'd made the situation worse by pushing him onto a train bound for the birthplace of the Reich. She was startled out of her panic when the door opened and Officer Müller walked slowly over her. "So your husband did not arrive in Munich, Frau Rosen. The Innsbruck train you shoved him on should have required passengers bound for Amsterdam to change to the northern line."

She was putting the puzzle together. He was only to pass through Munich after catching another train in Innsbruck bound for Amsterdam. He wasn't on a Munich-bound train at all. She didn't know how he did it, but she didn't care, either. "Where is my husband now?"

"I thought that you may be able to answer that question for us, Frau Rosen."

Elsbeth would have laughed if she wasn't convinced that she would get another smash across her face.

"We do know that he changed trains in Innsbruck. However, the porter only remembered that his ultimate destination was Amsterdam." He began to pace the small cell. "So, I would bet that he is in Switzerland."

Elsbeth was elated. "So, he was smart enough find a way without passing through Germany, avoiding your thugs."

The officer spun around and hit her so quickly that Elsbeth only saw his hand as it was crashing down on her cheek. This time she let her head follow the blow, hoping to soften its impact. It didn't help, and she could feel the wound open up and blood drip down her face again. "I hope you're enjoying this," she said.

"I am, Frau Rosen. Rarely do I get the chance to hit a Jew-loving whore."

Unable to control her anger, she lunged at the officer who caught her by both wrists. "Put your claws away, bitch. If we don't have your husband, we can't do anything about the divorce. But trust me, that will be sooner than you think."

"So if you can't do anything, I guess I get to go home?"

"Yes, Frau Rosen." He released her arms. "Yes. You may go. He may make it safely to Holland but we have people there. Should he attempt to return to Germany, we won't make the same mistake." He called for the guard and instructed him to return Elsbeth's belongings and release her.

As Elsbeth was leaving the police station, her mind spinning, she heard someone call, "Frau Rosen, over here!" Nervous, she kept walking until a hand touched her arm. It was Dieter who pulled her into a waiting cab.

"What are you doing here? How did you know I was here?"

He appraised her cheek, but said nothing, and then looked at the cab driver in the rearview mirror. Suspicious, he opened the cab door and pushed Elsbeth back onto the sidewalk. He slid out of the backseat and handed the driver a few Marks.

"Walk with me."

Without thinking, she followed Dieter toward Hallensee. "Don't look around. Just listen as we talk. I'm going to take you to the Tiergarten where you will find a cab. Go home and lock your door. You will leave your apartment only to get groceries or go to church. They will be watching your every move. There will be men stationed outside of our building day and night. They'll do whatever they can to catch you with him."

She didn't understand why she was even released. "Why didn't they just force me to sign the divorce papers?" She didn't expect Dieter to know, but he did.

"Your husband is a high-profile exile. If anything is forced, it will certainly make the international papers, particularly in Holland. The German government does not want the Dutch to become any more protective of the Germans living there than they currently are."

"Why do you help me?"

"Frau Rosen, it was me. It was me who let them into your apartment. I am so sorry. They are terrible people, but they trust me now. I hear things... I'm so sorry. Can you forgive me?"

So it was you. Elsbeth was flooded with emotions but didn't know what to say. He'd been a foe, but more importantly he'd been a friend. She hugged Dieter tightly and managed to get out a faint "thank you" before she let the young man go, and turned toward the Tiergarten.

The Grand Hotel sent a car to pick up Willy from the Amsterdam train station. Upon arrival at the hotel, he went straight to the concierge desk. "International call, please. Berlin."

Willy waited for what seemed to be an eternity before he was handed the phone. He could hear the ringing on the other side. "Please, Elsbeth. Pick up."

"Brabant 612. Hello?" Elsbeth heard the long-distance static, and couldn't imagine that her husband would call, not after what they had both been through.

His words tumbled out. "Elsbeth, it's me. How are you, my dear? What happened? Did they hurt you? Are you okay?"

"Calm down, I'm fine. They arrested me but once they realized that they couldn't charge me with anything, they let me go. Listen. You can't be on the phone with me. I'll write to you at the hotel. I'll go into more detail about things then, but you mustn't worry. I love you. Goodbye, my love." Elsbeth hung up the phone and collapsed in Willy's chair. She was deeply exhausted from the beatings, the rollercoaster of emotions, and what she feared would be many more dealings with the Gestapo.

On the other end of the line, Willy was speechless. He didn't even have the time to tell her that he loved her.

Franz approached Willy, happy to see that he had returned to Amsterdam safely. "How was Berlin? How is Max? And how's Elsbeth?"

"You won't believe it. Do you have time for a drink? I have so much to tell you that I don't even know where to start."

"Sure, Willy. You don't look so good."

April 2, 1939

Max was in his apartment following the closing of *Revue of Revues*, and he couldn't help but react to every sound coming from the street. He also couldn't shake the events he'd heard about after opening night. Elsbeth and he had met up a few days after her release from custody, her face still a bruised mess, and she told him everything. Although he knew why the Gestapo wanted Willy, he worried that they would do the same thing when he and Charlotte tried to leave. *Of course, we're both Jewish, so the Reich wouldn't care about divorce. And I'm going to Holland for work. Still—*

His concerns were interrupted by Charlotte. "Max, remember we're not coming back. You need to pack more than summer outfits."

"What if they open our trunk and notice that we have all these clothes? We're only supposed to be going to Holland for the summer."

"We can leave. We're being allowed to leave Germany. We'll immigrate to Holland only until we can go back to America. Until we get that settled, let's enjoy our time by the sea. It'll be good for you to keep your mind off things." Charlotte kissed her husband lightly on the forehead. "Now finish packing."

Charlotte Ehrlich was not normally sentimental. She placed a few pictures of herself and Max in her small suitcase, closed it up, and set it by the apartment door. "Are you ready to go?" Charlotte didn't hear anything from the bedroom. She called again... nothing. She found her husband sobbing on the couple's bed, head buried in his hands so as not to attract her attention.

He looked at her, the depth of sadness fully on his face. "I can't do this. This is our home!"

Charlotte sat on the bed and took his hands. "What does it matter where we are? We have each other, right? We'll be fine. We'll be among friends. Willy, Franz and the others... immigrants in a new country. We'll build a new life in Holland and, when it's time, we'll go back to America."

Max returned her look and saw again how truly beautiful she was; and how, after all he'd put her through, he was undeserving of her. "You're right, as always. What does it matter as long as we're together?"

"Exactly. Now, dry your eyes, put your clothes in the trunk, and close it up. I have my bag by the door."

"Charlotte, aren't you going to miss it? Our home, I mean... the apartment? Berlin? Germany?"

"No. It's no longer our home. Now, let's go. The taxi's waiting."

14

September 1, 1939

As the doorman of the Grand Hotel tossed the stack of newspapers down onto the lobby floor, he picked up a single copy which he held over his head. His face was pallid and his eyes the size of dinner plates. He hollered for everyone to hear, "Germany invades Poland! Germany invades Poland!"

Like everyone else in the lobby, Willy was beyond shocked at the announcement. He needed to find Max Ehrlich and Franz Engel right away, but the two were heading toward him after hearing the words echo throughout the marbled cavern.

"So, he's done it. Hitler's invaded defenseless Poland! First, the whole mess with Czechoslovakia, and now Poland. What's next? Holland? France?"

"Willy, calm down. We just heard, too," Franz told him while reading the cover story of the newspaper.

"Unbelievable," said Max, reading over Franz's shoulder.

Willy, however, had no concentration for the paper. His mind had wandered to the worst possible scenario with Elsbeth living in a country that was now at war. And it would undoubtedly get worse.

Franz looked up from the newspaper. "So, what's going to happen next?"

"I have no idea," Max said slowly. "All I know is that it won't be good."

He was correct. Two days later, on September 3, Britain and France declared war on Germany.

November 16, 1939

Elsbeth just arrived back at her apartment door from a trip to the grocery store when the phone rang. Still holding the bag, she answered it. "Brabant 612. Hello?"

"Hello? Elsbeth? It's Amalie."

"Mother, oh, my goodness. How are you?" Elsbeth suddenly realized that with all of the events she'd been through, she hadn't called her mother-in-law in a very long time.

"I'm afraid it's Arthur. He's passed." Amalie's voice cracked, and it was several moments before she could ask, "Is Willy there?"

Elsbeth had to quickly sort out what she could and couldn't share. Whether subconscious or intentional, she had at that moment realized that Amalie had no idea of the state of affairs her son had found himself in. *What was I thinking? How could I have left her in the dark for so long?* She would have to tell her without going into too much detail. "Mother, he's working in Holland. I'm so sorry that I haven't called more... that I haven't kept you informed. Willy can't come back to Germany. I didn't want you to worry, but the truth is the Nazis are trying to force a divorce on us, and the Gestapo will pick him up should he return to Berlin."

Amalie gasped at the news about her son, but to avoid having to say anything more, Elsbeth directed the conversation toward Arthur. "There's no way that he can come to the funeral. I will be there, I promise. When will it take place?" Amalie struggled with the words, but finally was able to say that he had passed away in the morning, and his internment should take place as soon as possible, preferably by sundown the day after.

"I'll be there in the morning, Mother. Take care and I'll see you soon."

Elsbeth immediately began to pack for the funeral, but she realized she had to get word to Willy, and it had to be right away. In her daze about her father-in-law and needing to tell his son, she didn't think about her actions. She picked up the receiver and asked for an international operator to connect her to the Grand Hotel.

Willy's stomach churned as he ran to the reception desk where the concierge was holding the receiver out to him.

"Hello? Elsbeth? Is that you? What's wrong?"

"Willy? Everything's okay with me, but you need to know that your father passed away this morning. The internment is tomorrow evening. I'm going to Magdeburg." Elsbeth heard nothing from the other end of the phone. "Willy? Are you there?"

He was jolted back into the conversation as if he had been in a dream. "Pappa's dead?"

"Yes. I'm so sorry, my love."

"How's Mutti? Wait, you're going to Magdeburg? Do you really think that's a wise thing to do?"

"Your mother is distraught, but Willy, she understands. Remember, she's the one who encouraged Edith to relocate, and Lucie and Rudolf too. She wouldn't want any of you risking a return to Germany." Elsbeth could hear his indecision through the deafening silence. She instinctively knew that her husband needed more reason to stay put, so she lied. "Your mother told me to tell you that your father loved you very much. He was so proud of you. Your service in the war, your success on the radio and in the movies. He wanted everyone he met to know that you were his son."

Willy was deeply surprised that his aloof father had felt so many emotions all these years. Arthur had barely spoken to him in his lifetime, so Willy simply assumed that he was indifferent to his son or his success.

"She said that you can't come to Magdeburg. And that if you do come, you'll not be allowed into the internment. She's right to say that, Willy. She just lost her husband. The last thing she wants now is to lose her son."

"You're right. The Gestapo will know that my father has died, and they'll be expecting me there. That's all the more reason for you to be careful when you travel. Please, tell me you'll be safe. Promise me that as soon as he is interred tomorrow evening, you will say your goodbyes and catch the next train back to Berlin."

Elsbeth had a bit of a different plan. "I think I'm going to stay in Magdeburg for a few days after the funeral. We all need to plan on what to do should the situation here in Germany get worse. Mother is old, and I'm the only person in a position to care for her." She suddenly became keenly aware just how much they had shared over the phone. "I must go. I'll be back in a few days. I love you. Stay safe."

"Stay safe, my darling. I love you. Please tell my mother I love her."

Placing the receiver down, he was again exhausted from bad news. Frau Rubino's rooming house was a short walk, and he needed a nap. As he entered his room, his thoughts wandered as he considered his life. It felt like everything in his past was now dead—his father, his country, his career in Germany, and even his war record. And in the present, he was an exile in a foreign country. Willy thought about his wife he couldn't be with, and instead of his comfortable apartment, he was living in a small room with a bed, dresser, and nightstand. Everything was being taken away by a madman at the helm of his beloved homeland. When his brain couldn't think anymore, when his sadness could no longer be contained, and when a long, hard cry had emptied him, he fell asleep.

March 8, 1940

Elsbeth ran down to meet the postman. Not a friendly man, but he was always punctual. "Anything for me today, Herr Spann?" She expected a letter every Thursday in return to one she mailed to Holland every Friday.

"Right here, Frau Rosen," he said, handing her a yellow envelope indicative of the stationary of the Grand Hotel.

"Thank you," she said, already going into the building. She sat on the sofa to read Willy's latest letter. She always read it quickly at first, and then reread it slowly to take in every word. She had barely got past the opening paragraph when there was loud pounding on her door. She jumped up, scattering the pages of Willy's letter onto the floor. As she neared the door, she could see it shake from the force of the pounding fist. "Who's there?"

"Gestapo. Open the door, Frau Rosen!"

Elsbeth couldn't move. She froze in place, not knowing what to do, but within seconds, the door was kicked in. She stepped back and watched as the second blow broke the old doorway into pieces, revealing three men in SS uniforms. Elsbeth screamed, and ran for the kitchen.

"Frau Rosen, halt!" The officer and two soldiers followed her, and as she fumbled for a knife she was spun around and punched in the face. Her limp body went reeling backward into the table where one of them turned her around and handcuffed her.

"What is going on? What's happening?" Blood poured from her nose, a steady stream spreading along the table and onto the floor.

"Frau Rosen, you are under arrest for collaborating with a known Jew. Your husband, Willy Rosen."

"But we've filed for divorce in Holland," she yelled at them, trying not to swallow blood.

"You're being taken to Gestapo headquarters where you will file for divorce in German civil court. If you refuse, you will be jailed."

The officer grabbed Elsbeth by her arm and half-dragged her from the apartment. She called out for anyone to help as he took her roughly down the stairs and out onto the street. She saw Dieter as she was tossed into the back of a black sedan. As he stepped from the sidewalk, Elsbeth mouthed something at him through the closed window of the car.

Dieter watched as the black car sped away before acting on what she asked of him. He ran into the Rosen apartment, carefully entering through the shards of broken door. There it was. The pages of a letter. He made sure to collect everything, including the envelope. There was the address of the Grand Hotel. Shoving it into his pocket, he raced back downstairs.

March 15, 1940

It wasn't unusual to get some of Elsbeth's letters delivered during rehearsal, but this one wasn't from her. Willy tore open the envelope. "Elsbeth's been picked up by the Gestapo!" he shouted, rising from his chair.

Everyone in rehearsal looked at him in stunned silence. Willy turned white, and the letter from Dieter dropped out of his hand. He couldn't think yet... too many thoughts rushed in at the same time. Where was she? Was she even alive? How? Why? He stood stock-still, and he let out the animal cry he had held back for months, maybe years. He doubled over, the sound not stopping as he continued onto his knees.

Erich was the first to reach him. "Franz, take Willy back to the dressing room and make him lay down. Give him some water but get him out of here."

Franz helped Willy up to his feet. "Erich? What's going on?"

"His wife has been arrested. Right now, all we can do is what anyone in our own family would do. Pray that our God is just and caring and will not allow her to suffer." He held out his hand to the nearest cast member, who did the same thing to the next person, and they continued until a circle had been made around Willy's empty chair.

"Let's give our hearts and minds to Willy and Elsbeth at this time." With those words, the cast squeezed their hands even tighter and lowered their heads, with many quietly crying for Willy, for Elsbeth, and for all they personally had lost.

Sitting on the cot in the dressing room, Willy played out in his mind the events of 1939 and these first months of 1940. He went to Berlin when he wasn't supposed to, and only escaped capture by Elsbeth pushing him onto a moving train. But Elsbeth was arrested. It was him alone deciding that he'd return to Berlin. And for what? The opening night of a show? It was that trip that instigated all of this. This put her in the Gestapo's crosshairs. *How stupid could I be? How reckless and stupid?* And he couldn't stop reflecting on the advice he had been given over the past year. No, for more than a year.

Why didn't he leave sooner, and take his parents and Elsbeth with him? They could all have been in Holland together. Why didn't he listen? He had to figure out a real plan to get his mother and Elsbeth out. But how? And now where was Elsbeth? Willy felt nauseous and his head pounded. *I just need some sleep.* He laid down, and complete exhaustion overtook him.

May 2, 1940

Elsbeth sat in the Ministry of Justice building looking carefully at her surroundings. Nazi flags, Nazi colors, Nazi stuff everywhere. A large set of heavy wooden doors suddenly opened across the hall from where she was seated. Two Gestapo held the doors open, and a small, bespectacled man with an unkempt head of hair approached her. He was shuffling through a stack of papers while he walked toward her.

"Elsbeth Rosen?"

"Yes."

"You are married to the Jew Willy Israel Rosenbaum?"

"His name is Willy Julius Rosen, and yes, I am married to my husband and he is Jewish." Hostility was funneling through her veins, and the very thought of acknowledging their questions made her nauseous. "He has filed for divorce in—"

"In Holland, yes," he said, getting to the point. "The Dutch courts mean nothing to us, Frau Rosen. The filing in The Hague is useless. You will file for divorce here, today, in our own German courts." He neither looked up from his papers nor stopped shuffling them while he delivered this news.

Before even thinking, she said, "No, I don't think so." She immediately felt empowered by her declaration.

The man stopped shuffling his papers, apparently finding the one he was looking for, and placed it on top. Still without looking at her, he straightened the stack, tucked them under his left arm, and with his right arm slapped Elsbeth to the hard marble floor.

"Is that all you people do? Hit women? I bet you feel like a real man now, don't you?" Elsbeth again found herself speaking before thinking.

The boot of the bespectacled man struck her squarely in the stomach.

"Get her up."

The two guards left their posts and lifted Elsbeth off the floor. When she hadn't quite regained her footing, she was punched again in the stomach, blood spewing from her mouth and onto her inquisitor. "It looks good on you," Elsbeth said between gasps for air. "Red blood, white shirt, black jacket. Just like your nasty flag." All Elsbeth remembered was a fist coming at her face. When she awoke, she found herself on a cot in a small holding room; this one with a sink and a toilet that was small enough to resemble a coffee can. As she took stock of herself, she could tell she had been unconscious for quite some time. The dried blood on her blouse and skirt had turned brown, bruising had set in around her wrists from the handcuffs, and she felt as if a large elephant was sitting on her abdomen.

Things were starting to filter back to her. Oh, yes. She had mocked that officer. *Why did I do that? That isn't going to help anything.* Someone must have been watching when she started to move, because at that moment the cell door opened, and her interrogator walked in. He stood over her, looking at her battered face. Elsbeth would get back some of her own sarcasm.

"Do you like my new shirt?" he asked, gesturing to his freshly pressed white shirt. "Of course, I did prefer the other one with your blood splattered on it. It gave it a, let's say, patriotic look." He grinned at her, making sure she saw it.

It didn't matter that she had trouble breathing. Her fury was raging again, and she would not be forced into anything. "Beating up women! That's what makes you happy? Well, go ahead. But I'm not filing for divorce, so you may as well find another woman to beat up."

"Oh, I'm sure there will be plenty of other women, Frau Rosen.

You, however... I will enjoy watching you suffer. You won't leave here until you file for a divorce from your dirty Jew of a husband."

Elsbeth gathered all of the moisture she could and spat right into his mouth. He slowly wiped away her saliva. "The worst part of this, Frau Rosen, is that this comes from a mouth that has kissed a Jew." He wiped the spit onto Elsbeth's shoulder. "It makes no difference to me how long you stay here. Just know that it will be painful for you but pleasant for me. Once you sign, you are free to go. It's up to you. Who knows? Maybe you like it here." He bent over Elsbeth and said in a softer voice, "Maybe you like me?"

He touched the side of her face, stroking her cheek.

Without thinking, she snapped hard at the finger and didn't let go until she had bitten it hard enough to draw blood.

"Bitch!" he screamed. "Guards!"

Elsbeth got one brief chuckle before she lost consciousness again.

May 10, 1940

"Okay, everyone, places. Let's take it from the top." Willy was throwing himself into his work, trying as best he could to keep the situation of Elsbeth's incarceration compartmentalized. His new revue was to open the following evening and the cast needed to know that his steady hand was at the helm.

By the time rehearsal ended, it was well into the early morning hours. Willy, Erich, and Franz met in the bar to discuss the final rehearsal and strategize for the evening's premiere of *Laugh, Pagliacci!* As they recapped the various high and low points, Willy noticed an absence of people milling about; the bar was empty except for the bartender, and no one was in the lobby. Even at this time of the early morning, the Grand was usually bustling with patrons arriving, partying, having drinks.

"What's going on? It looks like we're the only ones in the hotel." Willy called to the bartender. "Hey, Peter, where is everyone? Is something going on at the boardwalk?"

Peter looked at Willy aghast. "Where have you been? Don't you know what's happened?" The look on their faces made Peter furious. "You've got to be kidding me. You really don't know?"

Erich, annoyed at his questioning, asked, "What's happened?"

"Germany has invaded Holland. The Wehrmacht landed paratroopers just outside The Hague." Peter slammed his hands down on the bar top, yelling, "We're neutral. We've always been neutral. Why would the Germans attack us?"

The three froze at their table. Finally, Willy was able to sputter out, "The Germans are here? What are we going to do?" He looked at his two cohorts, and said, "Go get the cast and tell them to meet us immediately in the Lutine. Now!" Within minutes, he was in the theater waiting for cast and crew to arrive. Everyone came so quickly they were wearing only their night clothes. Once they were assembled, Willy spoke to them from the stage. "You may not have heard, or if you have, you are as shocked as we are. The Germans have invaded Holland." The assembled became visibly upset, many unable to control their fear.

"Please, please. There is no performance this evening. And for many of us, for quite some time. The German Army is at the outskirts of The Hague, just ten kilometers from us. While we have been rehearsing, most of the guests either left the hotel or are now locked in their rooms, waiting for the outcome of what may take days, maybe weeks, to unfold. I've asked the hotel manager if we can stay at the hotel until there is some resolution, and he's agreed. I don't see how we can leave Scheveningen, so I recommend going back to your rooms and waiting until there is news. If you are people of prayer, pray that Holland stays strong, as it has been our protector for years. Pray that our people remain safe, and that the Dutch Army will succeed in its mission to keep Holland a free state; free from the tyranny that has decimated our homelands. Good night and stay safe. I will reach out to all of you when I hear anything."

He left the hotel, and it was nearly dawn as he walked the sandy sidewalk to the boarding house. Willy was almost in his room when, in the far distance, he heard an explosion. "A bomb? Grenade? What does it matter?" he said to himself.

The concussive echo awakened what had been placid, and there was a swelling of sounds... seagulls, the ocean, the trees... Everything seemed to make itself known. He stopped and looked around one last time, as if it would all be gone tomorrow. He saw a beautiful sunrise, and couldn't remember if he ever noticed it. Inside the foyer, Willy saw the newspaper's headline for May 11: GERMANY INVADES HOLLAND – DUTCH VOW TO FIGHT ON!

Four days later, after the German annihilation of Rotterdam, Holland surrendered.

15

November 1940

"Have you heard any news about Elsbeth?" Eric asked.

"I heard a few days ago from Dieter. I know he's one of them. Anyway, he has access to Elsbeth. She's not doing too well, according to him. She's weak physically. They keep food and water away for long periods trying to break her."

"What do you think she'll do?"

"What I hope she does is file for divorce. It's not worth her dying over. I wrote to Dieter to tell her either she files for divorce or I'll come back to Berlin and turn myself in. I'm not going to have her suffer anymore. I just can't take it..."

"When do you expect her to get the most recent letter from you?"

Willy tried to clear his head. "Dieter has to find an opportunity to speak with her. He usually goes with a package from his mother. I expect he'd pass the news on any day now, but I won't know a thing until I hear from him."

Erich took his friend's hand. "Willy, she'll file for it. She loves you too much to chance your returning to Berlin."

"I hope you're right, Erich. I hope she loves me enough to let me go."

November 1940

"Frau Rosen?"

"Yes?"

"Come with me. You have a visitor."

The door opened, and a guard escorted her to a room with a large visitor table where she saw Dieter sitting across from an empty chair.

"Hello, Frau Rosen." Dieter had to appear unconcerned about her lest he draw attention; or at least until the guard left the room.

"Hello, Dieter. It's always nice to see you. How is your mother?"

"Mother is doing well, Frau Rosen. She hopes you are not finding this too unpleasant."

"Please, tell your mother I am just fine." Elsbeth's face was thin from lack of food and pale from lack of sunlight.

He noticed the fresh bruising at the base of her neck, and his face contorted. Gesturing toward his own neck, he asked, "Did they do that again?"

Elsbeth whispered, "It's okay. No emotion, remember?"

Dieter nodded.

"Now, is there any other news?"

"Yesterday. He said if you don't do it, he'll come to Berlin and do it for you."

She knew exactly what Dieter was talking about.

"He said that if you love him, you'll do it." He could see the effect of his words; she was unable to shoulder the weight of her husband's demand any longer.

"Frau Rosen, it's time. You must do it. If not for yourself, for him. I believe him. He'll come back to Berlin and be arrested immediately. You are doing nothing for him locked up here. I was ordered to come here by my superiors to convince you to see it their way. But Frau Rosen, I can see it's for the best." He saw Elsbeth soften, and her eyes looked so sad.

She brought her hands up to hide her face. Elsbeth knew her husband was right. What she was doing was not only hurting herself but also the man she was trying to protect.

Dieter placed his hand on her arm. "Frau Rosen, sometimes letting go is the strongest thing we can do."

Elsbeth lowered her hands and looked at her young neighbor. As she had done so many times before, she would judge him as both a boy and a man, never more one than the other. She realized that at that moment, though, she was looking into the eyes of a man whose wisdom betrayed his age. She pushed her chair back from the table, nodding.

Dieter stood as well, motioning to the guard. He took Elsbeth's hand as if to shake it but held it warmly, and said through barely moving lips, "I will let him know today. And you must leave Berlin immediately, for you no longer have an apartment." In full voice, he called to the guard, "Frau Rosen is ready now. You may take her to the captain."

In that same uncaring voice he said, "Thank you, Frau Rosen. I wish you luck." He then walked out of the room, not looking back.

The guard's voice shook Elsbeth back into the moment. "This way. The captain will be pleased to see you."

Elsbeth composed herself as best she could, pushed her chair back into place, and followed the guard toward the captain's office to officially end her marriage. She unconsciously rubbed her wedding ring. *When was the last time I even realized I was wearing this? Willy may not be my husband after today, but he will always be my man.*

Elsbeth Rosen walked into the captain's office of the Central Police Bureau, and after an hour of questioning and paperwork she officially walked out as Elsbeth Hoffman.

Once she was outside of the bureau, she could let the tears she'd held back for an hour stream down her face. She gripped tightly the loaf of bread and the ring that was ordered off her finger. Walking back to Cicerostrasse, she looked around at Berlin as if for the first time. *Dieter was right. I have to get out of here. But where?*

Arriving at her apartment, she turned the knob and the newly repaired door flung open, revealing a heavy-set man with a half-lit cigar dangling from his lips. "What do you want?" the man growled.

Elsbeth was shocked into silence. Dieter had warned her, but she'd had no time to comprehend it. Even now, after what seemed to be several minutes, she was finally able to speak. "This... this is my apartment."

The man looked at her and without hesitation said, "Jew-lovers don't have apartments anymore, especially if you don't pay your rent. Your stuff's boxed up downstairs in the basement." He slammed the door, and she stood there, unable to move.

After the shock subsided, she went to the basement, where she discovered box after box of her belongings. Her hands came to rest on the dress she'd worn to Arthur's funeral. *Mother... I'll go to Magdeburg.* She pulled everything out of the boxes, rifling through the pockets of every coat and dress, taking stock of the money she found. She didn't have enough even for the trainticket. Who could she ask for the rest of it?

Dieter and his mother have done enough. I can't ask them for another thing. In the pile she'd created when tossing items out of the boxes, she spotted a small velvet case. It was Willy's Iron Cross. For some reason, that sparked a thought. "Max and Anny," she said out loud, relieved she still had someone to turn to. She selected one purse, one coat, and a few dresses, shaking them out heavily. The last thing she took was the medal. She left the basement of 55 Cicerostrasse and with it, Berlin and her life with Willy.

"What now?" Erich asked, after Willy told him about the divorce.

"Back on stage. It seems like a lifetime ago since we last performed. Well, before May 10, anyway. It'll be good to get back to some sense of normalcy." Erich didn't say anything for a bit, and long enough for Willy to notice. "What's wrong? Why so quiet all of a sudden?"

Erich looked at Willy with bewilderment. "Normalcy? Nothing's normal anymore. It's our everyday. It's our life from now on. Realize it and stop living in this world of denial."

There was that accusation again. "I'm not denying anything. Amsterdam's not nearly as bad as Berlin," Willy said, although he hadn't been outside in months.

"Berlin didn't start out bad either, but then it became bad for all

Jews and, lest you forget, Jewish sympathizers. For crying out loud, your wife had to divorce you just to stay safe. How can you not think about it every second of every day?"

"If I think about it every second of every day, I would kill myself. Music is all I have. If I start to think about what's happening outside of these walls, I'll cry uncontrollably. I don't have a choice, you see? I have to think that my new normal is just that... normal... and not something that's been forced on me. I need to be back on that stage so that I can begin to figure out what my future holds. You can perform with me or not. That's your choice. I choose to perform and move forward making music with those I care about most. Are you in? Or are you going to let this new normal destroy you?"

Erich had lowered his head while listening. He raised only his eyes to look at his friend. He took a breath and said, "I'm in."

"Good." Willy put a stack of manuscripts and some pencils into his leather portfolio. "Let's go. We got a lot of work to do if we're going to get this show up before Christmas."

"We don't care about Christmas, Willy. We're Jews." Finally, a chance to make a joke.

"Well, Hanukkah, then. Let's get the show up before Hanukkah. When's the first night?"

"December 24."

"Then what difference does it make?" Willy said, laughing.

December 1940

It'd been years since Elsbeth strolled along Auf dem Grat, a main thoroughfare located in the upscale Dahlem section of Berlin. There were rows of beautiful townhouses whose views of the park were envious. Looking for the home of Max Schmeling and Anny Ondra, Elsbeth turned onto Föhrenweg and began counting down the house numbers until she found the one she was looking for. She had barely gone up one step when a hand roughly grabbed her from behind. "Can I help you?"

"I'm here to see Max and Anny."

"Are they expecting you?"

"No, but we're old friends. Could you tell them Elsbeth Rosen is here?"

"Wait here." After a few minutes, the man emerged from the house, gesturing Elsbeth to come inside.

As her eyes adjusted to the dim lighting, she saw Anny descending the staircase. "How lovely to see you again. Please excuse the security, but things are quite different now, as you well know." She hugged Elsbeth, kissing her lightly on the cheek, noting that it was bruised. "Max is over in America now. He would have loved to have seen you. How are you, and how is Willy doing?"

Elsbeth explained the events of the past eight months, going into great detail on the trouble she took to keep her marriage from ending. "Anny, I need some help, and I didn't have anyone else I could trust. I need to get to Magdeburg. Willy's mother's there, and I'm certain she's scared to death. With her husband dead, and all her children in other countries, she's all alone. Anny... can I have some money for a train ticket?" She hated the thought of asking anyone for help, let alone for money, but there were no other options.

"Of course. Let me get my purse."

As Elsbeth waited, a small figure ran by the living room door. *Was that a child?* Anny returned to the room, her purse in hand. "You and Max don't have any children, I know, but..." and she pointed toward the hallway.

Deeply surprised by the question, Anny simply got out, "We don't have children." She was silent as she figured out what she could tell Elsbeth. After a few moments, she said, "We're hiding children... the Mendelssohn's...Max's banker. No one must know, Elsbeth. The Nazis have arrested their parents and confiscated everything they had. This is why we have the guard outside. Our celebrity allows for the authorities to permit private security, so we're hiding the children of our Jewish friends, like Max did during *Kristallnacht*."

"Max? *Kristallnacht*? I don't understand."

Deciding she would share this story, Anny took Elsbeth's hands in her own. "Let me tell you a story that my husband would never share. On *Kristallnacht*, Max was staying at the Excelsior Hotel in Berlin. His friend David Lewin became concerned for the lives of his teenage sons, Henri and Werner, and asked Max to hide them in his hotelroom. David snuck his sons into Max's room, and then Max phoned the front desk to ask that no one visit him, that he was ill and didn't want to get anyone infected. It worked. For days the Lewin brothers stayed hidden in Max's room. Once Max felt it was safe, he arranged for the boys to return to their parents, helping the entire family relocate to Shanghai and ultimately to America. No one can ever know. It would be the proof that they need to ruin his career and take him away. I'm so proud of him, Elsbeth. He saved their lives and hasn't spoke of it since."

Elsbeth was mortified. "Oh Anny, here I am concerned only for myself, and you and Max are living every day in constant fear too."

They were both very still as Anny opened Elsbeth's hand and placed a sizable bundle of Reichsmarks in her palm. "There is no such thing as bravery in these times, my dear. There's only humanity and doing what's right." She glanced nervously at the clock on the mantel. "You better go now, in case you were followed. This neighborhood can be difficult. Heinrich Himmler lives close by, so there are always Nazis wandering the streets of Dahlem. He certainly brings property values down," she said, trying to lighten the mood.

She called for the guard who then escorted the pair to the entryway. Anny turned to Elsbeth before the door was opened. "This may be the last time we see each other. Please care for yourself, and bless you for caring for Willy's mother. He will love you forever, you know."

Nodding, Elsbeth left, walking quickly to the train station.

January 1941

The Prominenten's second revue in the Beatrix Theater, *Viel Vergnügen!* (*Enjoy yourself!*), felt like old times to Willy, opening on January 9, 1941. His cast had been stable for the past few months since moving to Amsterdam. Audiences filled the theater night after night; searching for anything to take their minds off the occupation. The accompanying festivities went on into the early hours of the following morning, leaving Willy, Erich, and Franz bleary-eyed on their way back to their rooms off Plantage Middenlaan. They were laughing and enjoying the feeling of artistic success, and the expected critical acclaim in the morning's newspaper.

"Have the papers been dropped off yet?" Willy asked, as if the other two were in possession of information he wasn't privy to.

"I don't see any bundles yet, but the shops aren't even open. What time is it?" Franz asked.

Erich looked at his watch but his eyes were having a hard time focusing. "It's half past four. It's early, but they should have been dropped off in front of the shops by now."

The trio raced up to the nearest stack to sneak a peek at the review. Erich took a paper out from under the binding cord and began to rifle through it. Meanwhile, Franz's eye caught an announcement that was freshly pasted on the nearest light pole. "What is this?" he asked, pointing to a poster with a large yellow Star of David. He read out loud, "*Joodse registratie om meteen te beginnen!* Willy, Erich. Jewish registration to begin immediately. What the hell?"

"It's starting. Oh my God. It's going to be Berlin all over again," Willy said, his voice going up and his brain no longer fuzzy. "What are we going to do?"

Erich, whose logic was always a stabilizing force, said, "There's nothing we can do. There's nowhere we can go. The only thing we can do is register. It's not like they're dragging people away. Besides, the Dutch would never allow for that." He was matter of fact about it.

"Of course. They just want to know who we are. Kind of like a census," Willy said, not quite believing his own words. "Everything will be alright." Wanting to change the subject, he asked, "Where's the review?"

"On page four," Erich answered.

While Willy read over Erich's shoulder, Franz worried about the registration and its counterpart in their homeland. He could only hope that the Dutch would never allow its Jews to be rounded up.

February 1941

Willy noticed people scurrying, as if wanting to get out of the way of something. He couldn't understand why everyone was in such a hurry, and on such a beautiful day too.

"Good morning, guys," Willy said on his arrival at the theater. "Are we ready for today?"

Fritz and Erich were surprised by Willy's attitude. "Did you hear all the noise last night?" Erich asked. "Did you sleep at all?"

He wasn't sure what he was getting at. "I slept like a log. What are you talking about?"

"There was a lot of noise last night. Kept me up most of the night."

"Me too," Fritz added. "People were running down the street, coming from around Waterlooplein."

Willy responded, "Nope, nothing," and changed the subject to the performance at hand. "What are our thoughts on last night's performance? I thought Franz was outstanding in his sketches. His songs were spot on as well. What did you think?" Getting no response, he said, "Will you two snap out of it? We have work to do. People pay to see us and it's our job to get it right."

Fritz started to protest but was stopped by Willy's look. "Sure, Franz was great last night."

Relieved to have steered the conversation back on track, Willy said, "Last night was good. Tonight? Let's make it great—"

As the three retreated to the back of the theater, they could hear more noise from the street than usual.

"What was that?" Willy ran to the back door, opening it just enough to stick his head out and look down the alleyway. "What the hell?" As he pulled his head back into the theater, Willy started to run across the stage and down the right aisle of the house. "Something's going on!" he called back to Erich and Fritz.

The pair followed Willy, trying to catch up as he neared the main entry to the theater. The three burst out onto Plantage Middenlaan only to be stopped by the sight of several large trucks filled with German soldiers driving by, followed by two flatbed trucks filled with rolls of barbed wire. Willy stood unwavering as the blood drained from his face. "I can't think about this now. Let's go back inside. We have a show to put on in less than four hours." The cast members began arriving at six o'clock for the eight o'clock show. Otto and Sylvia arrived at the same time, both with as many suitcases as they could fit into a shared taxi. They dragged their belongings onto the stage, with Willy looking on in amazement.

"What are you two doing? Moving in?" Willy joked.

"The Germans are cordoning off the area with barbed wire. We won't be able to go home once they finish," Otto told him. "So, yes, we're staying here until we find an apartment close to the theater. By the time the Germans are through today, we'll all be in a newly prescribed Jewish ghetto of Amsterdam, the *Jodenbuurt*."

"A Jewish Quarter in Amsterdam? What does that even mean?"

He shrugged ever so slightly. "I have no idea," Otto said. "All I know is, if there's going to be barbed wire between me and this theater, I intend to be on this side of it. Cordoned or not, this is where I have to be."

Sylvia, arranging her luggage in a pyramid, added, "Me too. If this is where we Jews are to be, then I'm here, and I'm not going anywhere."

"Guys, look. We may not have a choice," Erich said quietly. "The patrons are coming in an hour and a half early. What's going on?" He approached a couple in the front row. "Why are you here so early? The show doesn't start for a while."

"We have nowhere else to go. We're told that we have to stay here in the *Jodenbuurt* until the boundaries are set and checkpoints erected. It could be days. What are we supposed to do?" the man said.

Erich noticed that the wife sat motionless, staring into space as if in a trance.

"Of course. You are most welcome."

Willy was still having a hard time believing what he was hearing and seeing. "Yes, of course. You are welcome here until you... and all of us... are able to return to our homes." He watched as one displaced Jew after another entered the theater, some wandering aimlessly because they simply couldn't sit still in a seat.

Franz took Willy aside. "What are we supposed to do?"

"Perform," Willy said. "If there was ever a time these people needed us, it's now."

"What about the tickets?" Franz asked. "The box office isn't open yet; these people walked in."

"Forget it. Tonight's on us. Let's open the doors and let whoever wants to come in, come in. As for the Germans, let's deal with that later. Elsbeth always says that everything looks better in the morning." Willy gathered the cast members with a gesture of his hand.

"When do we start?" Sylvia asked in a whisper. "Should we wait until eight o'clock?"

Willy watched the theater filling up. In the balcony several dozen spectators sat, too shocked to show any emotion at all. It was in this moment that Willy knew what he had to do. He smiled and turned to the group. "We'll wait until half past eight. We wouldn't want anyone to miss out on the fun now, would we? After all, this is why we're here." Pointing out into the house, he added, "We're here for them."

Sylvia watched Willy disappear into the catacombs of dressing rooms and costume shops, and she could only think how lucky she was that she had found him. Really, that she had found this family.

"He's right. It's not about us anymore." She looked at the faces that were sitting in the seats: individuals, couples, families. Everyone sat in complete silence, as if a single word spoken might disturb what was becoming a sacred space. The statuesque redhead remembered her own plight in fleeing Vienna during the Anschluss, and just how many times words couldn't express the terror of being forced into a new reality. "We're here for them," she repeated and followed Willy backstage.

16

July 5, 1941

"I don't understand," Willy said. "What is this *Joodsche Raad* and why do we need one?"

"Because the Jews need a representative body and that would be the Jewish Council. Its members can speak to the Germans, that's why," explained Johan Sellmeyer, the manager of the Beatrix Theater. "The Germans have identified prominent Jews within the *Jodenbuurt* who can act as mediators between the German authorities and the Jewish population. Things are changing quickly. We have to be completely cooperative."

What troubled Willy was not having a voice of his own. "Fine, but who is this Frans Primo? Who does he work for?"

"He's with the *Joodsche Raad*, and he'll have the final say on who performs on the stage."

Willy was still having trouble believing that a theater manager was going along with this. "So Primo wants you to post a sign saying that we are an exclusively Jewish ensemble performing for exclusively Jewish audiences. That means I can't have any non-Jews as part of my troupe or in the audience, right?"

Johan slammed his hand down on the desk, silencing his friend.

"You still don't get it, do you? We have no choices anymore. We do what we are told. Period. We are now a Jewish theater in a Jewish ghetto in a German-occupied country. That's it. We don't argue, we don't resist. We only do as we're told. The sooner you get that through your head, the better off you and the rest of us will be." He wasn't done with Willy. "If you don't learn how to play nicely with the Germans and the *Joodsche Raad*, I'll have no choice but to cancel the rest of your performances."

"I get it, Johan. I think if I can speak to the Council personally, at least I can be a face to them rather than just some performer wanting special permission."

"If you get this theater into any kind of situation with them, I swear you will never step foot on this stage again. Do you understand me?"

Johan was serious and Willy knew it. He would have to put on his best clothes and his finest demeanor before meeting with the members. "I promise, no issues. I intend to wow them."

"No, you will not 'wow' them. Simply introduce yourself and ask for specific clarifications on the restrictions placed on non-Jewish performers in your troupe. That is it."

July 11, 1941

"Mother, is there anything you want in particular?" Elsbeth called up from the basement.

"Can you bring up some of the canned carrots?"

One of the benefits of living outside of Berlin, and sadly of being divorced from Willy, was that she no longer felt like she was being monitored, and as a result was enjoying a sense of security she hadn't felt for over a year. She set the variety of canned vegetables and pickled meats on the kitchen table and let Amalie begin her routine of selecting which delicacies to turn into the evening meal.

"Has the post come yet?" Elsbeth asked.

"It's on the hall table."

Elsbeth picked up the small stack of mail delivered that morning. Right on top she spotted the handwriting of her former husband, although the stationary was not what she was expecting. "There's a letter from Willy," Elsbeth called out.

"Let me know what he has to say." Amalie knew very well the circumstances that had forced Elsbeth's hand, and recognized the deep love she had for her son.

Opening the envelope, Elsbeth was a little disappointed to find the letter was only one page. No matter the length, she sat down to savor the read.

Willy's explanation of the Jewish ghetto and the *Joodsche Raad* cleared up the odd stationery. The only stable address for him now was the Beatrix Theater.

July 5

Since we have been forced to be a "Jews Only" ensemble that performs exclusively for Jews, the sense of community is outstanding here; it truly brightens my day. People are making too much out of the cordoned-off Jewish sectors. We are free to leave and return as long as we have our passports, which for identification purposes, have been stamped with a large red "J." Most of the cast members have moved into the Jewish Quarter around the Beatrix Theater. Elsbeth, you would be so proud of the work we're doing. If it weren't for us, I am certain that people wouldn't laugh at all! Nelson's revue, down the street at the Hollandsche Schouwburg, is running with great success as well.

Elsbeth, thank you for taking care of Mutti. Please let me know how you both are doing and what news you have of anyone else. It gives me great joy to know that you are and will always be a dear part of my life. I love you now as I have always.

Your Willy

Elsbeth wasn't sure if her tears were from joy or sadness. She only knew that Willy was alive and seemed to be happy.

July 30, 1941

The building that housed the *Joodsche Raad* was a former canning factory with an elaborate array of offices and workspaces. Looking for someone to point him to its offices, Willy opened a door behind which sat a row of young ladies at sewing machines making yellow Stars of David with the scripted blue "J" in the center. He hadn't realized that he was staring at one particular lady, or maybe he was staring at the Star of David in front of her. In either case, she had no intention of letting him stand there. "Excuse me. Can I help you with something, or are you just a fan of yellow stars?"

Willy didn't know if he should be embarrassed or not, but he did know that he was a fan of sarcasm. "I'm not sure. I do like yellow stars, but the 'J' is a bit obtrusive. Less subtle would be better, don't you think? Now, if it were me doing the sewing, I would make both the Star of David and the 'J' yellow."

"That makes no sense at all. If they were both yellow, then no one would see the letter." No sooner had the words come out of her mouth than she got the joke and burst into laughter. "Thank you for the laugh. It's been way too long since I've done that."

There was nothing he enjoyed more than making someone laugh. "Then you must come down to the Beatrix and see my show." He reached out to shake her hand, hoping that she would reciprocate.

She did. "I'm Olga Krauskopf but my friends call me Mara. And yes, I walk past the theater after work. I can't afford to come see you, but I get such enjoyment listening to the audience from the sidewalk."

Willy was fixated by the young lady, and extended the conversation any way he could to keep talking with her. "Mara? Isn't that an odd nickname for Olga?"

"My middle name's Maria, so Mara isn't too bad, is it?"

"Not at all."

He was charming and she certainly didn't mind talking with him.

"In any event, it's a pleasure to meet you, Mara. Can you point me to the *Joodsche Raad* office?"

"You'll have to take the steps. Third floor, turn left, and follow the hallway until the end."

"Thank you, Mara. May I ask, if you're not busy tomorrow evening, would you like see our show? I can leave a ticket for you at the box office. It would be my pleasure."

Mara couldn't remember the last time someone had offered her anything, let alone a ticket that would have been impossible to afford on her own.

"I would love to see it, Herr Rosen. Thank you."

"Willy. Please, call me Willy."

"Then Willy it is."

Going upstairs, Willy looked back at Mara, who poked her head out of the door. They exchanged a look, and she said, "Better not take your eyes off the stairs, Willy. Use the handrail."

Willy chuckled, and continued up to the third floor.

The Dutch Jewish Council was a self-governing agency that cooperated with the German occupiers to create lists of Jews, the property they owned, their bank holdings, and other financial investments, as well as any bank accounts located in other German-occupied countries. It also oversaw the establishment of the *Jodenbuurt* and the many other Jewish Quarters scattered throughout the city. Amsterdam already had several areas with large Jewish populations, and its intricate system of canals created natural boundaries that divided the many sectors of the city. By setting up carefully placed barbed wire and checkpoints, the Jewish population could move around the city by using their passports stamped with a large red "J."

The *Joodsche Raad* also oversaw the establishment of several institutions formed for the educational and artistic advancement of the Jews in Amsterdam. Funding for these programs came largely out of the private monies donated to the *Joodsche Raad* by the barrel manufacturer Bernard van Leer before fleeing Holland for America.

Van Leer left a substantial amount of money for the formation of the Van Leer Foundation which funded several artistic departments, including a Jewish orchestra, chorus, dance band, and, of course, Jewish theater and cabaret.

Each department was overseen by the top Dutch talent of the day. Dr. Werner Levie oversaw the coordination of all activities; Henriëtte (Heintje) Davids, sister of Louis, oversaw the running of cabaret and small-stage productions. Willy was comfortable knowing that the fate of cabarets and revues was in the hands of his talented friend. It was the larger organization that he had a problem with, and specifically their demand that theater be exclusively for Jews and by Jews.

As he neared the door to the *Joodsche Raad*, it occurred to him that starting with Heintje might be a wiser move. He was instructed to take a seat while she was located. Before too long, a rotund woman with an ill-kempt mop of hair pinned to the top of her head walked down the side hall of the office. She was dressed in what could best be described as a floral duster with large buttons running the length of the frock, yet the fabric was almost too worn to hold them into place.

Willy jumped to his feet. "Heintje, how are you? It's been way too long."

They hugged tightly, and she whispered in his ear, "Come with me. We can't talk here. Let's go into my office."

He followed her down a long narrow corridor to a tiny room with a small desk and a few assorted chairs. Willy took a seat, and she locked the door. "It's so nice to see you," she said in a voice that was both soft and thick with resonance. "What can I do?" She anticipated why he was there but was hoping she was wrong.

"Heintje, since when do we need to be a theater of Jews and for Jews? Has it gotten that bad? Are we at the point where we are self-isolating from our friends?"

She nervously adjusted herself in her seat, which was too small for such a large frame. "Yes. Things are that bad. The *Joodsche Raad* has received instructions from the Central Office for Jewish

Emigration to begin collecting the names of everyone and everything Jewish within Holland. Just as they did in Germany, Austria, and Poland. Do we want to self-isolate? No. We are being forced to, and the Council has no choice but to cooperate."

"You mean to tell me that Jews are helping the Germans isolate Jews? Has the world gone completely mad?"

"Because truly, only Jews know other Jews. And only Jews know who has what in their possession. If the Germans don't get this information through us, they'll simply start arresting people even more randomly than they are now. The *Joodsche Raad* is trying to buy time."

"Buy time until...?"

"Until we're the ones who are arrested. Those of us with prominent names and specific purposes that keep the Quarter calm and not in a constant state of panic. There will be a time, Willy, when we'll have to take care of ourselves as individuals. There will be no *Joodsche Raad* or any organization that can protect us from our imposed destiny."

"Which is what?" Willy could barely think. This was much more than he had bargained for.

"Which is the elimination of all culture, of all joy, and of all celebration within the Quarter. The Germans want us to have all of this so that, ultimately, they can take it away. I'm only here as a puppet and as a face that the Council selected to help keep the Jewish community tranquil and settled. I do nothing. I sit, and I do nothing unless they tell me to. I'm just a face, Willy."

He stood up without saying a word. As he reached for the doorknob, Heintje grabbed his hand. She looked at him with complete despair. "Willy, figure out how you're going to get out of here. That will be the best thing you can do for yourself. Get out of here. I can't. There's no way they'll let me out of their sight. It may be too late for you as well."

He walked down the narrow hallway, feeling disembodied after the news he had just

received. At the bottom of the staircase he opened the door to where the seamstresses were busily making their Star of David patches, looking for Mara. She glanced up from her machine and smiled at Willy. *What a beautiful smile. How can anything be wrong when you look at such a beautiful smile?*

Willy turned and headed through the entryway and onto the sidewalk. He crossed the street and gazed into the Plantage Muidergracht canal; the flowers along the sides betraying the feelings of loss and helplessness that flooded through his body. Looking up, he saw people walking about as if there weren't a care in the world. " Jews I suppose... and they look as if they hadn't a worry. Why can't I feel like that?"

It was at that moment that Willy knew. "I have no plan... what would I do somewhere else? In Cuba? In America? Anywhere?" Willy simply couldn't see that anywhere was better than where he was; that the best of intentions sometimes don't work as planned.

"I'm here and here is where I'll stay." Contented that he had made a "plan", Willy turned from the canal and headed back to Plantage Middenlaan for the afternoon rehearsal of *Het Klopt!*

October 1, 1941

My dearest Willy,

How I hope that this letter finds you safe and well. Things in Magdeburg are remarkably similar to Berlin. We are seeing the same restrictions placed upon Jews here as in the larger cities.

Food is scarce in Magdeburg, but you know your mother; she has a basement filled with canned vegetables from the garden and fruit she has collected over the years. My guess is that it will be just a matter of time until the Nazis hear of her surplus and confiscate it all.

You know that Lucie and Rudolf are still safely in São Paolo, Brazil. Mother wouldn't leave, as you well know, and to be honest, Willy, I am not sure how long I'm able to stay in this country. Lucie wrote for me to join her there, but your mother is so weak and vulnerable that I feel I must stay with her.

Willy, my heart breaks for you, but you must do what you can to survive this. I know you. I know that whatever plan you have for yourself will not be enough. Please find friends who can help you. Should you find someone you trust enough, and you care for her, keep her close to you, as companionship may be the one thing you can count on as the days pass.

My love, know that I will stay with your mother until that is no longer possible. Until then, I will continue to write and anxiously await your letters. Autumn is passing much too quickly for me, but as long as you continue to shine, the season is immaterial. Write soon.

With much love,

Your Elsbeth

Willy sent his next letter, responding to Elsbeth's news.

October 21, 1941

My dearest Elsbeth,

I am eternally grateful for your sacrifice in taking care of Mutti. Lucie should never have burdened you with this. Any news from Edith in London? What would I ever do without you?

After the run of our last revue, the authorities forced Johan Sellmeyer to remove the name of the Dutch Royal Princess from the theater, turning the Beatrix into the new Theater van de Lach. Johan is still the manager and does everything he can to secure our safety as the walls seem to be slowly closing in on our little troupe, which, by the way, is not a little troupe anymore!

The Hollandsche Schouwburg has been turned into the new Jewish Theater and Nelson's revue is still running there. News has it that it may not be running for much longer, but you know how these things are.

I am grateful that you are making plans to leave Germany. You mustn't be heroic with Mutti; she is extremely resourceful and has an entire neighborhood filled with Jews to help her. You should go to Lucie and Rudolf. At least I will be comforted in knowing that you're with family.

We hear little about the war in the *Jodenbuurt*. No radios are allowed, and our leaving is strictly monitored. As for companionship, I have my family here, which seems to expand and decrease at any given moment. Word is that Max Ehrlich will be coming back to perform with the Prominenten! I miss Max.

My dear, I miss you every day. I must go. Rehearsal is calling!

All my love,

Your man, Willy

December 8, 1941

"Did you enjoy the show, Mara?" Willy asked.

"I thought it was the funniest and most clever show I have ever seen. I don't know how you do it. You write all the music, the words, rehearse the show, and accompany the entire production. You're amazing."

Willy was smitten with Mara, although it was more for the flattery than anything else. As he had told Elsbeth many times, no one could ever take her place.

Sunday performances always meant late-night drinks after the show and conversation with Franz, Fritz, Erich, and now Max Ehrlich. The group of six eagerly walked through the cold and light dusting of snow to reach Café de Paris, one of few restaurants that catered to a Jewish clientele and stayed open past showtime.

Willy was always eager to hear the rundown of the week's performances. With Max back in the group, there would be even greater analysis. They sat in the Café de Paris for hours—analyzing, laughing, cursing, laughing again—as if they were in another time and another place.

"Look at the sun," Mara said, as if she were seeing it for the first time.

"How can anything be wrong on a morning like this?" Willy asked his friends as they sipped good coffee among great company. They looked through the windows of the Café de Paris, watching as shop after shop came to life. People were coming out into the streets, and the city was beginning its Monday morning schedule of events. Willy thought he heard a familiar crackling sound coming from behind the kitchen door. "Shhhh, listen! Is that a radio?"

Fritz snuck a look through the window of the kitchen door. "It is," he said to the group, but he abruptly backed up as the waiter entered the restaurant looking quite upset.

"Good heavens, sit down. You look awful." Max helped the young man to a chair while Mara put a glass of water in front of him. "What's wrong? Can we help?" she asked.

The waiter looked at the group, and then out the window at the people who were standing on the sidewalk. "There's nothing you can help me with. You'll need to help yourselves now."

Max asked, "What? What are you talking about? What happened?"

"The Japanese just attacked the Americans at Pearl Harbor in Hawaii. America's declared war on Japan." The young man stared at them, then stood up and walked back into the kitchen.

After a few moments, Fritz asked, "What does that mean for us?" He was hopeful someone had the answer.

"No idea, but America's coming into the war. That should help us. Right?" Max asked, as hopeful as Fritz.

"I would think so," Willy said, raising his coffee cup. "Let's toast to the Americans."

"To the Americans," the group shouted, as they downed the rest of their coffee, happy to face the day with a renewed sense of purpose.

. . .

On December 11, four days after the Japanese attack on Pearl Harbor and the United States' declaration of war against the Japanese Empire, Nazi Germany declared war against the United States. Had any of the remaining Prominenten wished to leave Holland for America—or, in the case of Willy, for Cuba—that option was now gone. Those in Holland would be forced to remain there and await their fate.

By order of the German Authorities Willy was forced on December 15 to officially register at the *Joodsche Raad* with the Occupying Forces as a Jew living within the German Reich. From this point on his every movement in and out of the Joodsche Buurt would be monitored and recorded, as well as employment and any change of residence.

Willy Rosen was officially a part of the German Pogrom for the Jews in Holland, and still had no grasp on the reality of the situation.

17

May 1942

"Willy, can you give the girls a break and come to my office?" Johan Sellmeyer never interrupted rehearsals, so Willy knew the news wasn't going to be good.

"Sure. Ladies, take ten. I'll be right back." He followed the theater manager to his office.

Johan folded his hands on his desk, covering an official-looking document. "Willy, bad news. The Nazis are shutting us down. Theater van de Lach is no more after tonight's performance."

Since the coal shortage closed the theater for three weeks, audiences had flooded the Joodsche Schouwburg, desperate for entertainment.

Willy responded, "Honestly, I'm not shocked. I must admit I'm not even surprised. The coal shortage had exposed that two theaters drain more resources than one. What are we supposed to do now?"

"After tonight, you and the entire cast are no longer protected from being deported. You could all easily end up on a train to the east." Johan could barely look at Willy at this point.

After several seconds of stunned silence, Willy said, "There must be something. I can't allow my cast to be unprotected. They're here because they trust me. They trust us, Johan. We can't just sit here and allow this to happen." He paused for a moment. "Heintje Davids. She'll help. Can you cover for me in rehearsal?"

"Of course. Go and see what you can find out."

When Willy reached Heintje's office, the door was already open, and her head was down on her desk, her loud snores echoing in the small room. He realized that she probably hadn't slept in days, but the disruption was absolutely necessary. He knocked on the door. "Heintje? It's Willy. Heintje?" his voice getting louder with each word.

She popped up as if an automaton, her back stiffened and her eyes struggled to see who disturbed her sleep. Seeing Willy, she got up to hug him tightly; she could see he was deeply troubled. "What's happened? What's wrong?"

"You haven't heard? The Council's closing our theater after tonight's performance." He was frantic as he relayed the information he'd just heard from Johan.

There was a long pause as Heintje struggled to find the words. "I'm so sorry. It was bound to happen. We can't keep both theaters now. The Germans are demanding that we curtail cultural activities and by closing the smaller of the two theaters, we're able to show them we're cooperating."

"Cooperating? Have you thought about the repercussions for my cast?"

"They can perform with Nelson, Willy. It's not that bad. It's Johan who is the biggest loser in this deal, and I'm trying to figure out where to place him so that he still has a job. Of course, he's not a Jew, but as a sympathizer—"

Willy cut her off. "The moment you close our theater my cast is no longer protected from deportation. You know this, right?" He looked into her eyes, looking for any indication that she clearly understood the situation.

"Yes, I know. Look, you have to trust me, if only for a few weeks."

"What?" He could not make sense of the situation. *Was she in on this? Was this her idea? Surely not...*

"The orders have come that there must only be one theater, and the Council chose the Joodsche Schouwburg. There are

168

hundreds of performers that are part of the cultural life of the Quarter, and all of you are protected by the Van Leer Foundation."

"But we will no longer be the moment the theater closes! We'll be unprotected, off the list." Willy was frantic at the thought that he and his cast were being sacrificed for the sake of cooperation.

Heintje tried to keep a conversational tone to calm down her friend. "Listen, you just have to trust me. It'll take time, but I intend on getting you and all your cast onto the Van Leer list for the Schouwburg. The Council want me to close the theater and give you up to the Germans as a sign of good faith and cooperation. I will not let that happen."

"Really? What's your plan?"

"You'll finish your performance this evening and give the cast a couple weeks off. During that time you'll meet with the Nelsons to work on a new revue, a collaboration.[1] If you can come up with a revue to open at the Schouwburg that uses every member of both casts before the Council can act, then I have grounds to get you and your troupe on the Foundation's list for the Schouwburg. Do you understand?"

Willy walked out of her office like he was walking to the scaffold. His mind was racing through the various scenarios that might play out should her plan not succeed when Mara met him at the bottom of the staircase. "Willy, what's wrong?"

"I can't talk about it. Not here. Can you come to the theater when you get off work?"

"Of course. I'll be there an hour before showtime. Are you going to be okay?"

"That's out of my hands now. It's completely out of my hands."

"Just tell us what you would like, Heintje," said Herbert. "We'll do anything you need. As long as I'm able to call the shots here at the Schouwburg, we'll take on any cast member we can... anything to annoy the Nazis. We can plan to have something up by mid-June. Will that work?"

"Yes, it's perfect. I need rehearsals to start so that I can put Willy and his cast on the Van Leer list. Can you give me a start date?"

"What's today's date?" Herbert asked, grinning.

"May 2nd."

"Then rehearsals just started!"

"Bless you, Herbert. What you're doing is—"

But he held up his hand. "We're just being human. Is it not too much to ask that we take care of our own? No, it's required that we take care of our own." Herbert walked toward the stage to watch the rehearsal and turned back to Heintje. "What do you think of our stars? And I don't mean the actors," he said pointing to Sylvie Grohs and the newly stitched Star of David on her red military costume. "Don't you feel it offers just the right amount of self-deprecating hate? But the color is not exactly what I would choose."

"Careful, Herb, you never know who's listening," Heintje said, but she hadn't smiled that big in a long time.

"Let them hear it. The Nazis need to know just how little taste in fashion they have," he said, heading back to rehearsal.

Heintje left the theater acutely aware of the current situation of Jewish artists. She drew a large breath as she opened the door of the Theater van de Lach, and entered to pass on the good news to Willy. Instead, she found Johan who was packing up his office. Upon seeing her he threw his arms around her expansive waist.

"Heintje, how are you? Long time no see," Johan said, giving her a peck on the cheek. "Are you looking for Willy?"

"Yes, but finding you is an added perk. How are you doing?" Heintje had known Johan for most of her professional career and was genuinely concerned. "Do you have any plans?"

He didn't have a response so pretended to keep packing.

She took his hands, turning him so that he could see her face. "Johan, you've done everything that you could for Willy and the cast. There is nothing you could have done to stop what's happening. All we can do is move on and figure out how to minimize the damage. That's why I'm here. There is some good news. Everyone is going to the Schouwburg. They'll be safe there."

Johan gave out a small cry and his knees buckled.

Heintje grabbed his arm and walked him to his chair.

"They're safe then?" He could barely get the words out.

"Yes, every last one of them is safe. Herbert Nelson's agreed to combine the ensembles. If you like, I can ask him to place you in the theater as well."

Johan shook his head. "I've had enough. I have to get out of here."

"I understand. Would you like me to tell Willy anything for you?"

"Tell him that he's made Amsterdam... no, the world... a much better place. Tell him I wish him and everyone only the best as they make their way through this storm."

"I will. You take care of yourself. If you ever need anything, let me know."

They gave each other a long hug to soften their broken hearts.

June 1942

"We got a letter from Willy," Elsbeth exclaimed as she went into the sitting room, where Amalie continued her knitting without raising her head. "Mother, did you hear me?"

Still, no indication that she had heard the good news.

"Damn hearing," Elsbeth muttered. "Could be completely gone by now."

Elsbeth couldn't take Amalie to the doctor because there were no Jewish physicians left in Magdeburg. Elsbeth decided to read the letter privately, and walked into the kitchen.

June 13, 1942

My dearest Elsbeth,

I pray every day that you both are safe and that, when I write, my letters find you happy and healthy. Things here in Amsterdam are quickly turning from bad to worse.

Sellmeyer's Theater van de Lach was closed by the German authorities. We have all been relocated to the Joodsche Schouwburg down the street thanks to the quick thinking and kindness of Heintje Davids and, of all people, Herbert Nelson! Yes! Herbert and Rudolph Nelson! We are all extremely grateful to them both!

Things in the city are quickly closing in around us. Whereas we had freedom to come and go out of our Jewish Quarter, that right has been taken away. We must stay where we are "assigned."

Yesterday was among the worst days since the closing of the theater. All Jews had to turn over their bicycles! Can you imagine that, Elsbeth? Amsterdam with no bicycle? Many of us simply live at the theater these days; 24 hours of constant Schouwburg! It makes us feel safe, anyway.

Increasingly, the Nazis are summoning Jews to the work camps. Van Leer protects us, but there is an added feeling of security when you're in the theater. Mara Krauskopf and I sleep here now with the rest of the cast members, which leads me to another point. Mara is a sweet, dear young thing. I met her while she was working as a seamstress at the *Joodsche Raad* and we've been spending lots of time together lately. She has family here in Amsterdam, in one of the other Jewish Quarters. Since she works here in the Middenlaan Quarter, she can't go home anymore so she lives in the theater with me. She's even begun to act in the revues! She's been a great comfort to me these past months, Elsbeth, and as things are appearing to get worse for us all, it would be nice to have someone to go through this with. I am going to ask her to marry me. I hope you will forgive me.

Elsbeth, Mara could never replace you or the love that I feel for you. It would be a different love; one that comes out of a mutual fear. Mara would be someone to go through this hell with, and I would like your blessing.

I must go now. I'll keep you posted as everything continues to develop, my dear. Write to me here at the Joodsche Schouwburg, Plantage Middenlaan 24 Amsterdam. Write soon, my love, as I will not move forward with my plans without your blessing.

All my love,

Your man, Willy

"Thank you, God," she muttered. "He's found someone to go through this with." She felt a profound and acute sadness, but she knew that Willy wouldn't have been able to continue all this without someone to lean on. He needed a woman to keep him strong, like she had done for him all these years. She was on her way to Amalie with the letter when she stopped midway. *Willy is a man of his word, and he won't do anything about the marriage without my writing to say I approve.* She took out her stationary and penned her reply.

June 20, 1942

My dearest Willy,

I am very grateful that you are doing well and that there is joy in your life. Mara sounds lovely and I couldn't be happier that you have found someone to love and support during these times. Willy, this is what I have prayed for since we divorced; that you meet someone you can love and who will love you in return. Love is the only weapon we have against hate. I not only give you my blessing, but I give you both my deepest love, and prayers that you will come through this safely together.

Your mother is doing well. She doesn't hear like she used to but seems to be well enough to knit nonstop, oblivious to anything outside these walls. I intend to keep it that way for as long as I can.

I must go. It's time for dinner. The food is holding up well, and we both are keeping the weight on, which does draw cynical looks from the authorities. I can only hope that they don't catch on!

Give my love to Mara, Willy. Tell her she is a lucky woman to have you! Write back soon, will you? Your letters keep me going. I love you, my dear.

Your Elsbeth

She folded the letter neatly, addressed the envelope to Willy care of the Joodsche Schouwburg, and placed it for the letter carrier to pick up on his second post. She then started dinner, crying the entire time.

July 2, 1942

The day turned out to be beautifully sunny and warm—perfect for a wedding at the synagogue on Plantage Parklaan. In increasingly dark times the joyous event gave people reason to celebrate.

"Do you, Willy Julius Rosen, take this woman to be your wife?"

"I do."

"Do you, Olga Maria Krauskopf, take this man to be your husband?"

"I do."

"Under the sight of God and all that is Holy, I declare you man and wife."

The pair took the glass wrapped in a white napkin, placed it on the floor, and Willy's lifted foot came crashing down.

"*L'chiam!*" The shouts were deafening, and Willy was afraid the noise may draw attention from a random guard walking outside.

He looked at his new wife. *So young and beautiful*, he thought. *What could she see in me?* He kissed her lightly on the lips and whispered into her ear. "*L'chiam, my dear.*"

"*L'chaim, Willy.*" They walked to where Mara's parents were standing who were clearly touched that their daughter found love where little existed.

"I'll take care of her, Herr Krauskopf, I promise."

Mara's father looked carefully at his new son-in-law. "And know that we will take care of you as well."

Willy understood the statement: if there were ever a point when the two newlyweds needed to hide, they had someone to help them. He knew little about Mara's parents, but given that they secretly lived in a non-Jewish area, they had more of a support network outside the Jewish Quarter than he did.

"Thank you, Herr Krauskopf."

Willy took the hand of his new bride and held it high above their heads as they walked down the aisle and out onto Plantage Parklaan. They were off to Café de Paris to celebrate, but barely got down the street when they were met by a group of Dutch youth who, initially smiled at the wedding couple until they saw Willy's yarmulke and hurled insults and slurs. "Dirty Jews! Marrying? What are you going to do? Have more filthy Jews? Get out of here, get out of Amsterdam!" One picked up a rock and threw it at the couple.

18

July 1942

"Welcome back, Willy. We've got a lot of work ahead of us if we're going to get this show up and running by July 18." Herbert didn't let the grass grow beneath his feet when it came to putting a show together. It didn't matter because Willy was more than anxious to get back to work.

Willy hadn't even finished his coffee and the cast and crew were already filing into the stage areas. He noticed that there were a lot of people, and not all of them were required for such a mid-sized revue. Some people even sat in the house as if they were already expecting a show.

"What's going on with all the people?" Willy asked.

"Why don't you ask Sylvie? She's the driving force behind this."

He didn't have to go looking.

Sylvia Grohs, or Sylvie as she liked to be called, ran up to him. "How was your honeymoon?"

"I don't know how much of a honeymoon it was, but it was nice to have a few days to ourselves. So, what's with all the people? Are we doing open rehearsals now?"

While he was away, Sylvie had come up with plan to help the

community that Herb thought was awe-inspiring, but there'd been no way to clear it first with Willy. "These people have nowhere to go. There's no safe place for them other than here, so I invited anyone who wishes to sit and spend their days in the Schouwburg with us." Sylvie studied Willy's face for a look to indicate his approval or disapproval of her idea.

Willy cracked a huge smile and said, "Brilliant, Sylvie. We owe it to them, don't we?"

"Of course we do. And anyway, it gives us a constant audience. I like it."

Sylvie gave him a kiss on the cheek before returning to the dressing rooms to prepare for the day's rehearsal.

Willy said to Herb, "She really does have a heart of gold." Yelling into the theater he added, "Okay, everyone. On stage in five."

Mara was awakened early in the morning by pounding on their door. As she neared the entryway, she could hear the pounding was actually at her neighbor's, and then it stopped. She pressed her ear against the door, eavesdropping on the conversation.

"Frau van Berg? Lania van Berg?"

"Yes, how can I help you?"

"I have a summons for a Stephan van Berg. Is he at home?"

"Stephan? What has my son done? Is he in trouble?"

"I am here to give him this summons. He is to report for work transport on Wednesday, July 8. He is to bring only what is allowed and report at Waterlooplein by eight o'clock in the morning."

Mara listened as the footsteps descended the stairs. When they were gone, she cracked open the door to find her neighbor staring at the paper. "Lania, I'm so sorry."

"They want to take my son. They say it's for work duty, but I've heard things. I've heard that the men go east and are not heard from again..."

Mara hugged her and walked her into the Rosen apartment. "Sit here. I'll be right back." Mara went into the kitchen to put the kettle on, then went into the bedroom where Willy had slept through it all.

177

"Willy..." She shook him.

He rustled under the covers and barely said, "What?"

"Lania is here. The police have given her a summons for Stephan. He's to report for transit to a work camp on Wednesday."

No response came from the bed. "Willy!"

"What? What about Lania?" he muttered.

"They've summoned her son to report at Waterlooplein on Wednesday for transport to a work camp."

"What am I to do about it?" Willy asked, now half-awake.

"Is there a way to get him on at the Schouwburg? If he worked there, they couldn't take him."

"Has he ever worked in a theater before?"

"Does that matter? Go talk to Lania. She's in the sitting room."

Willy stood up and put on his house robe. "Let me talk to her." He sat on the couch next to Lania, more clear-headed about the situation. "I'm so sorry to hear about Stephan, but Mara and I have an idea. When we go to the theater today, we'll ask if there's a position for him. If we can get him on the theater payroll, he'll be safe from transport. How old is he?"

"He's 19. I'll go get him. Oh, if you could do this..." She clutched Willy's hand for just a moment before leaving their apartment. A few minutes later, she returned with a tall, muscular young man. Lania hadn't even given her son the time to put on a robe. His muscular chest was lightly covered with a soft mat of curly black hair. His face, with sharp, chiseled features and deep-set brown eyes, revealed the fear that was consuming him.

Mara said softly, "Well, he could just stand onstage and look like he does. No one could argue with that."

Willy seized on her words. "Exactly. Stephan, you are the latest addition to our cast!"

Stephan stared at the couple, not knowing what they were referring to. He looked at his mother, who was crying. "*Moeder*, what's going on?"

"I'll explain later. Right now, go home and get dressed. And hurry. You're going with the Rosens to the Schouwburg." He did as he was told, and Lania reached out to Mara, giving her gentle hug.

"How can I repay you? Just tell me what I can do?"

Stephan returned, having dressed quickly. He was equally impressive in his orange, blue, and white checkered shirt. Willy thought the young man might be making a statement in wearing the colors of the Dutch flag. "Yes, you will make for an outstanding soldier. Of course, we may leave your rather patriotic shirt unbuttoned for the ladies. Mara, let's get dressed and catch breakfast on the street. We need to get his name and papers to Heintje. She'll have to postdate them, but I doubt she'll have any issue with that."

Stephan was still unclear on what had just happened. He barely knew his neighbors who, until this morning, he had seen on rare occasions, and only late at night.

"Herr Rosen, thank you. I know nothing about being an actor. Don't you think they'll notice?"

"Nonsense. All the Nazi officials do is walk in to make sure that everyone is doing something. It doesn't matter what it is. They have yet to question anyone on the Foundation payroll."

"Payroll? You mean, I'll get paid to do this?"

"Yes, you will. It's not much. Barely enough to eat on, but it guarantees protection and gives all of us a much-needed diversion from the outside." At the theater, Willy reached for the door handle but was stopped by a fast-moving young arm.

"Please, Herr Rosen. Allow me."

"Thank you, son."

Willy introduced Stephan to Veterman. "Eduard, meet Stephan van Berg. He's our newest Jewish actor. Do we have a soldier outfit that would fit him?"

Eduard sized up the young man and shook his head. "Not with those shoulders. Let's take him down to costuming." Before Stephan was led backstage, he reached out his hand to Willy. When Willy shook it, Stephan pulled him tightly into his chest. "Herr Rosen," he whispered. "I want to thank you. But you should know. I'm not Jewish."

Willy wondered what the Germans would want with him. "Why the summons? If you're not Jewish..."

"I'm a homosexual. They're rounding us up as well."

Willy took a step back to look at the handsome young man. He had been so focused on the treatment of his community that he had forgotten about the other persecuted classes whose only crime was to be homosexual, Gypsy, disabled, or part of a myriad of other groups despised by the Reich and considered unacceptable. Willy held onto Stephan's arm as he was pulling away. "It doesn't matter in God's eyes, son. What matters to Him is that you're safe."

Stephan again hugged Willy. He finally followed Veterman, whose only hope was that he could fit those shoulders into a rose-colored velvet tunic.

Those within the Joodsche Schouwburg still felt the safety associated from being on the Van Leer Foundation list. Willy, his troupe, and the nearly one thousand other employees of the Foundation would soon find their world moving in a different direction.

The SS, frustrated by the number of Jews refusing to comply with orders to report for work duty, requisitioned the *Joodsche Raad* to use the Portuguese synagogue as a collection site for Jews to be transported. However, this met with tremendous resistance by the Council of Parnassim, via the religious community's representatives to the *Joodsche Raad*. When the *Joodsche Raad* offered up the Schouwburg instead, the suggestion was immediately accepted.

On Sunday, July 19, during a matinee performance, SS-Hauptsturmführer Ferdinand Aus der Fünten, accompanied by members of the Central Office for Jewish Emigration in Amsterdam, noisily entered the theater and walked directly into the administrative office. The actors stood frozen on stage in front of a worried audience. They waited restlessly as it was explained to Dr. Werner Levie, the director of the Schouwburg, that from this point forward the Schouwburg would be utilized as an assembly and deportation site for Jews being relocated to the Westerbork and Vught Transit Camps. It certainly did not matter to the SS that Dr. Levie was a world-renowned economist and theater manager, one of the original founders of the Berlin *Jüdischer Kulturbund*, and champion of Jewish art, music, and theater for the past decade. In fact, it seemed to make their job easier.

"What about our cast members? All of the Van Leer employees?" Dr. Levie asked, trying not to panic in front of Hauptsturmführer Aus der Fünten.

"Your employees will remain on the list. However, their duties will change. They will stay here in the theater and work the processing and transportation of Jews until there are no more left to relocate." Aus der Fünten gestured to the SS officers who immediately walked to every exit. "Your audience will not be returning to their homes. They'll be given postcards to write to their loved ones. They will write that they are leaving for work detail in Germany immediately. They may put any other sentiment they wish. I really don't care. They must request that a relative bring them a suitcase or rucksack with the required items enclosed. Your employees will begin processing them for transport in the morning. Do you understand?"

Dr. Levie was too stunned to say anything.

"Never mind. I'll explain to your audience—"

That startled Dr. Levie into the present; he certainly didn't want the SS on his stage. "No, I'll explain what's happening." He walked into the theater and onto the stage, and stood at the edge of the proscenium. Everyone could feel the tension throughout the theater. "Ladies and gentlemen, please. Quiet. Please." It took several seconds for the buzzing of chatter to end. "Ladies and gentlemen, as of this moment, none of us are leaving the theater. We have just been turned into a processing and transportation center for Jews headed to work detail in Germany."

An explosive sound erupted through the house as many of the audience stood up to leave.

"You'll see that we are unable to leave. Each doorway is guarded with armed soldiers. Please return to your seats and listen to me."

The audience did as it was told.

"Being passed down each row is a stack of postcards. Please take only one. You are to write to your loved ones that you will not be returning home. Tell them you are being transported to Germany for work detail and that you will be okay, and that you will send them updates once you arrive at your designated camp." His voice quivered as he gave these instructions, but he had to keep going. After composing himself, he read from the list Aus der Fünten had given to him. "Ask them to pack a suitcase for you with the following: two underpants, two pairs of socks, one spoon, and food for three days. Have them deliver it here to the Schouwburg. It will be collected in the lobby. The cards will be delivered this afternoon by the SS, and then the suitcases should be brought immediately."

Dr. Levie noticed that the theater was completely silent. No one whispered to a neighbor, no one screamed or yelled. There was... nothing. What would happen to them would depend on many things, but especially luck. He watched his audience silently fill out their postcards. He advised them, "We are only here for a short time. Use it wisely. Reach out to those you love and tell them how much you love them. Know that over the coming days our family of actors, stagehands, and musicians will be here for you. We are one family now." He then watched as the cards were passed to the soldiers at the end of the rows.

He turned upstage and gathered his employees. "My dear family. This is it. We as entertainers have finished our duty here in Amsterdam."

Several of the actors panicked.

Dr. Levie raised his hand for quiet. "You are all employees of the Foundation, so you will be spared. However, your new 'job' will be to process the Jewish people of Amsterdam for transport."

Aus der Fünten appeared next to Dr. Levie. "I'll take it from here. If you do not show up for work at your scheduled time, you will be in violation of direct orders and arrested. I'll see to that." He looked at the blanched faces of many of Europe's finest performers. "You know, you Jews are the lucky ones. You've been lucky all along." When leaving the stage, he heard a distinct noise come from someone. Turning sharply to the group, he asked sarcastically, "Does anyone else have something to say?"

Dr. Levie stepped out forward. In a moment of defiance that

shocked not only himself but also the entire cast and crew, he stated, "We shall go on the last train. And who knows what might happen before it comes to that."

When Aus der Fünten reached one of the doors, he looked back at the assembled workers. "I wouldn't hold my breath if I were you, Dr. Levie."

The cast and audience watched silently as he left the building, purposefully slamming the door behind him.

Max Ehrlich looked at his cast as all of them stood silently before him, shocked by what they had been told. Realizing that he had to snap them into activity and that Werner was in no shape to continue, Max took the lead.

"Heintje, you, me, and Werner will draw up the list of assignments. Let's talk about how the theater will be used and what space will be used for what purpose. Unfortunately, we need some direction on what they want." He went to the front of the stage and called out to the soldiers positioned throughout the theater. "Is there anyone here who can help with space allocation?"

"I can."

The answer came from an officer who made his way toward the stage, and much to Max' surprise opened a long tube and pulled out what appeared to be building plans. He spread three large blueprints of the building, one for each floor, and pointed at each one, left to right, explaining the floors' former and future functions.

"The entrances to the theater will be guarded around the clock, beginning today." He asked Max, "Do you have a list of the Foundation employees here in this building?"

Max shook his head.

Heintje spoke up, telling the officer, "I do. It's not separated out by position, but I have a list of all employees of the Foundation."

"Please, Frau Davids. Bring it to me."

"Certainly, but it's in my office at the *Joodsche Raad*. May I go get it?"

"Yes. Tell them Untersturmführer Dieter Schaeffer has given permission for you to leave."

Heintje immediately picked up her hat and purse and headed for the front doors of the theater.

Meanwhile, Willy's ears perked up at the name of the Untersturmführer. *Dieter Schaeffer? Could this be the same Dieter Schaeffer from Berlin? My old neighbor who time and again came to the aid of my Elsbeth?* He studied the officer's face. Of course, it had been years since Willy had last seen him, and at that time Dieter was a boy. It didn't matter if he recognized him. Willy had to get word to Elsbeth to confirm if Untersturmführer Dieter Schaeffer and Dieter Schaeffer of Cicerostrasse might be one and the same.

While Willy rolled the possibility through his head, Schaeffer continued. "The lobby will be guarded as well, guiding people to registration, which will take place in the cloakroom. Once they pass through registration, they will carry their luggage to the orchestra pit and take a seat in the auditorium." He pointed to the orchestra pit as he spoke, drawing Willy's attention to the space. "The stage will be used for registration as well, for when the numbers are too great for the cloakroom. The backstage quarters, including the restrooms, will be reserved for the Jewish Council and guards. The general population, including yourselves, must use the main restrooms on the first floor."

Willy focused on the orchestra pit, and then the blueprint, but something was wrong. *They don't have the prints to the basement.* There should be four sheets, one for the small rooms under the stage, the ground floor, first floor, and second floor, but there were only three blueprints. *Maybe they don't realize that there are rooms under here.* Willy carefully glanced at the pit wall where two blended seams hid a small door. He instantly understood that he had to get someone he trusted stationed there.

Orchestra pits were usually constructed with a door that blends into the surrounding wall for the entrance and exit of musicians from under the stage, but it seemed the SS were not aware of that. Based on the missing blueprint, they couldn't know of this method of discreetly moving individuals so as not to distract from the action on stage. Anyone stationed there would have to be strong enough to lift luggage in and out alone to prevent an SS soldier from seeing the door. Willy looked around to find Stephan; and there he was, standing in the shadow of the fly curtain, nearly six inches taller than those around him. He was wearing the same checkered shirt as when they first met.

Officer Schaeffer was wrapping up when Willy turned his attention back to the instructions.

"Are you able to do this?" Schaeffer snapped.

"We can do it, Sir," Max said, nudging Warner.

"Yes, we can do it. Everyone, let these be my last words to you as your theater director. You will help your fellow Jews get through this experience with kindness and compassion, as it may very well be the last acts of genuine humanity they experience on this earth."

Heintje burst into the theater waving a thick manila envelope. "Herr Untersturmführer, here is the list." Breathless, she handed him the envelope containing the names of the 1,000 employees of the Van Leer Foundation.

"Frau Davids, if you and your designees would be so kind as to assign each to a location within the theater, I would be very appreciative."

"Certainly, Herr Untersturmführer."

Willy took Heintje's arm and pulled her to where they could see the blueprints. "Heintje, they don't have the plans for the basement. There are only blueprints for the other floors."

Seeing that he was right, she said, "Yes, but they probably don't have plans since it's only a prop storage."

"But there's a staircase, remember? It leads to the inner courtyard. And, even if they find out about the basement and its access to the courtyard, they won't know about the pit." Pointing to the plans for the orchestra pit with his chin, Willy continued. "See? They don't have the door in the orchestra pit even notated on the ground-floor plans. We need to keep this a secret. Knowing that there is a way to access the courtyard undetected could prove a valuable resource in the future. We need the right person to be stationed there." He looked over at the stage right curtain area and called, "Stephan, can you come here please?"

As he made his way to them, Willy asked Heintje, "What do you think about Stephan? Do you think he'll do?"

"I think he'll do nicely."

Willy explained to Stephan, "It will be your job to stay in the orchestra pit to take the luggage when it arrives and lift it out when people leave. Can you do that? By yourself?"

"Of course, but why can't I have help?"

Willy led him to the edge of the stage and whispered, "There's a door in the pit that you can't see. They don't know it's there, and they mustn't find out about it. That's why."

"Don't worry, Herr Rosen. They won't need to step foot in the pit, I can guarantee that." He hopped in and removed his checkered shirt, leaving him wearing only an undershirt that showed off his frame. He then easily stacked chairs once used by the musicians into groups of four, lifting them out of the pit and onto the stage.

"I think he's got this, don't you, Heintje?"

She watched Stephan single-handedly clearing out the space. "I think he's got this."

Within two hours of the official closing of the Joodsche Schouwburg, the first bags of luggage arrived. Max Ehrlich and Herb Nelson, among others, worked in the cloakroom with registrations. Heintje thought it best that friendly, well-known faces were the first ones seen when individuals entered the building. Max was instructed to "play the clown" and cheer up any adult or child struck with fear.

The employees of the Foundation who were unfortunate enough to be in the Schouwburg on Sunday, July 19, 1942, became witnesses to one of the tragedies of wartime Amsterdam: the transformation of a place associated with joy, laughter, creativity, and humanity into a site of tears, despair, loneliness, and terror. By Monday, July 20, the theater no longer existed. In its place, Jews arrived for processing and deportation to the east in what proved to be a quick and efficient way to move thousands of Dutch Jews to their death, as part of the Final Solution.

19

July 25, 1942

After what felt like years since he'd been home, Willy walked up to the door of Amsteldijk 16 smelling like something that had died in the canal. Mara flung the door open and took Willy in her arms to kiss him, oblivious to the rancid smell that was already permeating their tiny apartment. After receiving a bath and clean clothes, he debriefed Mara on the events of the past days. He told her of the horror of seeing friends and acquaintances being brought in as bounty by the NSB, the Dutch thugs who were given five guilders for each Jew they rounded up and dumped at the theater. And of the questions he had to listen to but not be able to answer except by lying that things would be fine.

"When do you have to go back?"

"In three days. That's all the time we have."

Mara shook her head. "Willy, we have to figure something out. This won't last. There will be a time when you, me, and everyone working for the *Joodsche Raad* will be put on a truck. I know there are people going into hiding every day. We have to figure something out before we're no longer safe."

Willy knew she was right, like the others before her, but he hadn't the strength or mental sharpness to hold this conversation. "Mara, I need something to eat, and I need to sleep." He was so exhausted that he fell asleep, and was only jolted awake when he heard Mara call out that dinner was ready.

After three days of rest, Willy returned to the Joodsche Schouwburg. The former theater was now the closest thing to hell on earth he had yet to experience. And he couldn't shake the thought that Untersturmführer Dieter Schaeffer was Elsbeth's Dieter Schaeffer. He was friendly enough, and not just to Willy. Rather, he was quite different from the other SS soldiers because he spoke to those held in the Schouwburg, showing real concern. Still, Willy had to find out. It had been months since he had heard from Elsbeth, giving her blessing, but he would include it in his next letter. His time to write came unexpectedly when Untersturmführer Schaeffer entered the Schouwburg. It was only half past three in the afternoon, and the sun was so bright it made it difficult to see out onto Plantage Middenlaan.

"Attention, Jews," Schaeffer shouted from the stage.

Everyone immediately stopped what they were doing and awaited instructions silently and obediently. "There are no more transports today. However, there will be at least one more coming in around midnight. Begin to clean up this mess. You, you, and you. Go clean out the toilets and dump the refuse into the courtyard sewer. You, reset the chairs, and remember that they are to face each other in groups of four or six." To Willy he said, "You, come here."

What could he possibly want with me? Is this my turn? Willy's fear showed on his face as he awkwardly made his way to the stage steps.

"Yes, Untersturmführer?"

"Are you not Willy Rosen? The singer and composer? From Berlin?"

Should I tell him? Does he already know? Before he could figure out what to share, the officer answered his own question. "I always liked your music as a child, and yes, even now. How is your ex-wife? Is she still in Berlin?"

Willy tried not to show what he was thinking. "Thank you, Herr

Untersturmführer, she's fine." Willy's head was spinning. Maybe Schaeffer had simply overheard him talking to someone else.

"Go backstage and clean out the dressing rooms. Throw out any costumes, decorations, and such. We will have officers needing overnight accommodations in this shit-hole, and those are the cleanest rooms available." He removed a notepad from his hip pocket and opened it. "There will be two additional beds brought in within the hour. See that the room is cleared before then. Move quickly. *Schnell!*"

Willy ran to the backstage dressing rooms to toss out anything that could be lifted into a large cardboard box and dragged out into the courtyard which was now filled with waste, rats and other vermin. Regardless, it was his charge and gave him plenty of time to consider what just occurred. Schaeffer didn't acknowledge anything other than Willy's name and that he had an ex-wife. Was that coincidence, a sign, or an omen? All he knew was that Schaeffer, while friendly enough, was a member of the SS and thus an enemy. Willy struggled with the large box until Stephan appeared. "Let me help." He pushed the box out into the courtyard, closing the door as quickly as he could. Turning back to Willy, he looked around nervously, making certain that no one was within earshot. "Herr Rosen, it's the pit door. What are you intending to do? It's been a week now, and the basement is filled with overflow from the sewer."

"I thought that was just the smell from the toilets!" Willy looked around to double-check no SS soldier was lurking by. "When the Germans no longer need the theater, they will no longer need us. I intend to get us out of here before the end of the work detail, which could be any day now. I want to be able to go back to Mara and then somewhere safe for as long as possible." When there was no response, Willy added, "You should leave with me. Get as far away from Amsterdam as you can."

Willy could see this idea made Stephan nervous, but he simply nodded his head. "You tell me when you're leaving. I'll go with you."

When all the cleaning and straightening was done, Willy fixated on the large mound of personal effects left from hasty departures: eyeglasses, candlesticks, clothing. Shaking his head in disbelief, Willy picked up a notebook with a pen attached. Taking advantage of the opportunity, he sat against the wall of the theater and began to write to Elsbeth, expecting not to be able to finish his letter.

Joodsche Schouwburg, Amsterdam

My dearest Elsbeth,

I am not certain that this letter will ever reach you. If by chance it does, know that I am alive and as well as can be expected. Mara sews 18 hours a day. Me? I spend my days in the theater cleaning up shit from overflowing toilets and starving in this stinking hellhole. The theater is now a collection point for Jews to be sent east; no more performances...

There is an officer here, an Untersturmführer Dieter Schaeffer. He asked about "my ex-wife in Berlin." Could this be the same Dieter as our young neighbor?

Please write back, care of Mara's parents at Biesboschstraat 19III, Amsterdam. The sooner the better. Know that you are forever my love; thank you for taking care of Mutti; I am certain that things in Magdeburg must be getting bad for her and the others by now. Pray for me, Elsbeth, my love.

Your man, Willy

Elsbeth received the letter and knew it was time for Willy to learn all of the news from Magdeburg, regardless of his situation. She had no choice but to tell him about his mother, as well as where she herself would be, should he be able to write again.

Halle an der Saale, Germany

Dearest Willy,

You will notice that I am writing you from Halle where I have a small apartment. I visit your mother in Magdeburg several times a week. Her spirits are high and her health quite well for a woman of her age. The relocation hasn't seemed to affect her nearly as much as I would have expected.

Lucie and Rudolf are still in São Paulo, but we only hear from them occasionally. They ask about Mother and you but seem removed from the events here in Germany. But, South America is safer than Germany, after all, and joining Lucie in Brazil will be my destination when it is my turn to leave. We have no news of Edith other than that she is still in Cambridge, England.

I'm doing fine. My days are occupied visiting your mother and volunteering at the Catholic church nearby. There is so much to do, my love, as the raids are increasing. The British bomb Magdeburg almost weekly and Halle receives most of the off-target missiles. Who would have known the British were such poor shots? I can only hope that their aim improves in the coming months as all of us want this war to end.

As for Dieter Schaeffer, mention Cicerostrasse. If he gives any indication that he knows what you're referring to, then it is our Dieter! The Dieter who saved me, who has a soul. He is not like the others, Willy, but he is still one of them, so be careful.

I must go now. You are in my every thought, my love. I'll let your mother know that you are well; we mustn't worry her. I pray that God watches all of you and never turns His back. Until the next time, know that I love you!

Your Elsbeth

August 1942

Word was circulating that when the Joodsche Schouwburg, as a transport site, came to an end, all the workers would lose their protection and be sent to work detail. Willy, looking at the armband that gave him permission to come and go from the theater, could not remember his life before it adorned his jacket. It had become as much a part of him as the Star of David that Mara lovingly stitched on every outer garment he owned.

As he left the theater for the day, Willy heard a sharp call and instinctively turned toward the voice of Untersturmführer Schaeffer. "You. Jew, come here."

Willy walked quickly to the officer, removing his cap and lowering his head as was expected.

"Jew, we need more workers here tomorrow. Bring your wife."

"My wife? Why?" he was panicking but attempted to appear calm.

"You have remarried, correct?" Willy nodded. "Then bring your wife. Tomorrow. She will help you clean the orchestra pit." Willy unconsciously snapped his head up. Schaeffer noticed but continued, "There are too few Jews left to clean." He reached into his pocket to pull out an armband, tossing it at Willy. "See that she's wearing this." Schaeffer turned back into the theater, but calling back he said, "Go home, Herr Rosen. Bring your wife tomorrow." The theater doors closed behind him.

Willy walked home quickly as if he'd be late for an appointment. Once there, he pounded on the door. He couldn't figure out if Schaeffer had warned him that Mara wasn't going to be here. The delay made his heart beat fast, which slowed only when his wife opened the door.

"Willy, what's wrong?"

Willy pushed Mara into the apartment and quickly closed the door. "Tomorrow you're to come with me to the theater." He pulled out the armband and handed it to her. "Schaeffer gave this to me and said you should help me clean out the orchestra pit."

"The orchestra pit? With the door that Stephan guards day and night?"

Willy nodded.

"Do you think he knows?"

"I don't know how he would. Stephan has never left except to use the restroom. We even bring his soup down to him. How could he know? Wouldn't they have done something about it by now if they did? Why would he ask me to bring you to the theater to help? Stephan is there, he could easily help. No. There must be something else."

Willy's breathing slowed as he began to calm down. Being home with Mara made the day fall away, regardless of the horrors he'd been witness to. He couldn't think anymore, so he changed the subject. "Is there anything to eat?"

"Not much. Mrs. Dekker gave me the rest of her chicken carcass to make soup, and a few slices of rye bread."

"A feast, my dear," Willy said, pouring the remnants of the day's tea into two cups, and raising his toward the apartment above.

During dinner, courtesy of the non-Jew upstairs, Willy wondered what lay in store tomorrow at the theater. He knew that something wasn't right.

August 2, 1942

The morning was chilly and blustery as Willy and Mara made their way to the Schouwburg.

They were greeted by Heintje, who, when she was caught off-guard, increasingly had a bitter expression rather than the joy-filled one she once wore all the time. She looked at Mara and the armband around her left coat sleeve. "Willy? What's Mara doing here?" Without waiting to hear the answer, Heintje scurried Mara back toward the door.

"Schaeffer told her to come. He gave me the armband to give to her."

"What could he want with her?" Her look of concern matched theirs. "Then do what he asked. Hurry!"

Willy kissed Heintje warmly on the cheek and looked carefully at her face. *This could be the last time I see you.* He then took Mara's hand tightly in his own and joined Stephan and Untersturmführer Schaeffer in the orchestra pit.

"This area," Schaeffer said, pointing into the orchestra pit, "is filthy. All of this shit must be removed, the floors scrubbed, and the walls washed down. Has this area ever been cleaned?" he asked, looking directly at Stephan.

"I don't believe so, Herr Untersturmführer," he said, his head lowered.

"Remove everything that is not attached to the floor and walls and throw it away. It stinks of filth." Schaeffer walked away, and as has been his ritual, called out over his shoulder. "This will take you three all day. I expect progress when I return this evening."

"Very good, Herr Untersturmführer." Turning to his cohorts, Willy said, "Well, we heard him. I just don't understand. Why here? And why with Mara?"

"Let's just clean. Keep your head down and clean," Mara said, making her way through the piles of discarded items that filled the once beautiful orchestra pit.

Stephan looked around the theater at the other workers. Every person had an assignment. Scrub the walls, the floors, the toilets, the stairways. It was as if the theater was being prepared to enter its next phase. He said to Willy sotto voce, "Do you think it's about over? I mean using the theater to deport Jews? Why would they be so concerned about cleaning this place if they didn't intend to keep using it? And what about the door? The courtyard? The gate?"

Most of the Jewish workers in the Schouwburg had heard that someone in the apartment building across the courtyard would leave the shared gate unlocked at night. In a defiant act of bravery, one or more unknown occupants would go out each evening after midnight and unlock the two locks that secured the gate separating their back garden from the courtyard of the theater. The occupants would also leave the doors to their building open to aid anyone brave enough to attempt an escape. Several employees of the *Joodsche Raad* as well as dozens of Jews interred within the theater made use of the system, wading through the cistern of human filth in the courtyard to reach the unlocked gate. They would then enter the building on the other side and exit onto Plantage Muidergracht as the occupants slept. Before the sun would rise, someone would awake, lock the gate again, and mop up the footprints from the hallway of their building. It was through the efforts of unknown

Dutch families such as these that hundreds, if not thousands, of Jews would find routes to safety.

"Do you think we should do it?" Willy asked quietly.

"What do we have to lose? Do you think that we'll be spared the fate of the others?" Stephan responded.

"Should we tell Heintje? Anyone?" asked Mara.

"No, absolutely not," Stephan said. "Too many people gone would immediately raise suspicion."

"He's right. When it's time, we'll slip out." Willy couldn't believe it. *Finally*, he thought, *I have a plan. Whether or not it will work, we have yet to see, but there's a plan.*

"What should we do until then?" Mara asked.

"Clean, keep our mouths shut and our heads down," Stephan said, tossing trash into yet another large cardboard box.

Without another word they worked together to clear out the orchestra pit that would soon be their route out of the theater.

It was well past midnight when the three made their way to the edge of the stage. Stephan lifted Mara down into the pit as Willy felt his way along the edge of the railing. He froze when a match was struck against the flint-lined edge of its box. As the match glow grew brighter in the darkness, the trio could make out the face of Schaeffer standing on the steps next to the orchestra pit. He finished lighting his cigarette before he spoke. "I see that you've finished your work here."

The three didn't respond; they could only look down.

"Well? What are you waiting for?" Schaeffer asked, following a slow exhale of cigarette smoke.

Willy realized that the wrong words would mean certain punishment. "Herr Untersturmführer? Cicerostrasse?"

Schaeffer was silent as he took another long drag on his cigarette. "Yes, Herr Rosen. Cicerostrasse. In Berlin."

The three remained as still as possible, unsure of what the next move would be. The darkness of the theater kept their inquisitor as a shadow, with his face lit only momentarily by his cigarette.

"And you expect me to simply let you leave through that little door, correct?" Schaeffer whispered, alarming Willy. The question seemed now to come directly next to him.

"Herr Untersturmführer, we would never—"

But Willy was cut off by Schaeffer. "Herr Rosen. If you and your party were to leave, how would I have known? I'm not even here, you see," he whispered. After taking another uncomfortably long drag on his cigarette, he leaned into Willy and said softly.

"Don't you think it's time for you to go, Herr Rosen?"

Willy could feel the smoke against his neck yet still couldn't see Schaeffer through the darkness. "Herr Untersturmführer, we would never—"

Then Stephan grabbed Willy, lifted him into the pit, and jumped quietly as a cat after him and Mara. "Thank you, Herr Untersturmführer," Stephan said, pushing his friends through the small pit door.

No more words were spoken; there was only a glow from the cigarette and soft footsteps as Schaeffer left the area.

Out in the courtyard the trio found the gate open separating the neighboring building from the Schouwburg, allowing them into the garden and through the apartment building where they paused before stepping onto Plantage Muidergracht.

"This is goodbye, Stephan," Willy said, pulling Mara and Stephan into a group embrace.

"I don't know how to thank you, Meneer Rosen. Without your help, I don't know where I would be."

As he spoke, Mara took out a seam-ripper from her pocket and removed the torn, dangling pocket off the front of his shirt. "There," she said as she shoved the fabric into Stephan's hand. "Keep it as a badge of honor... They are, after all, the colors of your country!"

Stephan looked at the fabric and then at Mara. "Thank you, Mevrouw Rosen. You both have been very kind to me. I wish you both luck." He kissed the couple on their cheeks before stepping out into the night.

Willy and Mara watched from the entryway as he disappeared into the shadows.

"God be with you, Stephan," Willy said, barely loud enough for his wife to hear. "Where do we go now?"

"We need to get to a safe house and ultimately out of Amsterdam. If we can't do that, we'll have to go to my parents," Mara said, lifting the collar on her husband's coat to hide his face a little. "We'll have to stay close to the canals." She used the seam-ripper to quickly remove their dingy yellow stars. Pulling off their armbands, she shoved the offensive material into Willy's coat pocket. "Are you ready?" Mara took her husband's hand and pulled him out onto the sidewalk, careful to hug the edge of the canal and stay out of the streetlight.

Turning the corner onto Plantage Middenlaan, Willy looked back at the theater. His thoughts went to Heintje, Max, and the others still inside. As his eyes moved across the three large glass doors that led into the lobby, something caught his eye. *What was that?* He moved silently along the banks of the canal, careful not to slip on the dew-covered grass. *Nothing. Maybe just a reflection of the streetlights.*

"Willy," Mara said, tugging on his hand. "Keep up and stay close to me."

From behind the center glass door of the former Joodsche Schouwburg, Untersturmführer Dieter Schaeffer, from Cicerostrasse 55 in Berlin, looked for the pair through the darkness. He took a long drag on his cigarette as he noted the reflection of light from Willy's glasses. *Best of luck, Rosens. You'll need it.* He took a final puff off his cigarette and tossed it onto the floor of the entryway, neatly extinguishing it with the tip of his boot.

20

September 1942

For nearly ten weeks, Willy and Mara Rosen went from safe house to safe house, trying to never stay too long at any one address. However, life was becoming unmanagable for the Rosens as an increasing number of families with children needed space. During the third week of October 1942, they made the decision to leave the Quarter and make their way to the home of Mara's parents, which was in a non-Jewish area of South Amsterdam.

Alexander and Helene Krauskopf refused to leave their home when other Jews were ordered into the *Jodenbuurt*. They worked diligently to stay under the radar of the Dutch NSB by limiting their out-of-home functions and refusing to wear the Star of David, itself a crime punishable by death.

In the early morning hours of October 23, 1942, Willy and Mara left the safety of their hiding space toward South Amsterdam.

October 23, 1942

The initial knock on the front door of her parents' home was soft so as not to disturb the neighbors. When there was no movement from the inside, Mara knocked a little louder and whispered through the glass. "Mother, it's Mara. Open the door quickly." Through the glazed glass, Mara could see a small light making its way toward her.

After what seemed an eternity, the door finally opened to reveal the slight frame that was an exhausted Helene Krauskopf. She ushered them both into a back bedroom and only then spoke. "What are you two doing here?" she asked in a hushed voice.

"We've been on the run for ten weeks, but we need to stay here until we come up with something else."

Helene stood motionless while Alexander entered the room.

"Papa," Mara said, throwing her arms around her father's neck and kissing him several times on the cheek.

"What are you doing here?" he asked, both happy and distressed to see his daughter.

"They're staying here," his wife responded. "They have no place to go."

"There isn't much, but let me fix you something to eat. Wait, what is that smell?" she asked.

"Mother, what do you think? We stink of shit from the canals."

"Well, go take a bath and get some clean clothes on. Take anything from my wardrobe. Willy, you're next." She sounded like a seasoned officer. "Alexander, go and get Willy some clothes. Get out of what you're wearing now so we can throw it into the garbage before it gets light."

His father-in-law led Willy into the bedroom, where he rummaged through a few drawers. "I'll get rid of these." Alexander gathered up Willy's and Mara's clothing and shoved them into a paper bag. Willy watched in amazement at the speed and organization to which his wife's parents had gone into action. "I'll be right back."

Willy, alone in the bedroom, stared into the mirror above the dressing cabinet, studying himself. He hadn't fully looked in a mirror for months. His once-round face was now drawn and pale, wrinkled from stress. His glasses were bent, and he noticed a small chip on the left side of the frames. He looked at his hair, or what was left of it. All that was there were thin black strands matted to his white head, as if a full moon through a spiderweb. "So, this is me now," he said, sighing. "Well, it's better than the alternative."

"Alternative to what, my dear?" Mara asked, now all clean and wearing her mother's robe.

"Nothing. I'm just rambling. I'll be better after my bath."

"When you've finished, come into the kitchen. I'm starving."

Willy enjoyed watching the tub fill up with clean water; it'd been a long time since setting his foot into a bath. As he bathed, he could make out some words in the conversation taking place in the kitchen —a word here, a long pause there, until he heard Alexander clearly say, "Curt would never have put you in such a situation."

Willy immediately got out of the water and cracked open the door while he dried off and dressed.

"This is not Willy's doing, Papa. And just what do you think Curt would have done? He would have left me. No matter where we were in our marriage, he would have left me to fend for myself. Curt Simons cared for no one but himself and you know that."

Willy had only heard secondhand about Mara's first husband, largely through Helene prior to the wedding. Mara and Curt, as had he and Elsbeth, met and were married impetuously in youthful exuberance. The difference was that Willy still loved his ex-wife dearly and would have never, under any normal circumstance, divorced the woman who had been his stalwart supporter and then defender for over a decade.

When she saw Willy come down the hallway, Helene stopped talking and reached for the coffee pot that had just begun to percolate.

"Mama," Mara said, putting down her spoon, "we won't be here long. We'd never put you and Papa in this kind of position unless we had no other option. We'll get out of here as soon as possible."

Willy let his wife do the talking while he ate. When his silence could no longer be ignored, he said, "We just need some time to figure out how to get out of Amsterdam."

Alexander gave Willy a sharp look. "If it were so easy, don't you think we'd be out of here? That "J" stamped on your passport keeps you right here."

"I know that, Meneer Krauskopf. I was just saying—"

"Just saying what? That you waited too long to leave? That my daughter is stuck here with you? With us? If any of us had a bit of sense, we would have left years ago." He stormed toward the bedroom and slammed the door loud enough to be heard throughout the apartment.

"Helene, I'm sorry. I never meant—"

"Of course you didn't, Willy. Don't worry. You and Mara may stay here as long as you wish."

November 26

Leaving her mother-in-law would be the second hardest event of Elsbeth's life. "Mother, you know that I have to go. I can't stay here anymore."

"What will happen to me? What will they do once you're gone?" Amalie was panicked about being relocated. It was only through Elsbeth's connections with Dieter that Amalie was still safe in Magdeburg. Elsbeth understood that even he had only so much authority.

"Mother, we have gone over this. You will be just fine," Elsbeth lied. "The Michaelis family is just down the street, and they promised to look in on you every day. I have to go. The cab is waiting." Elsbeth stopped talking for a moment to regain her composure. "You know I love you, right?"

"I know that, my dear. I love you as I would my own daughter."

"You know I love Willy, don't you? I'll never stop loving him."

"I know that, too. I know that he loves you as well."

As Amalie's final connection to her son was about to leave her life, her tears turned into deep sobs. Elsbeth kissed her on the forehead and walked to the front door before her own emotions broke through. Amalie called out to Elsbeth, who turned to look at this dear woman one more time.

"Thank you, Elsbeth. I will keep your kindness with me always."

Elsbeth heard her mother-in-law sobbing as she closed the door and walked to the waiting taxi, away to her new life and away from the misery of those she loved.

Six days later, Amalie Rosenbaum would be taken from her home and deported to Theresienstadt.

January 1, 1943 came and went like any other day in hiding. Willy and Mara Rosen were still in her parents' home, with no prospect of finding another place to hide. With no more Jewish-owned stores, food and other necessities could only be purchased through non-Jewish friends or on the black market, the latter being the preferred method. The Rosens and Krauskopfs worked hard to make no noise and not be seen: they read during the day, spoke rarely and only in whispers, and kept the curtains closed and the lights off. Only their neighbor on the other side of a shared outside wall knew. If anyone could be trusted, it was her neighbor and landlord, Dr. Pieter Glessfeld, a Humanities professor at the University of Amsterdam. Were it not for him, they would certainly have starved to death.

February 1943

"There's the tapping. It's Glessfeld. Tap back," Helene said.

Willy picked up the small marble elephant and responded with two taps, pause, one tap, pause, three taps.

"Go see what he has, Mara. Fingers crossed it's something to eat." Mara went into her parents' bedroom, which had a neighboring window with the bedroom of Dr. Glessfeld. She waited for another gentle tap. She opened the curtains and window, and a small bag was shoved through. Once safely in her hands, the other window was closed and the curtain drawn. Mara did the same, and eagerly opened the bag..

"What's in it?" Willy couldn't remember the last time he had anything of real substance.

"More root vegetables from the garden," she said, pulling out a pair of early sugar

beets, a few potatoes, and a winter squash accompanied by a small loaf of rye bread.

"Looks like more soup," Mara told them, both with sarcasm and gratitude.

Alexander was busy building a false wall in the back of the closet. He would say it was needed "just in case we need to hide your mother." No one, including Helene, had the heart to explain to him that should the Nazis get inside the apartment, there would be no place for any of them to hide. Mara glanced over at her mother who shrugged. "It keeps him occupied. He has no idea that I would never let him go without me."

"I know, Mother, but he can't make that much noise. You have to speak to him because he won't listen to me."

"I'll ask him to stop." And Helene went to have a word with her husband.

Mara and Willy went back into the kitchen to clean the vegetables. "How much longer do you think we can stay here, Willy? Isn't there somewhere else we can go?"

"I know. We have to figure a way out of Amsterdam. As long as we're in the city, we're sitting ducks, just waiting for the Nazis to find us."

"But we can't just wander aimlessly, either. We'll need shelter and food; we have all of that here. We could just be patient."

Willy paused. Surely, being where they were was much better than trying to find another place. However, he worried about Alexander and Helene. They couldn't begin to keep pace should they find it necessary to run. He decided no one had a choice but to stay put, so those thoughts did no one any good. He nodded in agreement and returned to peeling his potato, wondering if you could also eat the peels.

March 1943

Willy and Mara were awakened in the middle of the night by a series of loud booms in the distance. Willy's eyes popped wide open as he reached over for Mara. "Are you awake?"

"I am now. What do you suppose that was? Bombs?"

"Too far away to tell. It must be the Brits or the Americans bombing the railway again. I hope."

"What do you think happens? When they send people east?" Mara asked, not really wanting to know the answer.

"I don't know," Willy replied, but he did know. To garner sympathy, the Dutch Resistance spread the word about conditions in the German work camps, including graphic details of crematoria, mass deaths, macabre medical experiments, and days filled with backbreaking work. Jews were not being sent to work detail. They were being sent to their deaths.

"Willy, what will we do if they find us? If we are captured, along with Mother and Papa, would it be reasonable to make any type of fuss? I would be too scared to even look them in the eye." Mara had clearly given this a lot of thought, contrary to Willy.

"Listen, what's the best thing to do to someone who is acting inhumanely?" he asked.

Mara lay there, working to come with an answer.

"I don't know."

"Make them feel human. What makes people feel more human than laughter? Maybe that's how we get through to them, should we ever need to do so. We laugh!"

"And until then? Just lay here and listen to the bombs being dropped?"

"Mara, if we get caught and we end up somewhere despicable, all we can do is try to make the best of the situation."

Willy's optimism always seemed naive, Mara thought, *but maybe there's a thread of logic running through it.*

"I can only pray that we can stay together. As long as we have each other we can make it through this. We simply have to remember to keep our humanity and not turn into them." He leaned over and kissed her softly on the lips. "As long as we're together, we'll be okay."

The bombs continued in the distance as they drifted back to sleep, feeling calmer knowing that whatever were to happen, they would have each other to laugh with, to lean on, and to love.

April 8, 1943

Willy looked through a crack he'd made in the bedroom curtains. He could see streams of sunshine reflecting off Dr. Glessfeld's makeshift greenhouse, which was filled with beautiful red tomatoes, big orange carrots, and heads of green leafy lettuce. He watched Dr. Glessfeld walk from his door to the garden, remove the glass cover, and begin to pick a basket of vegetables.

Suddenly, Dr. Glessfeld's head turned toward the garden gate, as if someone were about to enter. Willy saw him set the basket down and hastily move toward the back of the garden where he lost sight of him. Willy could hear a conversation, and it seemed to get louder.

"There is no one living here. It's been vacant since last summer. I have it locked up." Dr. Glessfeld was speaking to someone now coming through the back garden.

"We need to check, Dr. Glessfeld. We've had reports," Willy heard.

"Reports of what?" Dr. Glessfeld said, loud enough for anyone inside to hear what was happening. "Of someone living here? There is no one, as you can see."

"We need for you to open the door. Now."

Willy ran into the sitting room, white-faced and motioning for the others to come to him. "The Nazis... they're here... they're in the back with Glessfeld," he whispered.

"What are we supposed to do?" Mara asked.

Alexander and Helene held hands, as they shared a previously made resolve.

Willy spit out, "We can't implicate Glessfeld. He'll go to prison if we do. We'll have to pretend to be squatters. Jewish squatters that he had no idea were living here."

From outside, the group could make out Dr. Glessfeld's voice calling out over a Nazi shouting. "I tell you, no one's lived here for almost a year. I closed it up myself."

"Good. He's playing dumb."

He told Mara's parents, "Go and get your pictures and anything you wish to take that you can shove into a small bag."

Helene sprang from her chair, grabbing her sweater and husband's jacket, and tossing mementos from the tables into a small satchel. They could hear the lock on the front door being opened. Alexander motioned for Mara and Willy to join him at the closet door. "Get in. Both of you. They'll take us, but you can hide. Get in there and stay quiet," Alexander ordered, as he pulled out the false wall and pushed Willy and Mara into the tiny hidden enclosure.

Within seconds the room was filled with five Nazi soldiers, guns drawn and pointed.

"Locked it up yourself, did you?" One of the soldiers turned his gun on Dr. Glessfeld who reflexively put his hands up in the air.

"I didn't know, I swear... I didn't know," Dr. Glessfeld pleaded.

"Shut up and show me your papers."

Dr. Glessfeld pulled a folded paper from his pocket and handed it to the officer.

"Not a Jew." Looking at the old man, he said, "Get out of here. Go home. If I see you again, you will not be so fortunate!"

Dr. Glessfeld hurried from the room without saying another word, his hands still up in the air.

"He didn't know," Alexander said, quite matter-of-factly. Before he could say another word, he was pistol-whipped, crumbling to floor with blood spilling from a sizable wound on his forehead.

"Alexander," Helene screamed, falling by his side.

All Willy and Mara could do was listen motionlessly; their horror restrained by fear of being discovered.

"Take these two," the officer said, motioning to the pair.

One officer lifted Arthur off the floor, and a second picked up Helene. The officers handcuffed them and shoved them out the door.

Then, there was nothing but silence.

After what seemed like hours, Willy pushed aside the false wall and helped his wife out into the hallway. Alexander and Helene were gone and their whereabouts unknown. The two stood there in a state of shock, and Willy turned back toward Mara just in time to catch her as she collapsed in his arms.

May 10, 1943

It had been over a month since Alexander and Helene were taken away. Willy and Mara's days were spent sleeping in the hall closet and the nights spent stealing from Dr. Glessfeld's garden. To minimize any potential risk to their neighbor they would have to manage on their own.

Mara, stricken with grief, could only speculate on the location of her parents. "I just want to know where they are. Don't we know anyone from the Resistance who can help?" She was desperate for answers.

"Mara, we can't go outside and we can't contact anyone. Do you think your parents would want me to risk you getting taken away? They would never forgive me."

She knew he was right, but it did little to ease the pain of her loss. "Why? What did my parents ever do to anyone?"

"What did any of us do? What does being a Jew have to do with being a criminal? Nothing. All we can do is hide. Alexander would never forgive me if I put you in harm's way. Why do you think he spent all that time working on the closet? It wasn't for Helene; it was for us. For you. All we can do is continue to hide and pray for their safety and ours. Let's just go in the closet and try to get some sleep. Inactivity makes me surprisingly—"

Before he could finish his sentence the front door was kicked in and several Gestapo filled the apartment in seconds. At the rear of the group was Dr. Glessfeld, bloodied and beaten nearly to the point of being unrecognizable. The senior officer sneered at Willy and Mara. Looking at Glessfeld, he barked, "You are under arrest for harboring known enemies of the Reich."

"No!" Willy shouted, but found a gun pointed at his head. "He didn't know a thing. We've been living here in secret. He's innocent."

The officer shoved his pistol hard into Willy's gut, knocking him to the floor.

"These two. Have them pack some clothing and put them in the truck with the others!"

Willy was forcefully pulled up to his feet. The pair each put clothing into small leather satchels. Mara added some small pictures of parents to hers, while Willy took as much music as he could, filling his bag until it was nearly bursting.

The officer, losing patience, motioned for them to walk out onto the street where a truck filled with nearly a dozen Jews was waiting.

Willy and Mara found a space on a bench across from an elderly pair.

As the truck started up, the four looked at each other in terror.

Willy could only think that this was it. This was the end. What he had hoped would be a continuation of his story was suddenly over. There had been several opportunities to leave but instead at every turn he had sabotaged himself. So many of his friends and loved ones left as soon as they could, in whatever manner they could arrange. This was his situation now and it was all his fault. He was a captured Jew, and he had seen enough foul treatment at his beloved Schouwburg to know what was in store for him and Mara would not be good. Willy had been so consumed with the idea that he wasn't considered German by the new Reich that he neglected to realize that, in their eyes, he wasn't even human.

Within minutes Willy felt the truck turn sharply and then stop. The officer sitting in the back with the prisoners jumped out and unlocked the truck gate, ordering them back out onto the street. When Willy exited the truck, he didn't immediately know his surroundings. He helped out Mara and the elderly couple, but it was only when he turned toward the street that he recognized that they were on Plantage Middenlaan. He was standing in front of the Joodsche Schouwburg, back where he had started nearly ten months earlier. He looked at Mara and could only manage two words. "I'm sorry."

The group was pushed into the theater where they began the all-too-familiar process of registration.

"This is the beginning of the end..." Willy whispered to himself.

21

Still May 10, 1943

"Next!" a voice shouted, startling Willy back into the moment.

He walked up to the table and carefully studied the face, wondering if he might recognize it.

"Your papers, please." The man didn't even bother to look up, but simply took the crumpled sheets of paper out of Willy's hands and turned to the second page, stamping the arrival day and writing in the location. "Where were you picked up?"

"Biesboschstraat 19, Amsterdam," Willy answered. "With my wife, Mara. She's here." He pulled Mara up to his side.

Once the paperwork was completed, the two were allowed to take their place inside the familiar surroundings of the Schouwburg. Willy looked around at the same set-up of chairs—groups of four and six facing each other. He wondered just how many people had gone through the process in the ten months since they had escaped. Willy searched the room for his former neighbor. *Maybe if he helped us once, he would help us again.* He scoured every Nazi he could find, but he didn't see him.

"Who are you looking for?" Mara asked.

"Schaeffer. Do you see him?"

"No, but I haven't been looking for him. I do see Otto Dürer over there." She pointed to an extremely thin and pale man. The once happy and jovial actor had been reduced to a shell of his former self. He was sweeping up remnants of the last group of occupants when Willy came up beside him.

"Otto," Willy said, hugging his friend, but he felt no reciprocation. He stepped back—Otto's stare seemed to look right through him. "It's me. Willy."

"Willy, oh my God. We were all so worried about you. You and Mara were here one minute and then gone the next." Otto hugged Willy as he spoke, and both men made sure not to speak loudly.

"We escaped but got picked up this morning. What's happened to everyone? Where are Max, Fritz, and Erich?"

Otto looked up sharply and then began sweeping. He picked up a second broom against the wall and handed it to Willy. "Sweep. Sweep and I can talk."

As the two swept the filthy floor of the theater Otto gave a rundown of the whereabouts of their former cast members. "Max and Erich were taken away a couple of months ago. When the numbers began to really dwindle, those who had been here from the beginning were carted off. Some, like you and Mara, escaped before..."

Willy knew what he was going to say. "It's okay, Otto. We thought we were cheating fate, but all we were doing was postponing the inevitable."

Otto was surprised by Willy's calm demeanor and changed the subject to something a bit cheerier. "Franz Engel is still here. He's upstairs manning the soup kitchen. Go up and get some food. You never know when you'll eat next."

The pair entered the small former wedding chapel, now soup kitchen, and Willy instantly recognized him. Although thinner, Willy knew Franz's frame well from having spent every summer with him in Scheveningen since 1938. He placed a hand on Franz's shoulder so as not to startle him as he served.

Seeing Willy, Franz crumbled to the floor, becoming nothing more than a mound of bones and tattered fabric.

"Franz, it's okay. We're here, we'll help you." Mara helped lift Franz up, took the soup ladle, and began serving others as Willy walked Franz to a chair.

"Oh, Willy, they're all gone. All of them. Wallburg, Poons, Grohs, Davids, Ehrlich, Ziegler. I have no idea where they went. One day they were here, and the next... I looked around and I was alone.

"Franz, trust me when I tell you that if there was any way we could have taken you, we would have—"

But Franz cut him off. "No, no, I wouldn't have gone anyway. I would have been much too scared to even try it. I never wanted to be the last one, you know?"

Willy nodded, understanding exactly what he meant. "It's okay. We're here. Now, let's dry those eyes and get these people some food. We'll help."

Forgetting about his quest for Schaeffer, Willy escorted Franz to the soup line, where together they stood side by side, tearing off pieces of bread and handing out bowls of soup to the nameless masses that lined up for what may well be their last hot meal for the week.

June 1943

Stephan sensed someone observing him as he walked down Beethovenstraat toward Corellistraat. As a member of the Dutch Resistance, he was constantly aware of his surroundings and the possibility that at any moment he may be dragged off the street and never heard from again. He was one of a group of resistance fighters, known collectively as the CS6, living at Corellistraat 6. They were responsible for many of the high-profile assassinations of Nazi sympathizers in Amsterdam, making its members sought-after targets of the NSB and the Gestapo.

Trusting his instincts, he stopped to assess the situation under the guise of lighting a cigarette. About 100 meters back he noticed a person making an abrupt stop to glance over the railing and into the canal. *Just what I thought.* He would have to shake the man before he could return to the safe house. He sprinted the remainder of the bridge, slowing his pace only after he could see the street sign for Corellistraat half a meter ahead. He had just turned down the street toward the safe house when he heard, "Halt, Stephan van Berg. Halt!"

He bolted past the first few townhouses, ducking into an alley and then running behind the homes nestled along streets named after famous Baroque composers.

"Van Berg! Halt or I'll shoot!" were the last words he remembered before a sharp pain like a hot poker went through his right shoulder, shattering his collarbone on exit and sending him tumbling into a garden hedge. He tried to get back on his feet but was kicked by the heel of a boot.

The man hovering over him wore the black garb of the Gestapo. The Nazi cocked his gun and pointed it directly into Stephan's forehead. "Stephan van Berg. You are under arrest."

Stephan tried to stand but was again kicked to the ground. He looked at his assailant. "For what? What have I done?" His left hand went up to cover the exit wound and attempt to stop the bleeding, which was now pooling around him.

"For crimes against the Reich."

"What crimes? Smoking on the bridge?"

A young Untersturmführer joined the guard who had done such admirable work by Gestapo standards. "Well done, Fritz."

"Thank you, Herr Untersturmführer."

"Lift him up." Fritz forced Stephan onto his feet, and the officer leaned in for a closer examination of the wound. "Go and get some bandages," he ordered. Fritz ran off in the direction of Corellistraat. Standing alone, the officer shoved two handkerchiefs into the bullet wounds. He then ripped off a sleeve from Stephan's shirt, and tore it in half lengthwise, weaving half under the armpit and neatly tying the two ends in place with a knot above the broken collarbone. Not knowing what to do with the other half of the sleeve, he shoved it into his coat pocket.

"There. That will stop the bleeding until he returns." The officer studied Stephan's features silently, and then looked at him as if he knew him. "You were in the Schouwburg. You are a friend of the Rosens."

Stephan's eyes grew narrow as the officer pulled out a thin silver cigarette case emblazoned with a large "S". He took out a cigarette and placed it between his lips. Without asking, he placed a second in Stephan's mouth, lighting that one first. He then took a long draw on his own.

"To think I actually wished you all luck that night. Here you are again. What am I to do with you?"

Now recognizing Untersturmführer Schaeffer, Stephan was alarmed by the sarcasm. "What do you want?" he asked, removing the cigarette from his mouth.

"I could take you in for any number of things, Herr Van Berg, least of which is your being a homosexual." He continued to study Stephan as if trying to decide what he was going to do next. "Why are you so nervous, Herr Van Berg? You know, we're much less concerned with the Dutch homosexuals than we are with the Jews. This whole incident could be over quickly if you just tell me what you know."

Stephan acted as if he had no idea what he was referring to. "I don't know what you mean."

In one quick flash, Schaeffer pounded his fist into the wounded shoulder, sending Stephan backward onto the hard concrete. "Do you think I'm stupid? Do you not think I know exactly what you do? Who your friends are? Do you really think I would waste my time with one homosexual if I didn't think you were worth it? I'll ask you again. Do you think I'm stupid, Herr Van Berg?"

"No, Herr Untersturmführer. But—"

"I would be very careful what your next words are. You wouldn't want to lie to me now, would you?" Schaeffer helped him stand up and then straightened his bandage.

"Now, tell me what you know about CS6." Schaeffer was much less polite, becoming bored with the questioning. "You'll either tell me now or you'll tell me down at headquarters, and I can guarantee you that headquarters is much less pleasant to homosexuals than I am."

"I don't know anything about CS6 other than what they are. Everyone knows what they are because it's in the papers every day."

Schaeffer raised his index finger as if to quiet him. "The

resistance papers, Herr Van Berg. Only in the resistance papers. We make sure of that." He took a long draw on his cigarette, this time blowing the smoke into Stephan's face. "Are you certain that you know nothing else, Herr Van Berg?"

"I am certain, Herr Untersturmführer. I don't know anything."

Schaeffer became very quiet, finishing his cigarette and tossing the butt out of the garden and onto Bachstraat. He took off his right glove and raised the back side of his hand to Stephan's cheek. He ran it caressingly down along his chiseled cheekbone as he studied Stephan's extraordinary facial features. "Pity that a thing of such beauty must die."

"Herr Untersturmführer, I—"

The sound of a single shot sent the birds that were nesting in the trees above, skyward.

June 20, 1943

It began like any other beautiful summer morning. It was sunny, and the sounds of the city coming alive permeated into the Schouwburg. Willy and Mara, along with Franz Engel and Otto Dürer, were mopping the lobby where hundreds of Jews would soon line up to register and be sent to who knows where. With the only guards posted outside of the theater, the four stopped to glance out of the large glass doors, taking in the beauty of a sunrise that made them feel as if nothing at all had changed in their city. Willy took Mara's hand and squeezed it tightly. "It's beautiful, isn't it?" he said, looking out onto Plantage Middenlaan. They all knew the street well but today it seemed a bit quieter, a bit more peaceful. They didn't notice the trucks quickly lining up outside the entrance to the theater until the center door opened and Untersturmführer Schaeffer burst into the lobby, moving swiftly past the entrance and into the holding area.

"Herr Untersturmführer." Willy spoke before he could think, which brought a swift and angry stare. He lowered his head as Schaeffer turned in his direction.

"Herr Rosen. I should say it's nice to see you, but I don't think you would agree," Schaeffer said with all the sarcasm he could muster.

Having removed the gloves from his hands, he tried to shove them into his coat pocket, but something was already in there. He pulled out the half-sleeve and tossed it onto the floor. Willy saw the blood-stained fabric resembling Stephan's distinctive checkered shirt. He gasped. Schaeffer looked at Willy, realizing that he had put the pieces together.

"Sad, really. It didn't need to happen, of course. All he had to do was give me some information." He ignored the shocked looks and continued into the holding area, saying as he walked away, "Don't let yourselves end up in a similar situation." He thrust open the doors to the holding room, blowing into a large silver whistle. It broke the calm of the morning with an almost unbearably shrill noise. "Out, everybody, out. Out into the trucks," he shouted. At his words, two dozen SS officers, rifles in hand, sprinted into the holding room and quickly forced the interred out onto Plantage Middenlaan.

"You two, out onto the street," the officer shouted.

Willy and Mara looked around to see who he was talking to.

"You two," the officer repeated, and was moving quickly toward them, rifle pointed directly at their chests. "Grab your bags. Now!"

Willy and Mara dropped their mops and followed orders, running out of the lobby with their small bags of possessions, and joined the others.

Schaeffer stood on the sidewalk. He removed a cigarette from his lips and said, "I'm afraid that your luck has run out, Herr Rosen."

The truck suddenly jolted backward before moving forward out onto the street. Willy watched Schaeffer as the truck moved further and further away from the Schouwburg. The man who had done so much for him, Mara, and Elsbeth had finally surrendered to his cause. *Does kindness have an expiration date?* he wondered, as the truck sped down the street with its cargo being tossed around like oranges in a crate. The image of Stephan's bloodied sleeve popped into his head, and he remembered the endemic trust that he had felt upon meeting the young man, and their faith in each other. That crumpled piece of fabric tossed onto the lobby floor of the Schouwburg was all that Willy needed to answer his own question. *Yes, I guess it does.*

. . .

"Everyone out, you have five minutes!" The gate of the truck slammed open. The same officer who forced them into the truck forced them out, again with the tip of his rifle. "*Schnell! Piss and shit!*" The occupants of the caravan jumped out and sprinted toward the tree line to relieve themselves. Willy and Mara stayed close together.

When done, Willy zipped up his pants and helped Mara stand back up, brushing the dirt and grass from the hem of her dress.

"Two minutes!"

"Hurry, my dear. Let's go before—" but he was cut off by the crack of rifle-fire. They looked over to the far end of the trees to see a body violently reacting to a bullet through the back and then falling like a bag of potatoes.

Willy took Mara's hand, aiding her up into the back of the truck where they resumed their position on the long, wooden bench with the others. No one spoke a word, again making the trip quiet and tense with fear.

Mara's fear began to manifest, and she wiped away her tears. Willy knew the guard wasn't looking, so he kissed her softly on the lips. "We may be all we have in this world, Mara. It may end up being just you and me. And if it ends up being just us, I'm okay with that."

Mara looked at Willy and without a word, without even checking to see if the guard was looking in their direction, she kissed him sweetly on the lips in return. "I'm okay with that as well, love." Having regained control of her emotions, she tucked her handkerchief into the side pocket of her dress. She realized that dignity is something that can only be given away; it could never be taken unless you allowed it. She gave Willy's thigh a gentle pat. "I'll be alright."

Three hours later, after the beautiful morning they had enjoyed had turned into a hot and humid day, the trucks pulled up to the gates of a large complex of roughly constructed barracks surrounded by a barbed wire fence. Willy and Mara looked out to see hundreds of men, women, and children. Everyone appeared tired and dirty, sweating through clothing that had been on their backs far too long.

The back of their truck flew open, and the guard, rifle again pointed into the back of the truck, told them to get out. Willy jumped out first and then helped Mara. He felt the tip of the rifle jut into his side, moving him toward a wooden table where three women were seated in front of typewriters.

The conversation was as staccato as the typing. "Next. Name?"

"Willy Rosen."

"Dutch or German?"

"German."

"Over there." She pointed to a table a short distance away with the sign *Deutsche Staatsangehörige*. He started toward the German Nationals table but stopped to wait for Mara. He felt the familiar jab of a rifle tip in his back.

He made his way to the table where he lined up to register.

As he waited a German guard walked up beside him. "Hey, aren't you Willy Rosen? *Text und Musik von Mir?*" the guard asked, with a huge smile on his face.

"Yes, sir."

"I used to see you in Berlin at the KaDeKo. You were so funny. Go on... sing."

Willy, reticent at first, remembered his own advice: he'd have to get through this with laughter and music. He took his hand out of his pocket and lifted it above his head in his trademark bow, loudly exclaiming, "Ladies and Gentlemen, allow me for just one minute to introduce you to the latest fad in American fashion! Frau Bess Mensendieck! Of course, Text and music by me!" To his great delight, the captive inmates applauded, because the humorous song had been so popular years earlier. Willy sang from his heart, regardless of his current situation. To the inmates and German staff that day, Willy's performance was like a breath of fresh air.

Among those observing the show was SS-Obersturmführer Albert Konrad Gemmeker, Commandant of the Westerbork Transit Camp, Willy and Mara's new home. He watched from the window of his office, and a faint smile crossed his lips. Willy was performing as if on the stage of the KaDeKo, a place familiar to Gemmeker from his early days in Berlin.

"Herr Obersturmführer, do you want me to have the guards stop that man?"

Gemmeker thought for a moment. "No, let him go. I know this man. He's Willy Rosen, a cabaret performer from Berlin. It's actually quite a treat to have him here, even if he is a Jew."

Mara, standing a few people behind her husband in line, smiled for the first time in nearly two years as she watched her husband receiving applause from a grateful audience.

"Did you see that, my dear? They recognize me, even here!" Willy couldn't have been happier.

"Willy, where are we?"

In a continuation of his performance, he took a dramatic step backward, flung his arms open wide, and in a voice loud enough for the entire camp to hear he shouted, "Welcome to Westerbork!"

22

Westerbork was built by the Dutch in 1939 to serve as a refugee camp for Jews entering the country illegally; that is, fleeing the occupied territories of the German Reich.

As a result, several train lines passed through the area due to its proximity to the German border. When the Nazis took control of Westerbork in 1942, its classification as a transit camp meant it was only a pitstop. The length of stay for an inmate in Westerbork depended largely on the individual's ability to stay "off the list" of those selected for the weekly transport.

Every Tuesday morning at nine o'clock, the train, with its long lines of windowless cattle cars, would arrive. The list, provided by the Jewish Camp Council, was as dependable as it was deadly: transporting approximately 1,000 Jews each week—and 2,000 during the first months of operation—to Auschwitz, Theresienstadt, Sobibor, or Bergen-Belsen.

For those prisoners who managed to be *Gesperrten*, locked safely from deportation to the east, life in Westerbork was relatively more humane than in other camps. For Jews arriving at the camp with the worst possible scenario in their heads, life in Westerbork seemed to calm many of their fears. Not only could they stay together with their loved ones, but they were provided with food and health care, and could lead a less traumatic existence than those less fortunate elsewhere.

Willy Rosen's arrival at Westerbork on the afternoon of June 20, 1943, would bring the world of Weimar cabaret into a place where joy was limited, the camp's inhabitants being in much need of anything to take their minds off their day-to-day existence.

Still June 20, 1943

"Do you think Mother and Papa are here?" Mara asked Willy, hoping that they too would have been brought to Westerbork.

"I don't know. We can ask and look around. You never know."

Before he could even consider trying to locate Mara's parents, he and Mara had to first find where they were to report for housing. Willy, short though he was, held his head as high as possible, looking over the throngs of people scattered across the large dirt courtyard. "Mara, I think we should go over here," and he pointed to a large row of primitively painted barracks.

He simultaneously felt a hand on his left shoulder and heard a deep voice he recognized. "No, not unless you want to take some children and pretend to be a family."

Willy swung around, and there stood Erich Ziegler, from the Prominenten.

Mara, not wanting to waste any precious time, gave Erich a warm but brief hug. "I'm sorry, Erich, but I have to see if I can find my parents here." She gave them both a weary smile before turning around and starting her desperate search.

"Erich, my God, I thought you were dead! How long have you been here?" Willy asked, bringing him in close for a tight hug.

"I arrived last month. I think. I don't know, maybe the month before that. You know, you lose track of time in here very quickly. Willy, I thought you were dead as well. We hadn't seen you at the Schouwburg for months, and then they took me, and Max and—"

"Wait, Max is here? Max Ehrlich?"

"Yes, he's been here as long as I have." Struck with an energy he hadn't had in months, he said, "I know. We arrived in December this past year. You won't believe who else is here. Camilla Spira. Can you believe it? I didn't even know she was Jewish, well, she says half-Jewish, but who knows these days, eh? And that's not all," Erich went on, barely taking a breath. "There's literally a plethora of performers, camera men, directors, and backup singers and dancers from throughout Europe here. If it were anywhere else, we could put on a hell of a show. Can you imagine that?"

Willy's mind was racing with the possibilities. "What if we do put on a show?"

Erich remembered that Willy was always up for a show, but this was a prison camp. "Impossible. Do you really think they would allow something like that?"

"Look, what if we get everyone together for a talk? Nothing formal, but just see what's on their mind? If Max is here, we have the director. The rest is easy."

"Easy? Are you out of your mind? Nothing is easy. Nothing! We're in prison! This is not a boys' camp, and this isn't talent night at the KaDeKo. This is a Nazi camp, and we're prisoners!"

"What harm would it do? Do people get to socialize?"

"Yes, for a Nazi camp. But I wouldn't want to test anyone."

Willy became quiet, and then raised his head sharply as if struck with an unshakable idea. "What if we could recreate one of the old Lutine Palace revues here? Do they have a stage?"

"Are you mad? Where do you think you are? Berlin?"

"Of course not. They would never allow us on a stage in Berlin. Now, is there a stage?"

"No, but there's a large assembly hall."

"If there's a large room where we could construct a stage, we have a chance."

"Oh my God, a chance for what, Willy? A revue? We're going to entertain the Germans?"

By this time, the idea had firmly taken root in his mind. "What if by entertaining the Germans we are actually entertaining the Jews?

The inmates? Why can't we give people one last glimpse of joy before they're sent to God knows where? Erich, think about it. Just say they allow us to put on a revue. They'll think it's for them, but we get them to allow the general camp population to watch as well. We can give Jews laughter. We can let them see beauty in the face of evil. I tell you, if that's all I can do before I die, I'd be happy. What about you? Do you just want to go, with nothing to say for your life?"

"Of course not. I just don't see how this will ever happen."

"I'm not giving up on this. I'm not giving up on you, either. And you're going to help me if it's the last thing you do."

"It may very well be the last thing I do, Willy."

"Can we get Max and Camilla and the others together tonight?"

Erich shook his head in disbelief. It wasn't that he didn't see the value in what Willy was proposing; on the contrary, it was so good it would be disappointing to see it not come to fruition. Erich knew that even though Willy had just arrived, when he wanted something to happen, he would make it happen. "Okay, I'll put the word out. Let's meet at six o'clock after dinner in the recreation room. If anyone can do this, you can."

"And Max, and you. I can't do this alone. It'll take all of us. We'll just have to talk to the Commandant."

Erich laughed at Willy's naivety. "You think you can just stroll up to the Commandant's office, knock on the door, and ask to see him? Who do you think you are? Why would he even want to see you?"

Ironically, at that moment, a guard walked up, interrupting the conversation. "Willy Rosen?"

"Yes, I'm Willy Rosen."

"Willy Rosen, the singer and performer?"

"Yes."

"Commandant Gemmeker would like a word with you."

Willy did as he was told, but couldn't resist turning back to Erich, left standing in the same spot with his mouth wide open. Willy's face broke out into a huge smile, and he said, "The Commandant wants to have a word with me."

"Sit here, Herr Rosen. The Commandant will be with you momentarily." The officer pointed to a chair outside a door labeled in large letters, ALBERT KONRAD GEMMEKER, COMMANDANT–LAGER WESTERBORK. The officer then took his place standing across from the door.

Willy sat and waited to greet his latest fan, excited that he was at a camp in which the Commandant knew of him. He was giddy anticipating Gemmeker to open his door at any moment.

But Willy waited, and waited. Had the Commandant changed his mind? All Willy knew was the same hard wooden chair that he'd been sitting on for well over an hour was very uncomfortable. He asked the guard, "Does he know I'm here?"

"Shut up, Jew! The Commandant will deal with you when he chooses to deal with you."

Willy's face turned ashen and the confidence drained from his body. His tall stance in the chair shrunk to almost a cower as the harsh facts slapped him into reality. He was at a transit camp. *What was I thinking?* That is when the door opened to reveal a tall and slender man dressed in the familiar tunic of the SS.

"Willy Rosen?"

"Yes, sir," he replied, a new degree of meekness settling into his tone.

"Herr Rosen, I am SS-Obersturmführer Gemmeker. You may call me Commandant Gemmeker."

Willy stood, putting out his hand to shake, but Gemmeker only nonchalantly glanced at it and kept talking. "Herr Rosen, I caught your act when you arrived here. Quite a show, I must admit. It's been some time since anyone has sung at Westerbork, I am certain."

Gemmeker reached into his tunic and pulled out a thin silver cigarette case, bringing back images of Schaeffer to Willy's memory. "Do you smoke, Herr Rosen?"

"No, Herr Commandant."

"Good for you. Probably not good for the singing voice, eh?"

Willy thought that was a rather casual observation, so he returned the pleasantry. "Herr Commandant, my sister Edith is the singer. I am merely an entertainer." He pointed to his throat, adding, "It's not the best instrument for Bel Canto singing."

Gemmeker chuckled as he lit his cigarette. "Yes, your sister Edith.

She had quite a voice. I so admired her performances of Wagner in Wiesbaden a few years back. Where is she now? England?" The Commandant said, exhaling a smoky mist over Willy's left shoulder. Willy was shocked that Gemmeker not only knew his sister but also her location. He fumbled his words and managed to get out a submissive, "Yes, Herr Commandant. Cambridge."

Gemmeker looked at Willy with a glance that made him feel more and more uncomfortable. "Yes. England," Gemmeker continued. "Pity. The English have no taste in music. Her Wagner will be wasted on an unappreciative audience." He took another drag off his cigarette, adding, "But I believe we got the better end of the deal, Herr Rosen. We have you. They have her. I believe you are much more valuable to me than your famous sister could ever be."

Willy's mind was scrambled into a thousand pieces. *What is he talking about?*

"Herr Rosen, I am a man of culture. Westerbork is a place with none. Hell, there's not even a decent radio station that reaches out into this God-forsaken place. I would like you to put on a show, like you did in Berlin. You would do it here in Westerbork. We have a very small stage in the assembly hall. I will see that a piano is brought in, but that's about all I can promise. Does this interest you?"

Willy could hardly believe his ears. What he had just spoken about with Erich was the exact thing Gemmeker was requesting of him. "Yes, Herr Commandant. Very much." Willy only said what he was certain wouldn't offend or change the Commandant's mind.

"Good. Look around here, Herr Rosen. You'll be surprised at the talent that exists within this camp. Go and gather your people. I will have a piano here by the end of the week. You never know. You may end up singing for your life." Gemmeker motioned to the guard that he was finished and walked into his office.

"This way, Jew," the guard said, motioning for Willy to walk down the hall and out into the courtyard.

Already Willy was formulating his plans and running down the list of performers Erich said were in Westerbork. He knew that there was Spira, Ziegler, Max. Max would have to be the director, and Willy would do the writing and some performing. Camilla Spira would be the key. Everyone loves a beautiful woman and everyone knows her. She'd only need to sing one song and the revue will be a hit. He had to find Max.

The guard opened the door and pushed Willy into the courtyard with the persuasive end of his rifle. The bright sunlight nearly blinded him, and he felt arms wrap around his neck and a bosom press against his chest. "Willy, I thought I wouldn't see you again," he heard Mara say, her tear-stained face coming into focus.

He held her tightly and then took a step back. "Mara, it's okay. We haven't anything to worry about. From now on, we're stars."

Mara slapped him violently. "Have you lost your mind?"

Willy rubbed his face, then pulled her away from the crowd. "What's wrong with you? The Commandant wants me to put on a revue, like in Berlin. If I can get him to trust me, maybe we can find out where your parents are. The better the show, the more Gemmeker may trust me. The more trust, the more information. Right?"

Mara looked at him with a renewed respect. She couldn't love him more than she did in that moment and whispered, "You, my dear husband, are a genius. Just tell me how I can help." She kissed her husband lightly on the neck, careful not to be seen by the guard standing nearby.

"Well, we will be singing for our lives. Singing and performing for our lives."

They turned and walked toward the mass of people standing in lines by the registration tables. "We have to find Max Ehrlich."

Since arriving at Westerbork, Max had been ordered to pound out metal salvaged from downed Allied planes during the day. In the evenings, he connected with cabaret acquaintances. Rarely did he let an opportunity escape to entertain; if there were more than two people in front of him at the same time, he had an audience. The sight of Willy walking into the salvage building made his heart swell.

"My God, Willy! What a sight you are," Max yelled, running to hug him closely. "I thought you were dead, you know."

Willy looked at Max as if he hadn't seen him in decades; or as if it might be the last time he would ever see him again. "No, Max. They may have wanted to, but here I am. You're not going to believe this, but Gemmeker wants a performance. A cabaret. He asked me right after I arrived today."

"What? You've got to be kidding me. How does he think that's going to happen?"

"I don't know. He said there was a small stage in the assembly hall. I don't even know where that is yet. Hell, we don't even know where we're assigned to sleep."

"Come with me. You'll stay in the glorious Barrack 15, because only the best for you, Willy."

"What about Mara? Can she stay with me? Or are we segregated?"

"No, families stay together. I'm telling you; we've dodged a bullet here. This place has everything. It's a literal town. Don't get me wrong, you're in a prison camp, but things could be so much worse. At least, I keep telling myself that."

Max talked very quietly and slowed them to a stroll. "There's only one reason Gemmeker wants to do this, and that's to impress other German officers who visit the camp. It's all about him, Willy, don't forget that. He's a mean son of a bitch who would just as soon shoot you as applaud you. Don't get any false ideas. If we're going to do this, it has to be great, because if it's not, we're deported. Shipped out east. Get it?"

"I get it. I know this isn't Berlin. I don't know what we have to work with, or what we'll even do. I do know that if I am going to die, then I want to go out performing. Singing. Playing. Living as best I can for as long as I can. I don't care what Gemmeker's motives are. I get to perform again and so do you, if you'll help me."

"I'm in. I always was. We'll be creating cabaret in hell, but at least it's cabaret."

"Gemmeker said we would be singing for our lives. Let's agree that by doing this, we'll be performing for our lives. Don't you think that if it goes well then he may want more? The more he likes, the more we do, the longer we get to stay here?" Max had processed a lot about Gemmeker's request but hadn't thought about performing to live.

By now, they had reached Barrack 15, and Max walked them over to a lower-level second bunk. "There you go, Willy, right across from me. Mara, you'll need to take the top bed."

Willy collapsed on his bunk with Mara going limp right above him.

"Well? Are we going to do this?"

Glancing at Willy, Max said, "What do you think?"

June 22, 1943

It took two days, but Max had finally assembled the performers. The cast was definitely strong.

Camilla Spira was an A-list actress before 1933, and one of the few to successfully make the transition from silent to talking films. She asked, "How will this work, Max? I mean, look at the size of the stage. There's barely room for the piano, and if both Willy and Erich play, we'll need two pianos."

"We'll put the piano on the floor. Can we even get another one?" Max asked Willy, placing the responsibility on his shoulders.

"I'll ask in the morning. What else will we need?"

Max looked at his troupe: a stand-up comic, a singer/actress, a dancer, a concert pianist, Willy, and himself. No lights and no curtains, but everyone was a seasoned performer.

"Erich and I will play some duos. We'll have to improvise, since there's no music, but we've done it before. Of course, I'll sing and play. Can we do any kind of vignettes?"

"Sure. Why not? I'll write a few and we can see how they read." Max was clearly back in his element.

"Are we sure this is a good idea?" The question came from Erich. He was always a reserved pragmatist, so it should have come as no surprise.

"What I mean is, don't we think that this could be viewed as disrespectful? You know, dancing and singing while people are being sent away? I think we must consider that not everyone will be viewing this as we are. Have we even asked the Jewish Council what they think?"

The room fell silent and Max's enthusiasm melted away. "He's got a point. Has Gemmeker spoken with the Council about this?"

Willy was flabbergasted. "Do you think that an SS officer gives a shit about what the Jewish Council thinks? He tells us to put on a show, so as far as I'm concerned, we're doing what we're told to do. Do you want to live? Because that's what's happening here. We're singing, dancing, and acting for our lives."

"I'm just saying that we should at the very least tell them what we're doing," Erich continued, not wanting to let this go. "It's the respectful thing to do. I know we can't control how everyone feels about it. And for those who choose to see this as something beautiful, as an evening of music and laughter, then I'll be happy to know I was a part of it when it's my time to go."

The impact of his words rendered the room silent. One by one, the cast members nodded in agreement, including Max. "Erich's right. I'll do it. I'll go to the Council and tell them what we've been ordered to do. It won't be asking permission, but it is the right thing to do, and why wouldn't we? They're the ones who come up with the list of transportees. If we're to be kept off that list, they should know." Max could always be counted on to approach a difficult situation with a calm head.

Willy saw that things were moving ahead, hopefully smoothly. "You're right, both of you. Thank you, Erich. And thank you, Max, for talking to the Council."

Max looked at the assembled group. "So, what are we going to call this show?"

The assembly hall at Westerbork had been filled with row after row of raw wooden chairs and benches for the prisoners of the camp. Allowing the inmates to be entertained had been Willy's guiding principle, and it was about to come to fruition. The first two rows were reserved for Gemmeker and the officers of the camp. One large over-stuffed chair was placed front-row and center for Gemmeker himself; and the officers also had chairs, but not like Gemmeker's "throne".

The stage was bare wood and small. Black cloth curtains were strung across a rope acting as a rear curtain. Two pianos were strategically placed at the foot of the stage, side-by-side, within ten meters of Gemmeker's chair. A matching pair of black curtains covered the areas offstage right and left, giving tiny spaces for the performers to change out of sight. There were no spotlights and no footlights; only the bare bulbs that hung from the wooden beams above the audience.

July 11, 1943

"Tremendous, don't you think? I can't believe this is happening," Willy said, happily dressed in a black jacket and matching pants that were given to him as part of the troupe's costumes. Gemmeker had managed to collect suits and dresses that would be appropriate for the show. Mara joined her husband in a preperformance inspection of the hall. It had been less than a month since they had arrived at Westerbork. The last thing they ever expected was to be standing on a stage getting ready to perform for a camp of German officers and Jewish prisoners. *Bunter Abend* (Colorful Evening), as Erich jokingly titled it, was opening in a few hours, on a Friday night at eight o'clock.

It would be a performance that would transform the troupe into something much larger than the six of them could have ever imagined.

The cast gathered on stage for preperformance notes when the front door slammed open and Gemmeker entered escorted by a pair of SS guards. Gemmeker didn't say a word as he slowly made his way to the front of the hall. The performers quickly assembled in a line, heads bowed, waiting for instructions. Instead, Gemmeker looked overhead, struck by the ingenuity of the curtain rigging. "Very nice," he said, as he continued his examination of the work done in the space over the past month. He lightly fingered the black cloth curtains, rubbing his fingers together afterward and stating that they were dusty but sufficient. He looked up into the rafters, noting the bare bulbs hanging by wires over his chair. "We'll have to fix those. Unacceptable." He then walked over to the large chair, placing his hand on the top of the curvature and looked at Willy. "For me?"

"Yes, Herr Commandant." Willy kept his head down.

Gemmeker slowly nodded his approval. "Very nice. Nice touch, indeed." He took one final look around the stage area and again nodded. "Herr Rosen and Herr Ehrlich, I applaud you."

"Thank you, Herr Commandant," the two answered in unison.

Gemmeker continued. "The word from my guards is that you have all worked tirelessly for this performance to go well. You do know that I am an aficionado of the theater. I have seen you, Herr Rosen. Actually, I have seen all of you on stage in Berlin and Düsseldorf. I consider myself fortunate to have such an array of talent within my camp." Gemmeker smiled a broad, toothy smile, that stretched across his exceedingly handsome face. "Should this evening go well, you will continue your work." Gemmeker walked halfway down the center aisle to the door when he turned back to them. "If it does not go well, you will be on the next transport to Theresienstadt."

He and the guards walked out, leaving the prisoner-performers standing silently, each replaying the words of Gemmeker over and over in their heads. The silence, for Willy, was deafening. "What are you worried about? You are all the finest in your craft. Even me," Willy said, smiling at them. It broke the tension as the group chuckled at his boastfulness. "Don't even think that this won't go well. These people haven't seen something like this in ages. They'll love it. Remember, we're giving them a glimpse of humanity before stepping out into the horror of reality." Willy looked at his watch, noting just how much time Gemmeker had taken. "Okay, we have to snap to it," and with that he turned the stage over to Max to give his director's pitch.

"Okay, well. How do I top Gemmeker?" This time they laughed out loud, grateful for Max's ever present humor.

The first audience members entered an hour early in anticipation of the evening's performance by the cast that now called itself Bühne Lager Westerbork. The Camp Westerbork Stage Troupe had developed a kind of celebrity in its own right. The freedom of movement among the prisoners provided all the advertisement needed to guarantee a large and receptive audience. Anyone against the performance in principle stayed in their barracks to pray that they would not be on Tuesday's deportation list. Meanwhile, those on the stage and filling the benches were looking for any way possible to escape their mindnumbing work.

Camilla stuck her head outside the stage dressing curtain to watch the audience. They moved aggressively into the front seats, but made sure not to infringe on the first two rows. Her happiness turned to grief when she watched men, women, and children fight for seats. She studied their thin, drawn faces. This was not an audience looking for a cabaret performance; this was an audience looking for a boxing match. The inhumanity she was witnessing became too much, and she pushed the curtains aside and stepped onto the main floor. "Stop it! All of you!" she shouted, loud enough to be heard over the screams of people being stepped on after they were pushed to the floor. The fight for seats had become a stampede. "If you do not stop this insanity... we will not perform. That's final! We will not perform."

The audience immediately stopped, staring at their beloved star with a sense of deep shame and horror. People reached down to help those on the floor to stand up, and offered their seats as gestures of kindness. Of humanity. Within 15 minutes, the room was full and quiet, with the exception of the first two rows.

Before Camilla could return to the stage, the doors to the hall swung open to reveal Gemmeker and his party of SS officers and camp officials. Instantly, the entire room stood silently with their hats off and heads lowered. The noise coming from the Nazis was rowdy and loud, the sound of drunkenness. As they neared the front two rows, Gemmeker announced, "Gentlemen, may I present the star of stage and screen, Frau Camilla Spira. She will be one of your entertainers this evening."

Camilla saw the hungry eyes of the officers, realizing that they were much more interested in her as a female than as a performer. As was to be expected of someone with her intelligence and training, she fell into playing the part of a star. And of playing for her life. "Herr Commandant, you do me a great honor. Gentlemen? I trust that you are all well?" She spoke to them as if she were the guest of honor at a state dinner; her casual ease with the enemy was remarkable. Her heart was pounding in her chest, but she wore a flirtatious grin, playing the Germans for the goons that she knew them to be.

"We are all well, Frau Spira," Gemmeker responded, showing his guests to their seats. Before she could turn away to join the others backstage, Gemmeker grabbed her arm to the point of bruising, and yanked her toward him, close enough that he could put his lips to her ear. "Let's not be too familiar, shall we?" Gemmeker then glared deeply in Camilla's eyes. "Don't make a mockery of me. Do you understand?"

"I understand, Herr Commandant." Camilla stood back from Gemmeker just enough to see the cruelty of his look recede into a soft and gracious smile.

He turned toward his compatriots, telling them, "Gentlemen, I believe that you are in for a real treat this evening. We have the finest performers in Europe right here in Westerbork. Let's enjoy the show, shall we?" Commandant Gemmeker gave a wave of his right hand to Willy and Erich, now seated at the duo pianos directly in front of him.

The audience sat silently, and Willy and Erich nodded to each other. They played an introduction, which was the cue for Max to come onto the stage for the welcome. "Good evening, ladies, gentlemen, distinguished guests and... others?"

The room burst into laughter and applause.

Max lit up instantly, settling into his natural element. "This evening, by the generous support of Commandant Gemmeker, we would like to present to you Gruppe Bühne Westerbork performing *Bunter Abend*! Here are your entertainers for the evening. There's the world-famous reciter of all things that rhyme, Josef Baar. The brightest star in Germany's firmament of talent, the lovely Camilla Spira. The greatest innovator of modern dance and Holland's siren of the *Lied*, Chaja Goldstein. At piano one is the legend of the concert stage, the extraordinary pianist Erich Ziegler, and at piano two is Herr *"Text und Musik von Mir!"*, Germany's finest cabaret artist, the performer-extraordinaire Willy Rosen. And I, performing as actor, director, and your emcee for this evening, am Max Ehrlich. Ladies and gentlemen. Welcome to *Bunter Abend!"*

```
                    B U N T E R    A B E N D
                  Leitung:  M a x    E h r l i c h

Mitwirkende: Chaja Goldstein - Camilla Spira - Josef Baar - Max Ehrlich
             Willy Rosen - Erich Ziegler

     1. Josef Baar plaudert und reint
     2. Camilla Spira in ihrem Repertoir
     3. Max Ehrlich in seiner Szene "Theaterbesuch"
     4. Willy Rosen (" ....der Text und die Musik sind von mir.... ")
     5. Chaja Goldstein in ihrem Repertoir
     6. "SCHACHMATT" (Sketch)
                     (Max Ehrlich, Camilla Spira, Josef Baar)

                      P a u s e .

     7. "DER MANN OHNE NAMEN" (Sketch)
                          (Max Ehrlich, Josef Baar)
     8. Willy Rosen - Erich Ziegler an 2 Klavieren
     9. Camilla Spira: Chansons
    10. "AUF DER RENNBAHN"
                   Der Neuling: Max Ehrlich, der Fachmann: Josef Baar

Ansage: Max Ehrlich, Josef Baar.    Musikal.Begleitung: Erich Ziegler.
Saaleinrichtung: Eugen Frankenstein.  Beleuchtung: Richard Türkel.

                       Beginn 8 Uhr.
            (Die Programme sind nach Ablauf am Ausgang abzuliefern.)
```

23

Still July 11, 1943

The evening's success was resounding. Following the show, Willy and Max were the first to go into the hall to greet the prisoners. Before they could walk down the small staircase leading to the floor they were stopped by Gemmeker who was grinning ear to ear and obviously delighted by the performance. "Herr Ehrlich, Herr Rosen. Superb, simply superb, gentlemen." Gemmeker looked at the throngs clamoring for the group. "Go greet your fans. Come see me tomorrow morning. Both of you. Nine o'clock." Gemmeker gestured to the other SS officers, and the inmates parted like the proverbial Red Sea, allowing the officers to leave the hall unhindered; the only sounds being the pounding of their heavy boots.

Looking around, there were so many smiling faces and so many wonderful people. The smiles hid the undeniable dread everyone felt, but they would take the memories of this evening with them, this colorful evening of music, dance, and song.

"Can you even feel anything?" Max asked.

"No, I'm numb," Willy said, being uncharacteristically quiet.

"It'll be okay. It's over," Erich said, joining the pair.

"Over? Oh no," Willy said. "I have a feeling that this is just beginning. Gemmeker asked to see us first thing tomorrow morning. He loved it."

"What's that supposed to mean? We do it again?" Erich asked, incredulous at the idea. "Can't you see what tonight did to us? Can't you tell how physically and emotionally drained we are?"

"Yes, but look what tonight did for them," Max exclaimed, pointing into the courtyard where inmates were still making their way back to their barracks, humming and singing as they went. "We did that. We brought them that joy. Screw what it does to us. This is about them."

The cast looked at each other. Realizing that Willy was correct, Erich spoke for them all when he said, "Tomorrow at nine? Sounds like a plan." He was straightening chairs that had been tossed around in the frenzy.

As Willy picked up one end of a toppled bench, Mara called out, "Let's get this place cleaned up and go to bed. The morning will come soon enough, and we have work detail before you see Gemmeker."

"You're right, I completely forgot about that," Willy replied. "Let's get moving here. This is actually triple-work."

July 12, 1943

Willy and Max found themselves waiting outside the office of Gemmeker, but this time without a guard keeping watch. Promptly on the assigned hour the office door swung open and out came a smiling Commandant, reaching out his hand as the two stood up. Neither man had ever known a Nazi to even consider shaking hands with a Jew.

"Herr Ehrlich. Herr Rosen. Good morning. I saw that you were out doing your work early. But performing isn't work, right?"

"Yes, Herr Commandant," the pair said, still with quite a bit of enthusiasm.

Gemmeker was surprisingly friendly as he invited the two into his office. "The performance was outstanding. Now, we must make it grand. Please, sit down." He gestured for them to take seats in front of his desk. "I would like Westerbork to be a model camp." He sat down and reached for his cigarettes. "Oh, I know that Tuesday mornings are horrible. I don't like them either, but I have my orders." The Commandant continued. "I would like you to do another show." Gemmeker slid several pages toward Max and Willy. "It's the manifest of each man, woman, and child in Westerbork. Go through the names to see if anyone on that list can be of use. I want the show bigger and better. You'll need things, I know. You tell me who and what you need, and I'll see that it gets to you."

Staring at the sheets of papers Willy looked at Gemmeker in disbelief. "You want us to tell you who and what we need? A bigger show?"

"Exactly. It shouldn't be too difficult to get the things you need. I can send some people into Amsterdam to get lighting, curtains, costumes, instruments... whatever you need."

Willy didn't hesitate. "Can we get a bigger stage? If we're going to have more people, we need a much bigger stage."

"And an orchestra pit for the musicians?" Max added. "There are a lot of musicians on this list. I count three on the first page alone."

Willy continued. "Perhaps manuscript paper? I could write songs and arrangements."

"You make a list," Gemmeker said, handing Willy a notepad and pencil.

Max was delighted. "Herr Commandant. If you can get us the supplies we can put on the revue."

Gemmeker stood up and again reached out his hand, first to Max and then to Willy. "Very good. Go and do your work. Gather your people. Write your list." The Commandant walked to the door and opened it for the pair to leave. "I am expecting great things, gentlemen." Without emotion or irony Gemmeker added, "You better hurry and find your people. If you don't get them off the list before Tuesday at one in the morning, you'll lose them."

The reality of the situation quickly returned. The good mood turned sour and they walked faster as they headed back to their work.

Willy and Max located a cadre of technical experts to work on the second show, titled *Humor und Melodie,* a revue Willy had done previously in Scheveningen. Willy was able to reuse several of the scenes he had written for other revues, and then created additional ones around the talent of the ever increasing cast of the Gruppe Bühne Westerbork.

It was the fourth year of the war and supplies were in great demand. Yet, Gemmeker was somehow able to acquire only the best for his theater project. He had velvet curtains and lighting brought in from the former Joodsche Schouwburg. However, it was the newly constructed stage that created the most controversy, not only for the performers and crew but also for the Jewish Council. Gemmeker, searching the area for the best and strongest material he could acquire for the supports and floor of the stage, settled on wood that had previously been the floors and walls of the destroyed synagogue at Assen, a short distance away from Westerbork.

July 31, 1943

"As if we weren't unpopular enough with the Council," Max complained, pointing to the floor that was about to be desecrated in the eyes of the Orthodox Jewish Council members.

"It's not like we requested it. It's what it is, so let's just make the best of it. At least it's allowing Jews to live, right?" Willy could always manage to find a brighter side to events.

"Good point," Max responded. "That's what we'll say. And everyone needs to keep our story straight. It might make them feel better. Erich, can you call them up?"

Within minutes, the cast of *Humor und Melodie* was assembled on stage. As they waited, each member took in the transformation of the hall. Curtain rigging was being secured to the ceiling rafters, lights were already positioned overhead in hanging rows or tucked neatly into floor pockets in the stage. The fly curtains were the same worn black materials previously used as a rear curtain, but were now hanging in a much more appropriate place.

"We'll need new fly curtains soon if he keeps this up," Camilla whispered to Willy who was seated on the stage floor to her right. "Hopefully, I won't be here by then."

Willy turned to look at her. "What do you mean?"

"Shhh, softly, Willy. My family is working with Hans Calmeyer to get me declared *Vollarierin*. If my family can afford the fees to pay this corrupt so-called expert Hans Weinert, then Calmeyer will have documented support that I'm Aryan. With that, my husband and I will be considered a Privileged Mixed Marriage and I can get my family out of here. Please, Willy, don't say anything to anyone about this."

"Who am I to judge? If I were able, I would do the same. In any case, your secret is yours to tell, not mine."

"Thank you, Willy. You're a dear."

"Are you two done?" Max called out to them.

"Sorry Max. We were caught up in something else," Camilla said, smoothing away a few tears.

Max, seeing that his star was upset, gave his final instructions. "I'm almost done, anyway. I'll wrap this up. Willy, do you want to take it from here?"

"Sure. So, some of you may remember that I did this revue at the Lutine back in '41. I'm using some of the same songs and a couple of the same sketches but much of the material will be new. Look around and you'll see some familiar faces and some new ones. I'll let the others introduce themselves. Mara, why don't you start?"

One by one the cast members stood up and gave a brief background on their performance career or, in the case of a few like Mara, their lack of one.

The formation of The Westerbork Girls added an element of professionalism because they'd be backup for the main talent and perform between sketches. Talent was less an issue for the dancers than looks. Talent, as their choreographer Simon Dekker-Dickson would say, could be manufactured as an illusion, as long as the illusion was beautiful.

Willy handed the stage over to Max to go through details of rehearsal schedules, fittings for costumes, individual musical rehearsal schedules with Erich, and dance rehearsals with Simon. "News from the Commandant. It seems that he has given permission for our rehearsals to count as work detail, so no more double-duty."

The cast was ecstatic. Up to that point, rehearsals had not been regarded as real work.

"And we're allowed to rehearse whenever we wish, without supervision. There will also be a change in accommodation for some of us. Several people will be moved out of the barracks and will be placed in houses. Willy, Mara, and I will be in one, and Camilla and her family will be in another with Esther and her husband. Hermann, Heinz, and Jonas will be in the third. Rehearsals of the small vignettes can be done in the houses. That way the girls can use the stage with the orchestra to work on the dance numbers."

Erich, who had been relatively quiet about the way events had played out, raised his hand and asked a question that many didn't want to know the answer to. "What do you think he wants out of all this?"

The question was answered by a raspy voice that was as loud as a bullhorn. "Who cares? He could get his damn jollies watching the girls. Or the boys for that matter. As long as he lets us do our thing, I don't really give a damn!" Hermann Feiner was not one to sugarcoat anything. A brash and foul-mouthed behemoth of a man, he was known primarily as a singer of Viennese operetta during the 1920s.

"Really, Hermann? Watch your mouth. There are ladies present," Camilla said.

"Where? I can't find a one."

Max jumped in. "Okay, you two. Let's just keep things civil." Turning to the group, he said, "So, we all now know the cast, and you know some of the plans. First thing tomorrow morning, we'll start with the dance numbers."

Willy realized that the Hermann incident had derailed answering Erich who sat in the same position looking at the two of them, waiting for a real answer. "Erich, I have no idea what he gets out of this. Maybe it's our *bashert*... our destiny to do something good, something that protects us from the inevitable. Let's just live in the moment, though. And if we can make people happy while we are, then all the better."

Erich wasn't buying the explanation, and his expression said so.

September 4, 1943

Before anyone knew it, the opening night for *Humor und Melodie* arrived. This production was twice as long as its predecessor, and considerably more impressive on every scale.

Willy and Mara stood together, looking out among the rows of chairs and benches, just as they had done prior to *Bunter Abend*. This time, however, the feeling was different. It wasn't just that their overwhelming nerves had given way to butterflies of excitement; it was what they had accomplished together. It was the number of people who were now a part of something so much bigger, and because of that were safe, for the time being, from being sent east.

Mara broke the silence. "Do you think he suspects what you're doing?" she asked, careful not to share the question with the wrong ears.

"What? What do you—"

She cut him off with only a glance. "Just promise me that you won't do anything too heroic. That you won't draw too much attention to the production."

"I promise you. Max and I are only doing what we were told to do. The Commandant wanted a bigger production, and we gave him one. Does he realize that the bigger the production, the more people are being saved? Maybe. Maybe not. It goes back to what Erich asked. There's something he's getting out of doing this, but I just can't put my finger on it." Willy's voice faded as he glanced out into the empty hall.

Mara squeezed his hand tightly and simply added, "Just keep your head down, Willy."

There's that phrase again... Willy's mind stopped when the cold truth hit him: should he not keep his head down, it could be cut off. He leaned over and kissed Mara.

"What was that for?" she asked.

"Nothing. Nothing at all." He helped her down the stage left stairs and toward the main entrance to the courtyard. "Let's go round up the others."

September 6, 1943

The final performance for *Humor und Melodie* was only three days after its opening, giving the prisoners one last taste of life before more than 1,000 would be herded like cattle onto transports headed east the following day. Mondays were hard on everyone in the camp, but even more so for the Gruppe Bühne Westerbork.

"September 27 is Gemmeker's birthday. I think we should give him a present. Something that shows him our appreciation for allowing us to perform," Willy said.

Max nodded.

"Why? He's only doing this for himself. Why should we go out of our way to give him anything?" Hermann asked.

Keeping his voice lowered, and looking to make sure no guards walked in, Willy said, "How many times do I need to remind you of this, as long as we're performing, we're not on the transports?"

Max jumped in. "Got it, Feiner? Keep your mouth shut, do your work, and maybe you'll get out of a Tuesday transport. Now, anyone have an idea for a gift?"

Leo Kok rarely spoke and never in cast meetings. He was an artist with an incredible talent for painting, drawing and designing sets. "What if we give him a picture book? We could make it for him. Rudolf Breslauer can take some photographs and I can draw some of the sketches we're doing. Some humorous moments, remembrances... something to make us human in his eyes. Hans Margules will help, and we can get the book bound by someone I know in the shops."

"Very clever, Leo. Let me know if there's anything I can do to help. We'll sign it and present it to him on his birthday as both a remembrance and a thankyou."

Willy stepped in to address the cast just before they were dismissed to get into their costumes. "Tonight, when the whistle blows, our audience will go back to their barracks. When they get there, as they start to sleep, they'll pray that their name won't be called out in the morning. For those unfortunate people leaving us tomorrow, let's make this the most unforgettable night of their lives."

Willy's emotions got the better of him, as he asked everyone to stand and form a circle and he said, "For whatever reason, fate brought us together. We are family now. Max and I thank you for your work, your dedication to helping those in the audience forget their nightmare, if only for a few hours. Let's pray that Gemmeker continues to find joy in our performance and that we're allowed to stay and work together as one."

Without any prompting, the entire ensemble said, "Amen."

Willy collected himself by turning on his performance mode. "Alright, let's get ourselves ready. One hour until showtime. Places in 50 minutes."

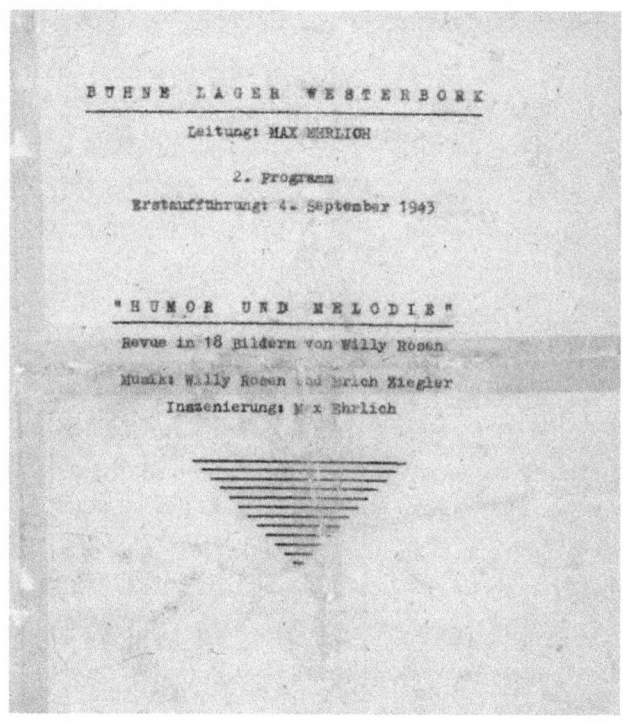

September 27, 1943

Max, Willy, and Erich made their way to Gemmeker's office to present him with his birthday gift; their thankyou for allowing them to perform. Walking into the camp's headquarters, Willy remembered that only a few months earlier he had been escorted to the office by an armed guard. Now, he could enter as he pleased. When they knocked on his door, Gemmeker gave out a resounding, "Enter."

The three walked into the office with Willy holding the book.

"Well, well, well. What do you have behind your back?" Gemmeker asked, with a surprising air of casualness. "Something for me, I hope?"

"We've brought you a birthday gift, Herr Commandant. From the cast," Max explained as Willy produced the book, entitled *Humor und Melodie*. "It's signed by some of us. We wanted you to know how grateful we are that you have allowed us to perform."

Gemmeker couldn't have been more astonished. He took the book with great care and studied its cover. They watched him read the dedication and slowly turn the page. He sat down to look through the rest of the book, as if the three of them were no longer in the room. After the Commandant read the final page, he stood up and extended his hand to all three. "Thank you. I am honored and will treasure this for as long as I can."

Gemmeker was clearly grateful, but what an odd way of putting it into words.

"You are welcome, Herr Commandant. It's from us all," Willy told him.

Gemmeker needed to change the subject and take back control of his emotions. "How is the new revue coming along?"

"Well, Herr Commandant," Willy assured him.

The three men understood by that question that their safety from transport would continue. "It's going to be even better than *Humor und Melodie*. We're calling it *Bravo! Da Capo!* It will be ready to open on Saturday, October 16. Kurt Gerron is here, Herr Commandant, and we'd like him to have a prominent role in this show."

Having regained his composure, Gemmeker said, "Yes, I saw he had arrived. I'm expecting to hear Jetty Cantor at this performance as well. Yes? She and her husband are living with you and your wife, I believe." Gemmeker looked at Willy who nodded. Jetty had been saved from living in the barracks because of her fame as a premier violinist and accomplished comedic actress with a long stage and screen career. Mozes, her husband, was an accomplished cellist in his own right. Their move into Willy and Mara's house meant the relocation of Hermann back into a barrack, with Max moving into another house.

"She's such a talent, a great addition to the orchestra and cast. You will be pleased, Herr Commandant."

Gemmeker looked at the three men in front of him, smiling, but as if by magic it immediately faded, and he addressed them in a serious tone. "There will be many important people at this performance including the highest German officials in the Netherlands. If they're pleased, you may continue your performances with all my enthusiasm. If they don't see the merits in such folly, they could end your troupe as suddenly as I had formed it. I don't want to be just 'pleased,' Herr Rosen. I want to be 'amazed.' The future of your troupe depends on it." The Commandant gestured for the three to leave. Walking toward the door, no one was sure of what had just transpired. As Erich turned the doorknob, Gemmeker said, "Thank you again for the book. I am very grateful."

Wanting to change the conversation to the performance, Willy spoke, "The orchestra has filled out a bit but we could still use a good trumpeter."

"Hey, there's a new guy in Barrack 12 who's a trumpeter," Erich said.

Willy's eyes brightened. The possibility of having another trumpeter to score for would be stupendous. "Let me go and see what he's up to. I'm sure Gemmeker can get us another instrument. I'll catch up with you two later," Willy said, heading toward Barrack 12.

It was a beautiful Monday morning, but as he walked Willy's mind began to wander. Tomorrow was Tuesday and the entire camp would be awakened at one in the morning, when an officer would enter each barrack and read the list of those unfortunates to be on the transport that afternoon.

Willy knew he was lucky but it seemed so unfair that he and his performing friends were being spared the horrors of Tuesday mornings when so many others had no safety at all. Why was he able to look at the beauty of a Monday when it brought such fear to so many? His pace slowed to a complete stop as he looked up at the bright sky, the sun illuminating a brilliant blue that was void of clouds. *Thank you.* His prayer was soft and poignant, and for his and God's ears only.

He made his way to the third barrack along the fence, the one reserved for single men without family members. Willy bounced in the door. "I'm looking for a trumpet player," he shouted.

From the back of the long corridor he heard, "Who's looking?"

"Willy Rosen. Who are you?"

"The Willy Rosen? I know you from Amsterdam," the young man said, eagerly shaking Willy's hand. I'm Lex van Weren. I played in Sellmeyer's orchestra for three years."

"I'm here because we need a trumpeter. Interested?"

Lex's eyes grew wide with excitement. "You bet! Can you get me a trumpet?" His voice raised up, sounding like a ten-year-old at Hanukkah.

"I'm certain. Go and meet Erich Ziegler and the other members of the orchestra in the hall by the main entrance."

It wasn't an hour later that Willy was back in the theater with the confirmation that a trumpet would soon be delivered for the newest member of the orchestra.

Lex could barely contain his elation as he listened to the ensemble rehearse. Afterward, he ran up to Willy, nearly shaking his arm off.

"You're certainly welcome, Lex. I look forward to hearing you. Now, go get some sleep. I'm sure it's been a big day for you."

Watching him leave, Erich said, "He's a good kid. He sat there the entire time fingering the parts as if he had the instrument in his hands."

"You're the one who found him. Let's see how he does when he has a real instrument," Willy joked, as they too headed out as the whistle blew for the evening.

Everyone in Willy's house was awakened shortly after one in the morning by a tremendous pounding on the door. Jetty ran into Willy and Mara's bedroom, terrified. "They're coming for us, aren't they?"

"No, no, we'll be alright. Something else must be wrong. I'll find out what's going on." Willy put on his robe and opened the door to find one of the orchestra members, Jacques Barendse, on the other side.

"Willy, come quick. They're taking the new guy."

"I'll be right there. Tell him I'm on my way." Willy hustled into the bedroom, tying the belt of his robe tighter and putting on his slippers.

"Where do you think you're going?" Mara asked.

"I've got to see Gemmeker. I have to get Lex off that list," Willy said but Mara was faster than her husband and yanked him by the belt back from the bedroom doorway. "Don't think for one moment that I'm going to sacrifice my own husband for a trumpet player I don't even know. Are you crazy? You will not go and wake up Gemmeker. You must remember your place, or you could get us all sent away. Don't go to Gemmeker until the morning. Calm Lex down and assure him that it's a misunderstanding."

Mara's words shocked Willy into realizing that his haste could have jeopardized everything. "You're right. I'll talk with Gemmeker in the morning. I'll be right back." Willy sprinted from the house and to the barrack where he found Lex crumpled on his bunk, head in hands, quaking with fear. Willy sat on his cot and tried to give a comforting embrace around the shoulders. "Lex, it'll be alright. I'll go to Gemmeker in the morning and tell him that you're the trumpet player that he ordered the instrument for. He'll understand and take you off the list."

"Do you really think you can help me?"

"I can help you, yes. I may not be able to do many things around here, but I believe this is something I can fix." Willy gave him a soft pat on the back. "Trust me."

"Thank you, Herr Rosen."

"Don't thank me yet. And it's Willy. Rest now. I'll come and see you in the morning." While Lex uncrumpled himself, Willy left the barrack and returned to his bedroom to ready himself for the morning.

Willy was waiting for Gemmeker before eight o'clock. Within a few minutes, the familiar cadence of many pairs of boots announced the arrival of Gemmeker's claque. Willy peered down the hallway until he caught the eye of the Commandant who came over to greet his cabaret star.

"Herr Commandant," Willy said politely.

"Herr Rosen, good morning. I am assuming that your being here so early means that there is something urgent. Come in."

The Commandant reached for his cigarette holder and lit a cigarette with one strike of the match. He turned to Willy and raised one eyebrow, silently letting his visitor know it was now fine to talk.

"Herr Commandant. The trumpeter I spoke to you about yesterday. He is on the transport list for this afternoon. I was hoping—"

"You were hoping I could get him taken off?" Gemmeker took a long drag before continuing. "Herr Rosen, do you know how the list works? Do you think it's as simple as erasing a name off a list of Jews? If you do, you are sadly mistaken."

Willy, for all his promises to Lex, only now realized that he had no idea how the list worked. Of course, he thought it was just about removing a name. How could it be anything else? "No, Herr

Commandant. I don't know anything about the list." Willy was ashamed that he had come to a battle so poorly prepared.

Gemmeker looked at Willy as if he were disappointed in a child. "Names are not just taken off the list. When one name comes off, another must go on in its place. It's all about numbers. I must have 1,047 Jews on that transport this afternoon. Now, you're telling me I need to have 1,046. That's not possible, even for me. If I'm to take his name off the list, you must supply me with one to take his place. Are you willing to do that?"

Willy's mind was fumbling, unable to grasp the situation. Was Gemmeker asking him to find a person willing to go in place of Lex? "Herr Commandant, are you asking me to find Lex's replacement?"

"I am, Herr Rosen. If you want your trumpeter, you must replace him. I'm sorry, but that's the best I can do." Gemmeker turned toward the window as he continued to smoke. Without looking at Willy, he added, "If I were you, I would find a man being separated from his family. Someone who would be willing to be put on the transport because his loved ones are already scheduled. You only have two hours. Do you understand?"

"Yes, Herr Commandant." Willy's face was white and drawn, a look of horror on it. He would have to find someone to willingly leave Westerbork. To go who knows where?

"I would get started if I were you," Gemmeker said, gesturing for Willy to leave. "I'll need the name by ten o'clock when the loading begins. If I don't have it, your trumpeter goes."

Willy walked as calmly as he could out of headquarters, but then dashed toward Barrack 12, looking for Erich and Max. After explaining the situation, Max offered a plan. "We'll go into each barrack and find a couple with the woman packing and the man crying. It's a start anyway, and it could be the situation we need. Wife on the list, husband is not. He may be willing to go with her rather than be left alone here."

Willy couldn't imagine going up to a complete stranger and asking him to willingly take the place of someone leaving in a couple of hours. "Horrible. But yes, I agree. It's the most reasonable way to find a substitute." He looked around to get his bearings. "We only have until ten, so we need to move quickly."

Leaving the barracks, the trio saw a man carrying a suitcase, having trouble moving forward. He was being slowed by a woman who held tightly onto his ankle, as if she had slid down his body. The frantic woman refused to let go as she screamed, begging him to stop. Despite his wife, the man tried to keep moving toward the main gate.

"I won't do it. I can't do it," Erich said. "We agreed that it should be a man to follow his wife, not the other way around."

"What does it matter?" Willy asked. "We need a name, and it doesn't have to be male." Willy half-ran to the couple, stopping in front the man. He looked at the face in front of him, which held watery eyes set deeply into leathered skin. He guessed the man to be around 50 and the woman of equal age. Willy noticed the pair wore weddingrings. He took a deep breath, gathering the courage he needed to ask the couple the most terrible of questions. "Sir, your wife wants to go with you. I can help make that happen. I just need a name to give to the Commandant... someone to take the place of—"

But then the man crashed his fist into Willy's stomach, sending him flying backward into the dirt. "Stay out of this. Just because I have to go doesn't mean that she has to," the man shouted. He then turned his attention to gently unwrapping his wife's arms from his ankle. The sobbing woman wouldn't let go.

"If she has a chance to live, she's going to get it. She's not coming with me," the man said, shaking his leg hard enough that he finally broke her hold on him. He knelt next to his exhausted wife, telling her, "You're staying here." Tears were streaming down his worn face as he told her again, "You're staying here, and I'm going, understand?" The woman wouldn't lift her face as the man continued, his voice much softer and intimate. "Martha, I love you. You have a chance here. I don't know what'll happen to me when I get on that train, but I know it will be better for you here. I just want you to have a chance."

The train whistle blew its arrival at Westerbork, alerting the inmates that boarding was near. The man gave one last look at his wife as she lay on the ground, shattered and broken. He lifted her head up and looked into her eyes, knowing that it would be the last time he would ever see her. He gave her the gentlest, most heartfelt kiss as a final gesture of his love. He then stood up, grabbed his luggage, and walked toward the train.

Max and Erich watched as the events between the couple played out, ignoring that Willy was still on the ground and holding his ribs. Coming back into the moment, they ran over and helped him stand up.

"I'm okay," Willy said, brushing himself off and taking a handkerchief from his pocket to wipe the dirt from his face. "I can't do this! I'm going to have to tell him... I can't believe that I'm going to have to tell him I couldn't fix this after everything I said last night." Willy was distraught, and Max did his best to comfort him.

"You only said what you thought was correct. This is not something that you have any control over. This whole thing is an inhumane shit-show, and all we can do is play the parts we've been ordered to play."

"I know. We have to find Lex and get it over with. They're boarding the train now." They started toward Barrack 12 only to be stopped by the wife who was now upright. In her left hand was a small handbag, and in her right hand she held something out to Willy.

"Take this. Here's your name." The woman took off running after her husband, leaving Willy holding the piece of paper that had just saved the life of his trumpeter.

24

Rehearsals for *Bravo! Da Capo!* were going extremely well. Jetty had stepped into the leading female role, filling the void created by the loss of Camilla Spira who had received the news that she was confirmed as fully Aryan. She and her two children were to be released from Westerbork that afternoon.

"Camilla, could you do something for me? Could you take some letters and mail them? This one's a letter to my mother in Magdeburg. I want her to know that I'm fine and among friends. This one is for Elsbeth. I don't know about the postage, but it's going to Brazil. I can owe you..."

"Don't think twice about it. I promise to get them in the postbox."

"Thank you, Camilla. You will always be my star."

"And you will always be my music director," she said, leaning in to give Willy a soft peck on the cheek. "I have to go. Hans sent a car for us." Reaching the gate, she turned to see Willy standing in the middle of the courtyard. She managed a weak smile and a small wave of her hand. It struck her particularly hard at that moment that she would never see him again. She'd never see any of them again. Hans opened the back door of the limousine. She climbed in and rolled down the window. As the car pulled away, she stuck her head out and shouted, "The world will know about the great things you've done here, Willy. Take care, my dear!"

Willy continued to wave until the limo was hidden in the cloud of dust. As he slowly let his hand down, he felt Max standing next to him.

"That episode took three years off my life," Max said, clutching his heart.

"And God knows, you don't have that many to spare," Willy quipped.

They took each other by the shoulder and walked back to the rehearsal hall, both relieved, no—joyful—that Camilla had really gotten away.

Her departure from Westerbork corresponded with the arrival of cousins Nol van Wesel and Max Kannewasser, known worldwide as the singing duo "Johnny and Jones," and their wives Gerda and Suzanne, respectively. Unfortunately, they arrived too late to be added to the current revue.

The orchestra was impressively large, which was a direct result of Willy's work to include as many of the camp prisoners as possible, such as Jetty's husband, Mozes Cantor, on cello.

Late October 1943

With each performance, Willy was becoming more comfortable, or maybe it was less uncomfortable, with the role that he and his entertainers played in the camp. He had no choice but to firmly believe that they were giving the prisoners their last glimpse of the best that humankind can give. He was grateful for the work required to stage such productions and knew his performers and designers and crew were safe.

Of all the scenes in this revue, none hit as strong a personal note for Willy as *Der Pojaz*, the soliloquy that Hermann Feiner performed[1]. Willy first presented a version of it in Berlin in 1938, set as a reflection of German society's turning against him. He had experienced his fame

252

and popularity curtailed by the Nazis. Then, having been stripped of his German nationality and labeled an enemy of the state, he had become an object of humiliation. He had decided to include it in the revue as a reminder that he worked like a puppet for the very people who stripped him of his dignity as a German, a Jew, a war hero, and a human being.

The Man About Whom One Laughs (The Buffoon)

After all, there's always one,
That one laughs about.
After all, there's always one
Who becomes the joke.
One is destined
To be the fool
It starts in school,
And remains their whole life.
One must be a perpetual clown
Wandering through their existence.
Oh, people like to laugh
At the expense of another:
Everywhere there's always one
That one laughs about.
Everywhere there's one,
Such as you - the *BUFFOON?!*

"What did you think? Pretty good, right?" Hermann was never shy about giving himself a compliment or two.

Willy couldn't speak. Rather, he simply looked at Hermann, teary-eyed, patted him on his protruding stomach, and nodded. He walked backstage to where no one could see him collapse into a heap. The poem was a microcosm of his entire life: the Iron Cross, Elsbeth, hiding, and Westerbork.

I'm the clown, Willy thought. *I could have left Holland but chose to stay. I am the buffoon.* He would always know that no matter how much praise was heaped on him by the Commandant and his Nazi cronies, he was still their clown, performing for the very people who had taken his life away from him.

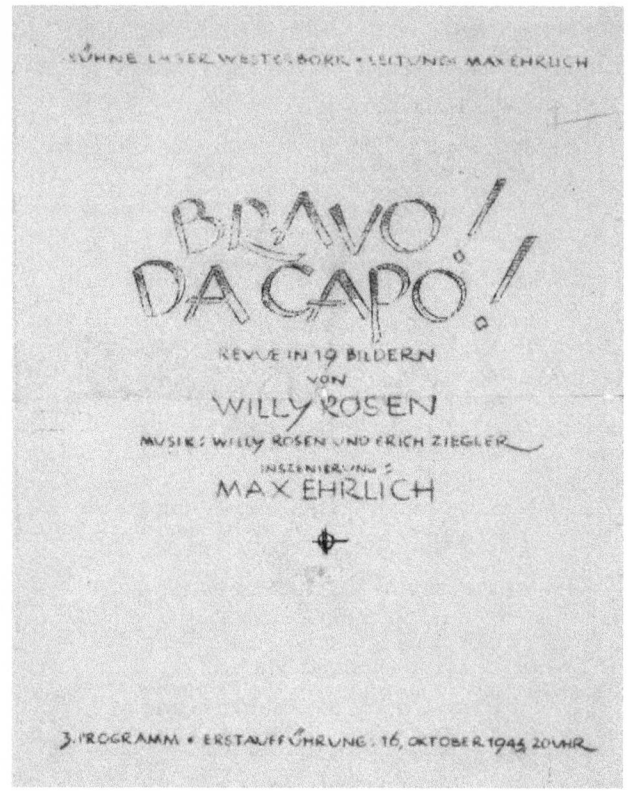

The camp audience would clamor for tickets which were now needed to control the number of people that could fit in the house. Still, there were many within the Jewish community of Westerbork who continued to vehemently disapprove of performing Operetta at an opened grave. Nevertheless, Willy and the Gruppe Bühne Westerbork performed *Bravo! Da Capo!* every day and night for just over a month, turning it into the longest-running revue to date in the camp. They would perform for the inmates at night, and daytime or evening for Gemmeker's prestigious guests. Only an outbreak of polio in November 1943 forced Gemmeker to halt the performances as well as all transports in and out of Westerbork. Finally, the troupe could take a break.

December 20, 1943

During the enforced shutdown of the revue, Lex van Weren was deported to Auschwitz, placed on the final transport prior to the polio outbreak, and this time Willy wasn't given the opportunity to save him. Commandant Gemmeker had intentionally placed the young trumpeter on the list of deportees to remind Willy and Max that he was in charge of everything at Westerbork, and that neither man had power over who was saved and who was not, regardless of their position within the Bühne. This decision shook each member to the *Der Pojaz* core when the transports started back up on January 11, 1944.

January 18, 1944

Willy's household was awakened shortly after one o'clock in the morning. Willy quickly put on his robe and slippers; all he could think of was who might be the next on the list. When he opened the door, a red-faced Max stumbled in, breathless. "They're taking Hermann Feiner," Max said, barely able to speak, and doubling over from running so quickly.

"What? Hermann? He shouldn't be on the list. He's in our next revue," Willy said, not quite awake.

"We should be able to get him off the list. Right?" Max was questioning their ability to fix anything, knowing that lightning rarely struck twice.

"I would think so," Willy said, and although he didn't sound fully confident, it was enough for Max to leave and go comfort Hermann until they had real news to share.

When Willy couldn't go back to sleep with this news, Mara joined him on the sofa. He sensed that things were going to be different with Hermann than with Lex. "There's a reason Gemmeker's doing this and I would bet my last guilder it has to do with power and control."

"Willy, come back to bed. You'll try in the morning, but right now there's nothing to be done. Let Max deal with Hermann tonight, and you deal with the Commandant in the morning." She led him back to the bedroom by the hand, and Willy laid down but did not sleep.

The next morning, after checking in on Max and Hermann, Willy went to the Commandant's headquarters and waited for Gemmeker. Once he was ushered into the office, all Gemmeker would say is, "It's his turn, Herr Rosen. You mustn't ask for so many favors." Gemmeker was enjoying the conversation and relishing the grief he was putting Willy through.

"Herr Commandant, please. Hermann is a key member of the troupe. We need him."

"You only need who I let you need, Herr Rosen. No. Feiner goes. He'll go to Theresienstadt. They'll have lots of things for him to do there, not to worry. They have almost as much cabaret and certainly more theater than we have here at Westerbork."

Willy tried one more desperate plea, though it was a dangerous one. "Herr Commandant, please. I want to keep the talent I have."

"But that's not your decision, is it? You may not want new talent, but perhaps I do. I've seen Hermann Feiner now in the last two revues, and he's tiresome. You'll find someone to replace him. Someone far better."

Willy was reminded once again that to Gemmeker they were all toys to be played with. He knew his conversation was futile, and his time would be better spent saying goodbye to Hermann.

Gemmeker seemed to agree. "You can go now, Herr Rosen. However, the Führer is planning on filming in Theresienstadt. I would start getting used to saying goodbye to your cast members from this point forward." He gestured for Willy to leave.

He went straight to the barrack where he found Hermann consumed with fear. He shook his head at Max and went straight to Hermann. "Hermann. It's Willy."

The frightened man kept his back to Willy, his face buried in his pillow to stifle the noises erupting from his lungs. "Let it out. I know you're scared. I could just—" But Hermann, in one swift move, buried his head into Willy's chest, the sobs no longer silenced. Willy hugged him for a few minutes, and then whispered, "Hermann. They're sending you to Theresienstadt. Gemmeker said that they're filming a picture down there and they want you in it. Can you believe it? You get to be back in the movies after all." Willy feigned excitement, hoping that the information would change even a little the way Hermann viewed his departure from Westerbork.

Lifting up his head, Hermann looked directly at Willy, unblinkingly. The color began to return to his cheeks. "Are you serious? Don't lie to me, Willy. I'd rather know the truth than be lied to."

"I swear. The words came out of Gemmeker's own mouth just a few minutes ago. He said that others from the troupe would be joining you, that he had to decide who would be the best for the film," Willy told him, feeling pangs of guilt for stretching the truth about the movie.

"Will you be coming? Will Max?" Hermann knew that if one of them were coming, then it was certainly true.

"I have no idea. I could be. But you're the first, hand-picked by the Commandant himself." Willy hugged Hermann one final time. "You take care of yourself, okay? Don't become too big of a star. Your ego won't be able to stand it."

Hermann chuckled at the thought that maybe Willy was right. "Thanks, Willy. Maybe they'll let me write to you from there. I can tell you how the film's going."

"I'd like that. I'd like that a lot. You better get down to the train. Are you packed?"

"Yes, for what it's worth. I don't have much."

"All the better. Let's go."

The two made their way through the courtyard and out to the Boulevard of Misery—the long dirt road that lay next to the train tracks leading into and out of Westerbork—where Hans Margules assisted the unfortunate masses onto the train.

"This is going to be the hardest trip of your life," Hans warned him. He reached into his pocket and pulled out a small container of water, shoving it into Hermann's hand. "Take this. You'll need it." As Hermann climbed into the cattle car, he took his final look at the camp. Sucking up his emotions, he called out, "Theresienstadt, here I come!"

February, 1944

Hans Margules's work on the infamous Boulevard of Misery was beyond torture. He was the last person to witness each cast member board their train, and there was a never ending flow of friends and strangers to be loaded like animals into cattle cars. The sorrow and stress were unbearable.

Hans was waiting for Willy in the theater early one Tuesday morning. "I can't build your sets anymore. I'm sorry."

Willy was overwhelmed by the announcement. He had lost half of his troupe, and now he was losing his best set designer and builder. "What's wrong? We need you!"

Hans was visibly tense. "They're making me work on the trains fulltime. They're increasing the number of transports. I'm sorry." Hans then confided something he hadn't told anyone. "When I came here, I thought I would last a month or so. My mother wrote a letter saying I wasn't a legitimate Jew. That my father was Aryan. I was deemed a half-Jew and told that I would have to stay here in Westerbork, that I'd never be transported. However, my fate would be to work at the trains and to have to watch every single Jew be carted away. I was spared by a letter but tortured by it as well. Now, I just can't..." Hans broke down, his head collapsing onto Willy's shoulder.

"I had no idea. I'm so sorry, Hans. At least you don't have to worry about being deported. That must mean something."

Hans immediately sat upright. "It means I have to die a bit inside every time I shut a door, every time I write a number in chalk on the outside of the car. I might be living, but I'm dead." Without another word, he stood up and headed to the train, needing to load another day's commodity.

At that moment, an SS guard entered the hall loudly, his boots thudding against the worn wooden floorboards. "Herr Rosen? Herr Ehrlich? The Commandant wishes to have a word with you. Follow me."

Willy and Max stared at each other.

Are we going to be told that we're next to go? What about Mara? Will they send her with me? Willy's mind raced with the memories of all the cast members that he had to say goodbye to over the past six months. Willy was deeply nervous as they walked into the office.

"Herr Rosen and Herr Ehrlich, I have a wonderful surprise for you both. I do hope your new revue is coming along well."

Although Max hadn't heard Hans's story, he lashed out. "Our revue? We hardly have enough people left to put on a show. They've all been taken away. I thought you said that we were safe from transport." He clearly didn't worry about facing Gemmeker toe-to-toe this morning.

"I'll remind you to speak to me with a civil tongue, Herr Ehrlich, or you will be on the next transport." He waited to twist the knife. "Yes, it's sad, however, the orders have been given."

"What orders?" Willy managed to ask.

"Orders that all Jews are to be transported out of Westerbork. New Jews are more likely to leave as soon as they arrive." Gemmeker reached for one of his ever present cigarettes. "Oh well, all good things must come to an end, but not your revues. You both will remain here and continue with your work." He stopped speaking as he took a long drag, watching the smoke trail toward the half-open window next to his desk. "Anyway, I wanted you to know that Johnny and Jones have been here in Westerbork for a few months. I believe they'll make a wonderful addition to your revue, correct? They are, I mean, they were, the biggest stars in Holland... teen idols, I believe. In any case, they're here, spending their days stripping downed Allied airplanes. They will continue their work during the day, and now they will spend their evenings rehearsing with you."

Willy was both relieved to have such talent and sickened to hear that one of the continent's most popular singing duos was in Westerbork.

"When do you expect the next revue to be ready?"

"At the end of next month, Herr Commandant. We'll go right now and find them. Thank you, Herr Commandant."

Willy's emotionless response didn't get by Gemmeker. "Herr Rosen, it would be good to remember that any of you can go at any time. Now go and find your stars." Gemmeker turned toward the window as a way of dismissing them.

The two men hurried out of the office and straight to the metal shop to find Johnny and Jones. They immediately spied the pair working across from each other at a long table, wearing the blue uniform of the shop's workers and their faces covered with soot.

"Hello, Johnny and Jones?" Willy asked quietly in Dutch, not wanting to startle them.

"Yes. Who are you?" Jones asked.

"I'm Willy Rosen and this is Max Ehrlich. We run the camp cabaret."

"Holy cow, look who this is, Nol. It's Willy Rosen. We know all about you. We knew you were here and really wanted to meet you! We grew up on your music. You must be really old now," Jones said, in nearly one breath.

Max burst out laughing when Willy's face turned red. "Yes, I'm older, but I'm still me," Willy zinged back.

Nol van Wesel, aka Johnny, reached out for Willy's hand, shaking it enthusiastically.

Meanwhile, his musical counterpart and cousin, Max Kannewasser, aka Jones, reached for Max. "Of course, we know you both. You were just getting ready to put your show on when we arrived."

Willy explained. "The Commandant sent us here to invite you to perform in the next revue. Can you do something cabaret-like?"

"Sure. Can you get us guitars?" Nol asked eagerly. "It seems like forever since we played, but we certainly know your music. We do a lot of your songs. Actually, we do a potpourri of your music as part of our set. Maybe we can do that here?"

"I'd be honored," Willy said, shocked that these two teenagers really did know his music.

"When can we start?" Nol asked.

The young men looked at Willy and Max with the excitement that only comes through youth and naiveté. Willy felt like he was looking into the eyes of lambs who would certainly be sent to the slaughter. "We rehearse tonight after dinner in the theater. I'll know about the guitars by then."

"We don't even need to list the orchestra in the program anymore. I mean, how many musicians does Theresienstadt need? I hear they have over 100 performers in their orchestra alone. We had a dozen, and now we have none," Willy told Max when they were alone.

"Well, if Gemmeker complains, I'll let him know it was his doing," Max said, still seemingly unafraid to say what he thought.

"I would keep my mouth shut if I were you, or you'll end up on the next train out of here," Willy warned.

At the first rehearsal, Johnny & Jones stole the show with their delightfully fun rendition of several of Willy's songs strung together. The problem was that Willy's German songs were interspersed with some Dutch and even some English songs. Willy knew this would be a serious problem with Gemmeker who had ordered that only German be sung in the cabaret.

Willy had consulted with Max about what to do. "Do you think maybe he'll overlook it because they're such a well-known act?"

"Well, if he doesn't, we'll lose them, as well as a lot of credibility with the Commandant." Max knew it was a risk, but there was little they could do, since the only songs the pair could sing in German were Willy's.

"I know. We'll just have to wait and see after opening night. I'm sure he'll let us know in no uncertain terms afterward."

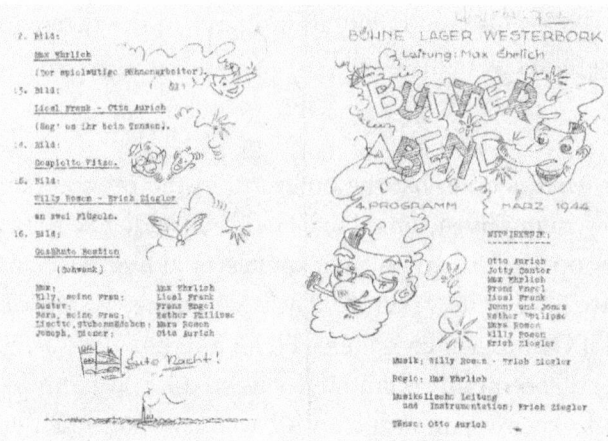

They were right. Immediately following the opening, Gemmeker informed Willy and Max that the Dutch heartthrobs would no longer be allowed to perform in the cabaret. Willy pushed his luck by asking Gemmeker about allowing such talent to perform anywhere else in the camp, playing into the Commandant's belief that he was a cultured man.

"Guys, I'm sorry," Willy said, finding the cousins after the crowd that had swarmed them left. "Gemmeker said if you're not singing in German, you're not singing in a revue, and he means it. He said you could sing in the coffeehouse while you stay here, but that's all." Willy was as apologetic as possible, knowing that the young men would be crushed. He was wrong.

"That's alright," Nol said. "As long as we can perform, we don't care whether it's with you or in the coffeehouse. If Gemmeker had said that we couldn't perform anywhere, now that would have hurt!"

After one evening's coffeehouse performance, when he hadn't seen the boys in a while, Willy stayed to find out how they were doing. "We're fine. Gemmeker's sending me and Nol to Weesp to pick up some airplane parts. We haven't been out of the camp since we arrived here," Little Max explained, plainly thankful for the opportunity. He had earned the moniker "Little" to differentiate him from Max Ehrlich.

Westerbork was a rarity in the Nazi camp system because it routinely allowed prisoners to leave for short periods of time to either carry out financial business, such as get money out of banks or make property arrangements. Or, in the case of the two young musicians, pick up crates of airplane parts. Nol gestured to Willy to come closer, so he could whisper their plan. "We've written a couple of songs since we arrived here. When we're in Weesp, a friend is going to set up a studio for us to record them, one of which is called *Westerbork Serenade*. I have a feeling it'll be big. But you can't say a word to anyone. Maybe Gemmeker wouldn't care, but maybe he would. In any event, we'd rather ask for his forgiveness after than try to get his permission before."

"Sure guys. I'll see you when you get back. We're starting our next revue soon, so I hope that we have an influx of new talent. Right now, the only new person is Flip Sanders. I don't really know him."

"Only Flip Sanders?" Nol exclaimed, back to his normal speaking voice. "He's one amazing kid! He'll be great for the revue."

"Thanks for the vote of confidence. Best of luck in Weesp!"

With that, the two singers left the coffeeshop and headed back to their barrack.

Willy, walking back to his house, felt better now that Johnny and Jones had made a plan for themselves. And he'd have to find Max and Erich in the morning to begin putting together the third incarnation of *Bunter Abend*.

25

Without new performers to work into the Westerbork cabaret, much more time could be spent finetuning the acts. Logistically, there was little to go through, with the exception of the exceedingly overworked Leo Kok, who had taken over all design elements from Hans Margules. The increased frequency of the transports paired with the loss of the safety net that once protected the performers from deportation had left the troupe smaller on all accounts. For *Bunter Abend 3*, to be performed in April 1944, the lineup included only ten performers: Willy Rosen, Max Ehrlich, Erich Ziegler, Mara Rosen, Esther Philipse, Lisl Frank, Jetty Cantor, Franz Engel, Otto Aurich, and Flip Sanders. Flip did not perform in the last review, and no new talent arrived, leaving only nine for the sixth and final revue to take place a month later.

Westerbork, being an open camp where individuals could leave and return on occasion, had more than its fair share of accurate knowledge about the war outside of the camp boundary fences. News of the Allied forces weakening the German army offered hope and at the same time brought fear of increasing repercussions from their captors. No longer did Max Ehrlich and Willy Rosen wait along the Boulevard of Misery in search of talent coming into the camp. By this time, the only people arriving at Westerbork were families with small children and large numbers of Gypsies picked up along the countryside or sent from other camps in Holland. The troupe had to focus on the talent they had and work their hardest to create a show that upheld the reputation of the finest cabaret in Europe.

The 16 scenes of *Bunter Abend 3* were exactly as the four previous revues had been structured. Many were solo acts, interspersed with short vignettes by several members of the cast. Now, however, there were no longer large ensemble numbers, and no chorus remained.

Gemmeker was still enthusiastic, but he was no longer attending every performance. His time was now occupied with train schedules and how they could be increased.

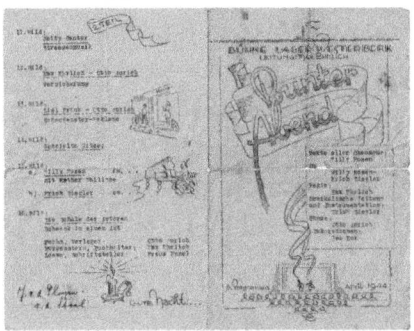

May 8, 1944

After *Bunter Abend 3* ended, Willy needed to know what the future may hold for himself and his tiny troupe, which is why he was in Gemmeker's office. "Herr Commandant. Thank you for seeing me."

"Herr Rosen, it's always a pleasure. Your cast was marvelous this past weekend."

"Thank you." Willy was incredibly nervous and apprehensive to bring up his next points, but knew that if he didn't do that now, he may never have the opportunity in the future. "Herr Commandant. What will happen to us? To the cast and crew? Are we to be sent away as well?"

Gemmeker reached for his cigarette case but, opening it, found it was empty. The man would have to have the conversation naked, without a cigarette to help him get through the questioning. "Herr

Rosen. Willy, may I?" Gemmeker had never used his first name. *What could that mean?*

"I have no intention for you or your members to be caught up in this death trap. I can only imagine that at some point you and the others will have to go. When that day comes, there are a few things that I can still do to help. You should trust me. I will not let anything happen to you or your remaining cast members. When you and your cast leave, I can make sure that you are sent to Theresienstadt. They have quite excellent entertainment, if you hadn't already heard."

"I have heard, Herr Commandant."

Yes, there were shows, but no loyalty by the camp administration to protect the performers from deportation. One of the stories he had heard from Hans was the fate of Kurt Gerron, who had been ordered to film a propaganda piece in Theresienstadt. Once completed, Kurt was immediately sent away. Some noise had come back about a camp in Poland from where no one returned: Auschwitz-Birkenau. *Had that been where Kurt was sent? Was he alive? Were any of the deported cast members still alive?* Willy's mind raced with the possibilities. He saw an opening. "Herr Commandant, is there anything that you can do to ensure that we're not sent anywhere else once we get to Theresienstadt? I've heard things—"

But Gemmeker raised his right hand. "You must not believe everything that you hear. When it's time for you to leave Westerbork, and that time is coming soon for everyone, I will send a letter to the train personnel that none of you should ride in the cattle-cars, but in the third-class cars. I will also send word to Theresienstadt that you and your members are to remain there as part of the cultural productions of the camp for as long as it is in operation. Now that, Willy, is the best I can do for you at this point." Gemmeker looked out the window, bringing his hand to his lips, forgetting that he didn't have a cigarette.

Willy was ecstatic—he had received a guarantee that everyone he loved would be safe in Theresienstadt until the whole damned thing was over. "Thank you, Herr Commandant."

When he was already in the hallway Gemmeker called him back. "You've done some remarkable things here at Westerbork. Things that other camps and other commandants could only dream of. This war... this shit-box of a war... will be over soon." He swallowed hard and deeply, as if he were a bit overcome with emotion. He quickly regained his composure. "You have brought great honor to me, and I intend to do everything in my power to help you and your cast survive this war. You have another revue in the works, yes?"

Willy nodded, wondering if he was going to be told to cancel it and instead prepare to leave.

"I think you should call it *Total Verrückt!* because *Totally Crazy!* is what all of this is. I was a normal man before this war. I don't know..." He stopped to look out the window at the goings-on in the courtyard, at the inmates going about their daily work detail and at the armed guards lounging around the gates. The choices he made in the coming months could have a major impact on how his life would be after the war. That's what he needed to worry about.

Willy listened and, for a moment, almost felt sorry for the Commandant. It was short-lived, however. This man sent tens of thousands of people on trains to go who knows where. The friends he had performed with one day, were gone the next. The Nazis destroyed Jewish theater and culture by eradicating his people. No, he wouldn't shed a tear for Gemmeker. All Willy cared about was making sure that he, Mara, Max, Erich, and the others would live to see the day when this war was over. He realized he hadn't responded when he saw Gemmeker looking at him.

"*Total Verrückt!* Yes, Herr Commandant. I believe the name is perfect."

"Plan your revue as you see fit."

Willy was dumbfounded.

Gemmeker walked over to Willy, touched him on the sleeve looked him directly in the eyes as he spoke. "I promise you. I will do everything in my power to see that you and your cast make it out of this. You have my word."

Gemmeker sounded like a man who wanted to follow through with his promise but wasn't certain if he even had the power to do so. Willy felt a degree of uneasiness, yet had no choice but to hope that Gemmeker would stick to his word. He said, "Thank you, Herr

Commandant," and left the office pondering what had just played out in front of him.

Willy reached the theater where Leo was sketching out the scenes for the upcoming revue. "*Totally Crazy!* That's what he wants the show called. Well, the opera piece will fit well within the title. As long as he's not expecting cheery and happy, I'll be fine calling it whatever he wants," Willy announced. In the back of his mind, he decided that sharing Gemmeker's promise with the cast could be an energizing factor in their upcoming performance, as grotesque as it was planned to be.

The revue was to be a dark premonition of events to come. Even the number of scenes, 13, served as an ominous reminder that although they had been lucky up to this point, the future looked entirely different. The revue was brilliant, if not disturbing, and the performances intense, uplifting, and thought-provoking. It premiered on a Monday evening, June 5, 1944.

The following morning was D-Day when the Allies landed at Normandy.

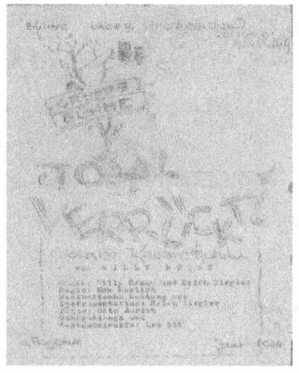

June 6, 1944

Gemmeker had Willy gather the cast so that he could address them personally. "My entertainers. I wish to thank you for all that you have provided to me and this camp over the past year. However, there will be no more performances of your show. I must stop all rehearsals until I receive further instructions on how Westerbork will be affected by the latest turn of events. Until that time, you must return to your previous work duties." Gemmeker paused as he looked at the cast. There was no more to say, so he walked down the stairs to leave.

When he reached the door, Willy called out. "Herr Commandant?"

"Yes, Herr Rosen?"

There was a distinct pause as Willy noted an abrupt change in Gemmeker's attitude. He had spent the past 11 months creating some of the finest cabaret performances in all of Europe and working with some of the most renowned talent. Willy hoped that the promise Gemmeker had made to keep them together would come to fruition should the worst-case scenario play out. "Herr Commandant, thank you for allowing us to live and giving us the gift of giving to others. To help make their lives brighter in the face of fear. Herr Commandant, we are human. Humans need to feel love. Your allowing us to perform has given us that gift. Thank you, Herr Commandant. And we are grateful, very grateful, for the promise you made to us. May God bless you, Herr Commandant."

Gemmeker reflected upon his sentiments. Yes, he knew they were Jews, but was that so bad? What had they really done? Had this been other circumstances, he could have been seeing them in any theater in Amsterdam or The Hague. Was Hitler wrong? He had to answer that for himself. After a few seconds, he had decided... Jews were not human. "Thank you. I wish you all well. Good day." Gemmeker exited, realizing that he cared little for the Jews he'd come to know.

26

It had been nearly two months since the first and final performance of *Total Verrückt!* and the members of Gruppe Bühne Westerbork were experiencing the day-to-day monotony of being regular members of the inmate population. However, the coffeehouse still had performers entertain in the early evenings after the day's work was done. Between Willy at the piano and Johnny and Jones singing there were regular evening shows.

As the news of Allied troops taking town after town from German control reached Westerbork, Gemmeker and his fellow officers became increasingly tense, restricting all movement of prisoners out of the camp and forcing more brutal labor details, as if to break the spirits of those inhabitants secretly holding a glimmer of hope that one day the Allied troops would reach this desolate outpost in Drenthe.

August 2, 1944

"Do you actually think Gemmeker will keep his word?" Jetty asked the others gathered around the small table, sharing what little food had been allowed them for the day. She picked at the two bread slices for four adults. "I mean, why would he? What does a Nazi think he owes a Jew? Nothing, I say. I don't trust him. Sure, he speaks of thanks and wanting to do what he can for us, but in the end, why should he?"

"Jetty, shut up. Can't you see you're upsetting them?" Mozes said, pushing the other piece of bread toward Willy and Mara, making sure that his wife didn't eat that one too.

"Thanks, Mozes," Mara said, appreciating the gesture. She split the slice, giving Willy half. She had hoped that he would jump into the conversation, but only through a look of pleading did he give in and attempt to set the record straight, as he saw it. "I don't believe that Gemmeker would give us any false hope. Why would he? Like you said, Jetty, he doesn't owe us a thing, so why even mention it if his intent is false?"

"How about the reason that he's a pig and a sadist just like the rest of these monsters? I think he's just toying with us to make the end even worse than—"

"Worse than what?" Mara asked. "Worse than a simple death? An unexpected death? We're not fools, Jetty. We've been here a year. We've seen it, haven't we? A few executions, death by exhaustion, starvation, rats, disease. What can they do to us that would be worse than that?"

Understanding the effect of her words, Jetty said, "I'm sorry."

Mozes took his wife's hand and then kissed it. "It's alright, my love. We're all just tired. Tired of everything. Why not go to bed?"

Willy looked at his watch. "Let's go to the coffeehouse, Mara. I need a little bit of cheering up. You want to come with us?"

Mozes shook his head and gestured toward the bedroom. "Duty calls."

"Understood. Let's go, my dear." Willy held open the front door for his wife, and both immediately had to protect their eyes from the wind-swept dust. Willy stopped in his tracks, tightened his grip on Mara's hand, and turned to look her in the eyes. He looked like someone carrying the weight of the world on his shoulders, and his breath became shallow and quick. "I want you to know that no matter what happens, I love you."

"And I love you." Mara was taken aback with his sudden burst of sentiment. "Willy, what's wrong?"

"Everything. Everything and nothing." He stood there, memories of his loved ones flashing by him like a transport train. He thought about his mother and father, Lucie and Edith. And about Elsbeth. It was as if she were right here with him. Elsbeth would always be his first love. Yes, he loved Mara, but it was Elsbeth he would always carry in the center of his heart. Had this madness not forced them apart, he would still be with her.

"I love you," Willy said softly, as in a trance.

"I know, my dear." Mara's voice shook Willy out of his stupor and back into the present. He gave a faint smile at Mara.

Going to the only spot of happiness in the camp they enjoyed an evening of entertainment by the hottest duo in Holland. The coffee was fake, pressed from rye, but the music was real. As real as his love for Elsbeth. He wondered where she was.

During a work break the previous week, they had let Willy know that their song *Westerbork Serenade* was getting a great deal of airplay throughout Holland on the underground radiostations, as well as on Radio Free Europe. Their plan to record it when they were in Weesp had worked out well.

The simplicity of the song's story reminded him of his own Westerbork love affair. He was extremely lucky to have had Mara with him through all of this. He admired her. She was a quiet pillar, always supporting him no matter what was asked of her. When he needed a Westerbork Girl, she stepped in. When he needed her voice in the ensemble numbers, she did that. She was young and beautiful, seemingly spared from the scars of life while in the claws of monsters. Willy never imagined anyone replacing his Elsbeth, but how fortunate he was that, throughout this horrible ordeal, he had found someone to ease the misery and share the hunger that never left. Truly, if he couldn't have Elsbeth, he was grateful to God for Mara. Deep within his retrospect, Willy hadn't realized that Johnny and Jones had finished their set and were calling out to him. "Hey, Willy, it's your turn."

"My pleasure, boys!" After the piano was in place, he put on his biggest grin, and with a hearty voice, called out, "If you know this one, join in. Text and music by me, of course!"

When finished he walked over to Mara, took her by both hands, and lifted her up to gently bring her from behind the table. He wrapped his arms around her delicate frame and kissed her with a deeply passionate kiss; the kind forbidden by the authorities. The audience burst into enthusiastic applause and cheers, grateful to see a truly human moment amid all the inhumanity.

The evening ended when the 9:50 p.m. whistle blew. Willy and Mara took their time as they walked up the dirt path, fingers again intertwined. For all the ugliness, they had a beautiful life. They had a home, they had friends, they had music, and they had each other. No Nazi camp could take that away, they thought.

News trickled down to the troupe members as they each began their morning work duty that all cultural activities would now cease. Willy, who only the night before had been in an unexpected state of bliss, was again knocked back into reality. The beauty of the previous evening was stripped away to reveal the putrid horror that was being a prisoner.

Max found Willy reading Gemmeker's order tacked to a light post in the courtyard, his face drawn and pale. "You've heard, obviously," Max said.

"Yes. I can't believe they've done it. They've succeeded in taking away the one thing that kept us human. First, the revues, but there was the coffeehouse. Now what do we do? What's going to happen to us?" Willy barely spoke loudly enough to be heard.

Max shrugged his shoulders as if he were doing his routine. "I don't know, Willy, but what do any of us know?" With no response, Max understood the level of suffering and the severity of the questions. Humor wasn't going to work this time, so he turned Willy away from the sign and toward him. "We didn't want to be here, but here we are. We were given the chance to perform... to laugh, to sing, to cry, to love. God placed us here, together, for a reason. I don't know why, but I'm sure glad he did. We've all spent the past year making others feel alive, doing more good for people here than we did with all our work at KaDeKo, the Lutine Palace, and the Schouwburg put together. What more could anyone ask of us? We did well, Willy. We did very well."

Willy took in everything that Max had to say. He truly heard that their work there together was the most important of their combined careers. "You're right, Max. But what do we do now?"

"Now? We keep our heads down, that's what."

"There's that phrase again. I just hate it, and you know that's not me. I've never been able to do that, and never will."

"Well, I guess I can't expect you to do something that's not you," Max told him, sensing his friend was coming back to himself.

Max and Willy together could always lighten any situation, even this one.

Willy smiled, and asked, "Do you think they'll let us hum?"

"I don't know, but I wouldn't push it if I were you."

"Come on, let's hum. Let's hum *Im Weißen Rössl*."

"Benatzky? The White Horse Inn? Can't we at least hum to a good Jewish composer?"

"Well, he married a Jew."

"Is that really good enough for you? Is that all it takes?"

"Hey, you're the one who said not to push it," Willy said, and the two laughed.

An officer noticed the pair standing there, not at a work detail, and forced them toward the metal shop. Along the way, the strains of Ralph Benatzky's 1930 operetta could be heard via a faint humming.

By the third week of August, trains were arriving not just with Jews but with prisoners from many different cultural groups, though mainly Gypsies and other dark-skinned people from the extremes of Western Europe. They would stay in the cattle cars, not allowed to exit, and a random group of Westerbork prisoners would be sent to join them, creating, in the later oral testimony of Hans Margules, an "impossible living situation where the people were crammed in the cars like sardines in a tin can." This process of "topping off" the transits took only a matter of hours. The camp inhabitants feared these special transports even more than the regularly scheduled Tuesday trains.

There was also a dramatic increase in the number of regular

transports. The new transport schedule would have two trains leaving weekly. By late August, that number would double. Those deemed "necessary workers," such as those doing the heavy work in the fields and the metal strippers and recyclers, were spared from transport, at least for the time being. The Gruppe Bühne Westerbork, as well as Johnny and Jones, were fortunate enough to be among those whose work details protected them from immediate deportation. For how long that would last was anyone's guess.

August 26, 1944

With the camp emptying at an alarming pace, Willy and Max wanted some reassurance that Gemmeker would hold to his promise of protection for the company, should they be ordered to leave.

"Come in, Herr Rosen and Herr Ehrlich. What can I do for you?"

"Herr Commandant," Willy said, maintaining as much cool as he could. "It's concerning our situation, well, your promise to help us should we be sent away. We were hoping that—"

Gemmeker waved his hand. "Herr Rosen, I'm afraid all bets are off at this point. Of course, I can and will provide a letter expressing my desire that you and your friends are treated well if and when you must leave. Unfortunately, I have no authority once you get on the train itself, let alone what happens should you reach your destination."

"*Should* we reach our destination, sir?" Max blurted out, disturbed by the change of direction in the conversation.

"Yes, Herr Ehrlich. If you and your friends are sent away, I can only assume that it would be to Theresienstadt, as per my request. However, I'm afraid that even going to Theresienstadt can't guarantee much of anything these days."

"What do you mean 'these days,' Herr Commandant?"

Gemmeker reached for a cigarette, but realizing that he didn't have a match, he threw it on the ground in disgust and crushed it with his boot. "These days we are just following orders and doing what we are told to do. The end is coming quickly, and that has forced the Führer to play his final hand." Reaching deep into his pocket, he found a match, so he selected another cigarette and lit it before he continued. "The Allied Forces are advancing at a much faster pace than the Führer expected. Just yesterday, Paris was reclaimed by the Americans, and our troops are on the run back through the French countryside. There seems to be a never ending supply of Americans these days..." Gemmeker walked over to the window to examine the activity on his Boulevard of Misery. "Look at them. But orders are orders, and the camp must be emptied as quickly as possible before the Allied troops cross the Dutch border, which will be soon I expect." He paused to take another sizable drag off his cigarette, never turning to look at his guests. "You both will be going soon, as well as the rest of the troupe."

"We're being sent away, Herr Commandant? When? To where?"

Gemmeker's voice rattled Willy's head. "You will be leaving on the next to last transport of September 6. I would have put you on the final train out, but I had to leave that for the children." Gemmeker seemed nonchalant.

Willy finally spoke. "To Theresienstadt, Herr Commandant?"

"Yes. As promised, I drafted a letter to give to the train commander. Whether or not it is obeyed, well, that's another question." Gemmeker inhaled deeply on his cigarette and turned to the pair. His demeanor was quite calm and relaxed. Perhaps it was the nicotine. "You have both done very well. You have given your people hope where there may have otherwise been none. Now, if I were you two, I would go. September 6 will be here far too soon, I fear." Gemmeker had turned back to look out his window, staring out into the vastness of the trainyard, watching body after body being aided into the cattle cars through billows of dirt and dust. When the door was shut, Gemmeker closed his eyes to think, to contemplate the repercussions of his sending thousands upon thousands of humans to the unknown. He knew where they would be going at first but, worse still, he knew where they would eventually end up. Auschwitz.

27

Gemmeker was correct. The day of departure was upon them in what seemed like a matter of hours, as opposed to the two weeks it took. Only those half-Jews and Jews with money to pay off Gemmeker and the guards would be spared transport to other camps. All that was left of the Gruppe Bühne Westerbork was Willy and Mara Rosen; Max Ehrlich (and his wife, Charlotte); Nol van Wesel (aka Johnny, and his wife, Gerda); Max Kannewasser (aka Jones, and his wife, Suzanne), Otto Aurich and his wife, Lisl Frank; Leo Kok and his wife, Kitty, along with the unmarried Esther Philipse, Flip Sanders, and Ulla Gross. They were told to report at the Boulevard of Misery to be transported to Theresienstadt.

September 6, 1944

Although not called up for transport, Erich Ziegler planned to accompany the group to the platform, desperate and horrified by the deportation of his remaining friends. As the group walked, though, Erich fell further and further behind, his emotions not allowing his feet to keep up. Finally, sobbing, he called out. "Willy... I can't go. I can't watch you leave. Why do I have to stay here?"

Willy turned to see his dear friend of so many years kneeling in the dirt of the courtyard. "Stay. There's no need for you to see any of this. Just know that I love you like the brother I never had. Bless you, my friend. Know that you are very, very loved by us all." Willy turned and headed toward the train station to join the others. He could hear Erich's sobs as he walked, but knew if he turned around, he would lose the strength he needed for himself. When he arrived at the station, Willy went to see the train commander. "Excuse me, sir. Do you have a letter from Commandant Gemmeker about the transportation of the actors from his troupe?" Willy asked as politely and humbly as possible.

The train commander gave him a puzzled look, and spit on the ground directly next to Willy's foot. "Letter? Yeah, sure. I've got a letter. What's your name?"

"Rosen, Willy. My wife, Mara is over there, and the director Max Ehrlich is—"

The conductor spit again. "Yeah. You're special. You're in car number 7, reserved for only the best. Go and get your friends. They're waiting for you."

Willy led the others the length of the train to Hans who was helping to load the human cargo onto Transport XXVI to Theresienstadt. When they got closer, Willy sprinted up to him. "Hans, we're leaving as well. Gemmeker gave us a special car to ride in. Number 7."

Hans looked at him, too mortified to speak. After what seemed an eternity, he replied, "Yes, you're all in number 7, but it's not a special car," pointing to the filthy cattle car already occupied with approximately 50 other prisoners.

Willy turned white, the blood leaving his face. So, he had been played the fool. For how long? Had any of it been true? Had Gemmeker lied this whole time?

"Willy, are you okay?" Hans was snapping his fingers in Willy's face, trying to break the stupor that had taken over.

"This can't be right..."

Hans pulled him aside from the ghastly noise and confusion. "Willy, this is it. This is your reality. I'm sorry." Hans reached into his back pocket and pulled out a thin flask. "It's water. Take it. Water's like gold on the train. You won't get much of it and, when you do, it'll usually give you diarrhea."

Willy stood there too numb to think. As Hans hugged him, Willy suddenly pushed away and shouted at the top of his lungs. "This is how you repay us?!" He ran to the other side of the train and repeated his question directly at the window of the Commandant's office. "This is how you repay us? For all we did for you?" Willy's face was now red, his arms pounding the air, and his voice hoarse from his screaming. A few seconds later, he could see Gemmeker at the office window, with his cigarette in hand. He stared out at Willy nonplussed. He took a long drag off his cigarette, turned up the left corner of his mouth and let a steady stream of smoke pour out the half-open window. Without a word, the Commandant slammed the window closed and walked away.

"Rosen, Mara! Rosen, Willy!" The call came from Hans, still loading car 7.

Willy ran back around to the car opening. "Rosen, Willy. I'm coming!" He could see Hans helping Esther into the car, having allowed Mara to wait for him.

"Willy, they could have killed you," Mara yelled at him, hysterical that she'd have to make this trip alone.

"I just wish they had. It would save us all valuable time," Willy yelled back, his anger preventing his ability to think clearly. He knew he had to control himself or it would affect Mara and the others. As he looked around, he saw Max and the rest of his cast in tears. Willy's feelings toward Gemmeker only multiplied now as he saw his friends suffering. Somehow, instinctively, he knew that as bad as things were for Gemmeker and his kind right now, they would eventually get worse. Replaying Gemmeker's conversation about the proximity of the Canadian troops and the inevitability of the Allies pushing the Germans out of Holland brought a brief smile to his face.

Mara noticed his sudden change of emotion. "Why are you smiling?"

"Nothing really. Just a conversation I had earlier with Gemmeker. Fate has a funny way of rewarding people for their actions. Bad things happen to bad people. *Schicksal,* some call it. And Gemmeker and his kind will get what's coming to them, and they'll richly deserve it." He noticed Mara's disbelief at what he was telling her. He kissed her, and said softly, "You're right. Let's count our blessings." Willy took her hand and led her next to Max and Charlotte.

As the train entered a tunnel, the car went completely dark. A loud voice called out in the darkness. "Hey, does anyone have a flashlight? And a bagel?" It was Max, of course.

Life on the train to Theresienstadt was hell incarnate. Water was scarce, and the buckets used to collect human waste had long since filled up, spreading across the slat floors and onto the gravel tracks below. Theresienstadt was still a day away and the conditions were deteriorating rapidly; the coughing was constant, certain to spread among the other prisoners. Dysentery was rampant as the lack of fresh water created situations where even a urine-soaked rag provided relief from the delirium brought on by dehydration.

Sleep was as rare a commodity as food, and on the occasion that there was a stop on the trip, the prisoners were given only enough time off the train to relieve themselves, grab a drink of water and some bread and return to their assigned cars. Those too slow would be on the receiving end of a rifle butt, tossed back into a car with a broken jaw or worse. Having re-staked their spots in car number 7, Willy and Mara leaned against the back wall, Willy reaching inside his coat to pull out a piece of manuscript paper. Mara instinctively pulled a pencil out of her bag, knowing that this was Willy's way to keep himself from going crazy; either from fear or from the sheer horror of their situation.

"What are you writing, my dear?"

"I'm not sure. A song about being on this train." Willy listened to himself say it; but trailed off thinking that he could potentially write something no one would ever hear.

"You should absolutely write a song. You never know, we're going to Theresienstadt. Maybe you could do a revue there? If that's a possibility, you'll need songs. How many did you bring with you?"

"I brought a few, but certainly not enough for a revue." Willy's voice lightened up a bit. "You know, maybe there will be an opportunity to perform once we get there. They say they had great performances there as well. Maybe as good as Westerbork. I should write."

"Yes. Write a song about the train. I'm going to try to sleep for a bit," Mara said, resting her head on his shoulder.

Willy worked diligently, as if it was the only thing that mattered in that moment. Once he finished, Willy hummed through the melody. He was figuring out the refrain when his mind began to race again. *Text und Musik von Mir! For what? Would anyone even hear this? Will anyone remember me?* He felt his wife against his shoulder, and thought of his friends and the others on this dismal journey. All this contemplation created the unspoken fear to rise up in him like a fire. *What's going to happen to us?*

September 8, 1944

The trip from Westerbork to Theresienstadt took a little more than two days; two days of absolute misery watching those you love suffer from the inhumane conditions placed upon Transport XXVI. The train arrived in the small Czech town just before 5:00 p.m., with officers ordering all on board to debark quickly and line up for the processing of each prisoner. Once papers were examined and stamped by officials, the group began the walk to the fortress town previously part of Bohemia. As they approached the outer walls of the city, they were in awe of the height of the brick-and-mortar structures, all topped with earthen paths which enabled guards to move quickly from one point on the wall to another. Passing under the main entrance to the fortress, Willy noticed the same words emblazoned in black letters on a white background that he had become familiar with in Westerbork, "*Arbeit macht Frei* (Work will set you free)".

Funny... he thought. *Does anyone really believe that? Even the Nazis? Surely not...* He almost chuckled to himself but thought it inappropriate for the moment. Instead, he simply grabbed Mara's hand tighter and lifted his head up proudly, not wanting his wife to detect the terror he felt at that moment.

Theresienstadt was no Westerbork. There were no passes out,

few leisurely strolls around the camp and certainly no wearing of street clothes. Once inside the city gates, Willy and his troupe were taken to a changing station where they had to give up their personal clothes for the first time since their imprisonment and exchange them for horrid-looking blue-and-white striped outfits with a yellow Star of David emblazoned on the chest. The outfits were filthy, stinking of urine and fecal matter and stained in bodily fluids of all kinds. As Willy paused, his senses overwhelmed, he felt a sharp, cold jab in the middle of his back. "Move Jew! Change now!"

Willy took off his clothes, seeing that the others had obviously moved faster than he. He had set his satchel down while he changed and, once finished, reached for his bag, only to have it snatched out of his hand by a supervising officer. "What have we here, Jew?"

"Sir, it's my music. For the camp."

"Music for the camp? Well now, we don't have much of that anymore. Who told you that you could bring music here?"

"Commandant Gemmeker from Westerbork. We were his performers and—"

"And you thought you could perform here? Well, that may be possible. Maybe not." The officer threw Willy's satchel at him, nearly spilling its contents across the stone floor of the room.

"Thank you, sir," Willy said, making sure to keep his head down. He profoundly understood that if there were ever a time to keep his head down, it would be here. This wasn't much different from being on a battlefield, where drawing attention could get you killed. He had to decide if it was even a good idea to ask to perform.

They walked the cobblestone streets of the former Bohemian city, and everywhere were buildings that had been converted into barracks for the prisoners. As they stood in front of a building marked B IV, an officer shouted at them, "Men here," and pointing toward the much larger C III building across the street he added, "Women will be there." His German was poor and difficult to understand; maybe he was a Czech national forced to fight for Germany? Willy didn't know, but the gesturing of his rifle made it perfectly clear what he wanted. As they entered, the guard pointed down a hallway lined with stack after stack of wooden bunks, three tall in a stack.

Willy could tell that the previous occupants left suddenly and violently. Personal objects were left wedged between the bed frame and the wall; large chunks of human hair were tangled in the splintered boards; dried blood and urine stained the mattresses.

Men and women had entered the barracks together.and were happy they were not yet separated. Mara froze, unable to take another step. She was shaking uncontrollably, so Willy wrapped one arm around her to warm her, although it wasn't at all chilly.

"Look," she said, gesturing to the bottom bunk of the stack of beds in front of her. Willy followed her gaze. It was a human finger that had obviously been ripped from the hand of a young person, caught between the bottom slats of the bed and the support post.

Before he could process exactly what he was looking at, Mara moved quickly to the nearest window and vomited profusely, but it splattered on the wall and floor, missing the open window completely.

The guard gestured toward a mop and bucket filled with grimy water. "You clean it," he ordered, pointing his rifle at Mara.

Willy stepped back, allowing room for Mara to clean up the vomit, which seemed an incredible amount for such a small woman. Pointing the rifle at Esther, the guard said sharply, "Help her." Esther quickly found a piece of fabric on the nearest mattress and started to wipe vomit off the floor.

Willy looked at Max. His ashen face contrasted vividly against his coal-black eyes, which were glassy from lack of sleep, food, and understanding.

Willy inched toward his friend, whispering, "Max, are you alright?"

"Yeah, just dandy, Willy. Couldn't be better." His delivery was monotone, a statement of shock rather than sarcasm.

"Hang in there. We just need time to regroup, to talk and get our minds straight. The strain of all this has been too much for us all."

"You think? And here I was thinking we were going to the cultural center of Jewish life in Europe. Instead, we're watching your wife and

Esther clean up vomit. If that doesn't constitute emotional stress, I don't know what does."

"You two. Quiet!" the guard barked, thrusting his rifle in their direction.

Esther began to stand up, and Max reached for her arm to help. Barely on her feet, she looked at him, said, "Thank..." and passed out.

Max caught her, setting her down on the nearest bunk.

"Can we get some water?" Nol called out, having watched the events silently but no longer able keep his mouth shut.

"Water? I give you water," the guard said, propelling the butt of his rifle directly into the young singer's forehead.

Nol crashed backward into Little Max, sending both to the ground. Nol touched his head, recoiling from the pain. There was a tremendous amount of blood covering his hand.

Leo Kok tore off a part of his uniform and tied it around Nol's head to absorb the blood. Within minutes, it was soaked red. "Is this how we are to be treated? For all we've done for Commandant Gemmeker in Westerbork?" Leo shouted at the guard, who was taken aback by the degree of outrage and insolence. The guard lifted his rifle to assign the same fate but chose not to strike him. "Stupid, but brave, Jew. Go. Take others and get bunks. Women with me!" The men watched as the guard pushed the female members of their troupe out of the barrack.

"I thought he was going to kill me," Leo said, shaking from the encounter.

Willy was furious. "He very well could have. What were you thinking?"

"I was thinking that I couldn't show any fear. All I have is my dignity." The effects of what he'd just been through exploded outward. "Willy, that's what's important to me right now, not some chance to perform in this shithole. If you think for one moment that this place is Westerbork, well, look around! These people don't give a damn if we can sing, dance, act, or speak in tongues. Look at us, for God's sake. Look at these clothes. Wake up, Willy. You'll be singing over an open grave here."

Willy was stunned, but before he could think of what to stay, Max stood inches from Leo. "You know what? You're the one who needs to wake up! Your anger isn't toward him. It's toward them. Keep it that way. All we have is each other, and you better remember that."

Leo lowered his head. "You're right. I'm sorry. It's just this place..." Too weary from everything, Leo sat on the bottom bunk of the nearest stack, covering his face and nearly keening.

Willy sat next to him, holding him tightly around his shoulder. "Leo, no matter what happens to us here, we have those we love closest to us, even in this God-forsaken place. That's what we must focus on."

Before Leo could say anything else, a bombastic voice rang from down the narrow hallway of the barrack. "What on earth did you do now?"

Everyone turned to see from who was coming toward them, but Willy already knew. "Hermann Feiner!"

In a mockingly diminutive voice, Hermann said, "Did you miss me?" He spent the next few hours explaining how Theresienstadt worked. Things were grim. There was now only the occasional performance. He told the group of the "glory days" of shows at Theresienstadt, both of those he saw and performed in as well.

"Who do we ask about performing here?" Willy asked.

After no one spoke up to condemn the idea, Hermann answered. "Everything here is approved by Commandant Karl Rahm. He's young and Viennese. He's kind of an odd duck, but he knows good music. He loves Benatzky, Stoltz, Strauss, really anything operetta. You could ask about putting a revue together, but I wouldn't hold my breath. I mean, look around. There's a lot of shit going on here. The International Red Cross was here not too long ago, and Rahm had the place looking like a model city. I mean, impeccably clean and culture everywhere. However, as soon as the IRC left, it all came crashing down. The activities stopped and the city was back in ruins. All the flowers, statues, water fountain, all gone. Pausing for a moment, he looked at Willy and the group. "So, still want to put on a show?"

Willy waited for the information to sink in before answering, "Yes, I do. I think performing here would be just as important as it was in Westerbork. It would give these people hope again."

"I wouldn't be too sure about that," Hermann said. "It's different here. You can come in one day and leave the next. There's little rhyme or reason in the decisions on who stays and who goes. But I suppose it couldn't hurt to ask."

Willy didn't care. He would rather die performing than die not performing. "Where can I find his office?"

September 10, 1944

"So, you'd like to put on a revue here in my camp? You were Commandant Gemmeker's performers in Westerbork? We all heard of the performances. Actually, I am quite shocked that he sent you here. He was very proud of you all. Particularly you, Herr Rosen."

"Thank you, Herr Commandant." Willy was pleased to have garnered such a reputation, but he could tell that Rahm was no Gemmeker.

Rahm was young but hardened. He studied Willy, making him extremely nervous and uncomfortable. He finally turned his attention to Max. "And you, Herr Ehrlich. What is it that you do? Are you a singer of songs as well? A *Text und Musik von Mir!* also?"

Willy was taken aback that Rahm had used his trademark statement. Surely it was deliberate to let Willy know that he was not only familiar with his name, but was aware of his celebrity as well.

"No, Herr Commandant. I leave that to Willy. I'm the director. I put all the pieces together."

"I see. And you would like to do one of your shows here? I don't see why not. It would be nice to have entertainment again. We've had so little since the Red Cross left. Pity really. Seems like no one stays in Theresienstadt for any length of time anymore. You Jews, you know how to create, don't you? Well, there's a large rehearsal hall on the second floor of the hospital where the blind are kept. You may rehearse there. I will let the guards know. Send me your cast and song list for my approval."

Flabbergasted that it was this simple Max said, "Thank you, Herr Commandant. When may we start?"

"Today. Bring your actors to the hospital and report to

Untersturmführer Leber. He will show you the room you may use. There's already a piano, but I can't swear to its condition. You'll make do, yes?"

"Yes, Herr Commandant. Thank you," Willy said, keeping his head lowered.

Motioning to the guard, Rahm gestured the pair to leave.

Once they were in the barrack, the guard peeled off, leaving them to talk quietly but openly. "It went well," Willy told them, his exuberance difficult to contain. "Can you believe it? We get another chance. I even wrote a song on the transport here in anticipation of it."

Max was uncharacteristically quiet. After a few seconds, he warned, "Let's just rehearse and see what happens. Try not to draw too much attention to ourselves, right?"

"Right, I understand. Let's keep it down until we have a show to put on. Then we can let the word out."

After Max and Willy explained the rest of the conversation with Rahm, the troupe made their way to the hospital to find their new rehearsal space.

Once there, they found the young officer who didn't seem particularly interested in their request. "Go on up," he said, curling up the left corner of his mouth before he spoke. "Just be prepared for what you'll find there."

Willy's energy was higher than it had been in a long time, which sent him charging up the stairs and through the door to the rehearsal hall. He was hit with a stench so foul that he slammed the door shut. "What the hell?" Willy said to the others coming up behind him. "What is that smell?"

Hermann stepped out of the group and reached for the door handle. "Only one way to find out," and he pushed the door. They were looking at dozens of decomposing human corpses in the center of the room, rotting in the September heat.

Hermann slapped his hand over his nose and mouth. "Holy shit! What in the hell did they do here? And what are we to do about it?" Hermann asked, his eyes watering from the stench.

"Well, if we're going to rehearse, we have to get these bodies out of here," Esther said. She was disgusted by the thought but firm in her conviction.

"Really?" Hermann said. "I ain't touching them."

"Here's a thought," she said. "This is a hospital for the blind, right? Let's get the patients out of their rooms and lined up in a single file from the front door, up the stairs, to here. We'll have them pass the bodies down like a conveyor belt, one at a time, until they are restacked outside the building on the street. Once they're outside, we can press that they are buried properly."

Willy was appalled at Esther's idea but it made complete sense. The patients here were blind, so there'd be no revulsion from the sight. The smell would be equally awful for them, but if they were told they were helping to get the bodies treated with the respect they deserved, it might work.

"Well, who's going to go around and ask the patients?"

From the back, Little Max and Nol raised their hands. "We'll do it."

Esther continued as the leader for this ghoulish exercise. "As they get the inmates out of their rooms, I'll get them lined up. The rest of you help get these poor souls into their hands, okay? I know it's gruesome, but if we're going to have rehearsal, it must be done. We can only hope the Germans will deal with the bodies with more dignity than they have already shown. Yes?"

"Okay, let's move some corpses," Max said, enunciating as if he were performing a line from a skit.

Within four hours, the bodies were moved; the stack relocated from the rehearsal hall to the sidewalk outside the hospital building to be brought to the crematorium. Mara was amazed at Willy's ability to compartmentalize the situation. Here was a stack of dead bodies, humans who had passed from whatever cause. In any case, they had to be moved in order to rehearse, and it was done. Floors, walls, and furniture were scrubbed until the smell dissipated. Mara would have thought her husband unable to even look at such a situation let alone quickly begin to move the piano into the center of the space previously occupied by corpses and begin to play. "Hey, it's not that out of tune! Listen," he told them, and played *Charleston,* one of his more well-known if not outdated songs. He spoke above his own playing, telling them, "Gather round and get ready to work."

"What'll we call this one, Willy?" Nol asked.

"Let's ask Max. Herr Director, what shall we call our latest revue?"

"Well, it's worked before, so why not do another *Bunter Abend?* In honor of Erich Ziegler, of course. After all, he's the one that came up with the name in the first place."

"Perfect. *Bunter Abend IV.* For Erich. Are we all ready?" The enthusiastic nods from around the piano were all Willy needed. He opened his satchel, pulled out a stack of music, and put it on top of the piano for them to examine while he began to sing. "This song, I feel, should be the opening number of the show..."

And it all began again. For the next two weeks, the Gruppe Bühne Westerbork, relocated to Theresienstadt and rehearsing in a hospital, prepared for the fourth incarnation of their *Colorful Evening.* The performance would never take place though

28

September 21, 1944

The morning started like any other day in Theresienstadt; the group first walked to the cafeteria to find a loaf of bread and some clean water. What they found instead was something unusual. Paul Eppstein, the head of the Jewish Council, had posted a flier stating that an important public address would be made this evening; every inhabitant of the camp was being requested to listen. Hermann studied the flier as if it were written in a foreign language. Finally, he spoke. "Something's not right here," he said, pointing to the flier. "Since my arrival, there has never been a public address by anyone on the Jewish Council, not to mention Eppstein. Hell, he rarely comes out of the Hamburg Barracks."

"The what?" Mara asked.

"The Hamburg Barracks. It's where the Jewish Council and other officials live. You never see any of them around. Probably afraid they'll be killed or something. The Council selects who's transported out, just like in Westerbork." He was obviously troubled by the announcement.

Trying to break the tension, Max said, "Hey, it may not be bad at all. It could be good news. Who knows? Maybe we'll all get real food to eat."

"Laugh, funny man, but I have my instincts, and they tell me it's not good." Hermann headed toward the front door. "Count me out of the festivities today. I don't feel much like celebrating." They watched him leave, and then turned into the cafeteria to locate something to eat. Much to their surprise, there were multiple slices of still good bread by the sink.

"Okay, everyone," Willy chimed in, "let's take our breakfast and go upstairs. Rehearsal in ten minutes."

"Slave driver," Ulla joked, savoring the last bits of her bread.

"Just you wait, my dear. Your dance number is up first," Willy said, leading the group up the stairs and into the rehearsal hall.

Mara raced past a few people to join her husband at the head of the pack. "Willy, should we be concerned about this announcement? I mean, Hermann's been here a lot longer than us. If he thinks this is unusual, shouldn't we pay attention?"

"This whole thing is unusual, wouldn't you agree? Not long ago, we were moving dead bodies down these stairs like an assembly line would move car parts. I would say that everything passes for unusual. Here, it's the ordinary things that should draw our attention." Willy opened the door to the rehearsal room and ushered the cast inside. Everyone gathered around the piano as they normally did, waiting for instructions from Willy and Max. It was during times like these where they truly felt like a family—a family put together by fate.

Max stepped to the front of the room. "You know the drill, everyone. Stretches. And 1 and 2." While the cast warmed up, Willy made last-minute adjustments to the day's numbers. "I had planned to punish Lisl and Ulla with their dance number first, but I've decided to work instead on this full-cast number. I wrote the song on the train from Westerbork."

As they began work, Mara broke down, the song hitting too hard for her. She had spent nearly two years either on the run or in hiding, she had no idea what had happened to her parents but presumed the worse, lived more than a year in a transit camp, had seen so many friends taken away, and now Hermann's foreboding concern about the post. It all came crashing down around her.

Willy stopped rehearsal to sit next to her, "Mara, my dear, what's wrong?"

"This song. I know you tried to keep it light, but I just can't do it. Must I sing?" Mara had never made a request against participating in one of the numbers, so he knew she was terribly upset.

"Of course. Sit this one out, that's fine." He kissed her on her cheek and finished working on the number. After a few more hours of dialogue, dancing, and singing, rehearsal was over, and just in time to return to their barracks where Hermann was waiting for them. The strain and tension coming off him was powerful. "What's wrong?" Esther asked.

"You all missed the announcement. You missed it!" Hermann broke down.

Willy hadn't seen him like this since he was transported out of Westerbork.

"What did it say?" Max asked, although based on his behavior, he wasn't at all sure that he wanted to hear it.

"The Camp Commander's Office has ordered a work transport of 5,000 men between the ages of 18 and 50 to be dispatched immediately. We're assured that they will return in six weeks, after the work's done. The selections will be made on the basis of age only." Hermann tried to keep it together as he continued, although that was nearly impossible. "The Council asked that we maintain our discipline. We're all just supposed to make it easier for them." He was unable to contain his dread any longer. "Where were you guys? I had to listen to this all by myself!"

Willy understood that Hermann's reaction was directed in the wrong place. "Hermann, we're not the bad guys here. It's unfair for you to be mad at us. Be mad at them." Willy's brain registered the ages. "Wait, between the ages of 18 and 50? That would mean all of us except for you. You don't even have to go!"

"Which is the worst part," Hermann said, his emotions bursting out again. "I finally find you all again and you're taken away. I hate this place!"

"Oh my God, Willy, that means you," Mara said, her eyes showing that her worst fear was coming true.

"It will be alright, my dear. It's for six weeks, and I'll be traveling with Max, Otto, Nol, and Little Max."

"And me! I look old for my age!" Flip said. He had rarely spoken since leaving Westerbork except an occasional word or two with Ulla. They were young, kids, really. Flip, at 12 years old, was not yet a teenager; Ulla was only 20.

"Good boy. All we can do is stay together. Those of us who have to go will look out for each other, as will those of you who have to stay," Willy said, as he gently caressed Mara's face.

She leaned in to kiss him, her face cracking from such deep sadness. "We will, my dear. We'll take care of each other."

Willy turned to Hermann who had collected himself. "When and where are we supposed to go?"

"On September 29... to build a new labor camp near Dresden, called Riesa. You'll be on the train for a day, so you're to bring only light luggage. The Council has arranged for food for the day, but just to get you to the camp site. While you're gone, all spouses and family members are protected from deportation. The Jewish Council promised this. You'll be gone for six weeks and then return to Theresienstadt. You'll be able to write, which is something at least."

Raising his arms in a strong-man pose, Max joked, "Do they really think I'll be much good at physical labor? Look at these biceps. They couldn't carry an empty bucket."

Charlotte Ehrlich didn't find that funny at all, throwing her arms around his neck in an uncharacteristic display of emotion. "Just promise me you won't try anything heroic. We've come this far, and I don't intend to lose you now."

"Darling," Max quipped, "you couldn't lose me if you tried."

"So, two days after Yom Kippur we have to be separated. That's pretty crappy," Willy said, looking into Mara's eyes.

"We'll be okay here," she tried to assure herself. "After all, we have each other."

Esther agreed. "Yes, we have each other," and wrapped her arms around Ulla.

"So, we have a plan," Willy said, hoping to change the direction of everyone's mood. "The men who leave will stay together and take care of each other until we get back, and the same for the ladies and Hermann." Willy asked point-blank, "Hermann, we're counting on you to watch out for our girls. Can you do that for us?"

Without thinking, he said, "Damned straight I can." Hermann was in better physical condition than most of the younger men, since he'd had the most weight to lose. He actually looked strong and capable as the future protectorate of the former Gruppe Bühne Westerbork women.

"That's it, then." Willy looked around at his group. "The fourth *Bunter Abend* will simply have to wait until we return." He turned to Mara, who still looked deeply worried. He took her hand, asking her, "Shall we take a stroll, my love?"

"Why, I'd be honored, Herr Rosen."

Under the close scrutiny of the guards, they intertwined their fingers before walking out into the star-lit night o enjoy each other's company for as long as they could.

Between September 24 and 25, 2,500 men and boys were given notice of selection for work detail in Germany. Willy, Max, Otto, Nol, and Little Max all received notice to report to the *Schleuse*, the quarantine area at the Hamburg barracks on the afternoon of September 26 to receive their provisions from the Jewish Council. They were instructed to return to the Hamburg barracks on the evening of the September 28 to be processed and loaded onto passenger cars for the day's journey to Dresden. During the afternoon of the 28th, everyone met in the hospital's rehearsal room for one final time.

"Everyone here?" Max asked, knowing the answer.

"All here," Willy replied, his fingers tightly intertwined with Mara's.

They sat in chairs in a circle. This was their family, a family created out of necessity and united by choice.

Willy stood up and spoke first. "Many of us were strangers only a year ago. Fate and God brought us together to endure this hell as a group, for surely we are stronger together than we are as individuals. We helped others endure these times with laughter, joy, humanity, and dignity. We did that. All of us together. For many, we were the final glimpse of a kinder and gentler world, one that believed all humans as worthy of life and love. For us, we were part of something much bigger than a simple theater group; we were a gentle transition for those leaving Westerbork for the unknown. I, for one, would have never made it through these past months without Mara and without you. I know we're to be back in six weeks, but we also know the possibility—" Willy stopped himself. "Regardless of what the future holds, you will all be a part of me for as long as my soul cries out. Our voice will be one voice that will resonate for eternity so that our work is not forgotten. So that what has happened to us will not be dismissed as an error, or a dark spot in history where those who were lost became a number and not a name." He touched his chest. "We are Gruppe Bühne Westerbork, and there will be someone who will be able to tell our story. No matter what, we will live, even if that life is a memory." Willy welled up as he looked at carefully each member. "I want to thank you all, each one of you, for all that you have done to make our performances... no, our lives... possible these past months. Max, you have been the one to keep us focused and professional, never accepting less than our absolute best, even under dire circumstances. Thank you, my dear, dear friend."

Max stood up and hugged Willy. No words needed to be said. Max Ehrlich and Willy Rosen, two names which for over a decade had become almost inseparable, would surely continue to be so. Max turned to the group for one final request. "Let's just remain here and enjoy each other's company, shall we? There's a piano. We have singers, and dancers and no guards in sight. Let's go out with a bang."

Willy hopped behind the piano with Mara at his back. Max sorted the others around the keyboard. Willy played, randomly at first, and then a familiar strain became clear: *Warum hat bloss das Zebra so viel Streifen?* As each person remembered the words to *Why Does the Zebra Have So Many Stripes?* they joined in until a full chorus sang the refrain to one of Willy's most popular tunes; a song that questions the unknown universe disguised as a children's song.

When the singing grew louder, Max leaned into Willy and whispered, "Isn't this how you always envisioned it?"

"Envisioned what?"

"Our family."

As the music grew louder, the smiles grew bigger.

Willy leaned back toward Max and answered, "No. It's far better than I could have ever imagined." Willy gave Max a wink, and joined in on the final refrain.

September 28, 1944

At seven o'clock in the evening on Thursday, September 28, all men who had received their work orders reported to the Schleuse to begin processing. Each man was given a transport number to place around his neck for tracking purposes.

As Willy and Mara entered the courtyard, they were taken aback by the beauty of the setting. Lights were strung across the length of the yard, creating a canopy over the thousands of people milling about, eating, getting their number, checking their luggage, and kissing their families goodbye. The troupe stayed close to each other, determined to remain together throughout the process. As they stood in line, Willy noticed Mara crying, as he suspected she would. He hugged her tightly into his chest, which only made her cry harder. He softly whispered into her ear, "My love, you must be strong. You've always been strong. Strong enough for the both of us. After Elsbeth, I thought I could never love again. You brought me back to life. You gave me a reason to live, to fight, to write, to perform. Everything wonderful that we accomplished in Westerbork was due to you. If God hadn't brought you into my life, none of this would have been possible." He kissed her on the forehead and then pulled her lips close to his.

"Remember this. I will love you until my soul turns cold." He kissed her deeply through her tears, and then wiped her lovely face dry.

She looked into her husband's eyes and managed to get out a faint, "I love you so much. Come back to me."

"I promise I will."

Max, with Charlotte at his side, tapped Willy on the shoulder. "Hey, you two. Sorry to break up the party, but we have to go. Bye Mara, see you next time around."

It was just after midnight when Willy gave Mara one final kiss and then let her go, watching her as he moved with the line toward the loading dock. Hermann, being 56 years old, stood watching as his friends were separated once again from each other. The sight was too much for him, so he went back to the barrack. Esther and Ulla stayed with Mara as the others said their goodbyes.

"Hey guys, we're going, come on," Willy shouted.

Giving their wives final kisses, Leo, Little Max, Nol and Otto ran up to join the others. Flip ran quickly to catch up when he was stopped by one of the armed guards. "We're all full. Only 1,500 on this trip. The rest have to go out later. You're too young to go, anyway." Flip was desperate that he couldn't follow his friends, but realized he still had a job to do in Theresienstadt: stay and help Hermann until it was his turn to go.

Finding seats together, Max turned to Willy and remarked, "Nice to actually have windows on this trip, eh?"

Willy continued looking into the courtyard at Mara. "Yes, it's nice."

Max noticed Willy fixated on the group of women. "Hey, it'll be okay. We'll be back in six weeks. Look, even the train's different. All the comforts of real travel."

Willy finally redirected his gaze to Max. "You really believe them? Do you really think we'll be back here in six weeks?"

Max's usual jovial expression turned harder. "What choice do we have, Willy?"

After a few hours, just outside of Dresden, the train stopped. Willy and Max as well as the other men in their car stood up to gather their bags, now that they had arrived at their destination. Instead, guards walked down the aisle, passing out postcards and pencils and demanding everyone to remain in their seat. Each man was ordered to write to his family back in Theresienstadt the following lines: "I am well. Arrived safely. The work is bearable. The food is sufficient. Hope to see you soon."

"Pass the cards forward. If you do not write a card, you will be shot," a guard shouted down the length of the car.

"What the hell is this all about?" Willy asked Max, who was equally confused.

"I have no idea, but just write the card, and hurry. They mean business," Max said, and took his and Willy's cards, handing them forward as instructed.

A voice came from the back of the car. "This is Dresden. Are we here at the work site?" The guard moved quickly down the aisle, and with one swift motion pulled a gun out of his holster and fired one bullet through the right temple of the man, his brains splattering against the window.

Max and Willy froze in their seats.

"Any other questions?" the guard shouted.

Silence filled the car as the dead man slid onto the floor. A sharp jolt indicated that the train had started to move again.

Once the guard passed by, Willy whispered, "Now what? Where are they taking us?"

"Your guess is as good as mine, but I doubt it's to Berlin."

The pair barely spoke for the next several hours, and neither did the rest of the car's passengers. The men now knew that the tale of building a work camp outside of Dresden was another lie; a ruse to keep calm among those remaining at Theresienstadt.

Long after nightfall, Willy looked out the window. In the distance, he could see lights of a city. They were faint, darkened due to bombing raids, but he knew he was in Poland, so there were few choices as to which city it could be. Wroclaw? Opole? He scoured the area for any indication of a city, anything along the tracks, any station. Anything. Then he saw a sign for Katowice.

He nudged Max awake, wondering why they would be so far south in Poland to build a German work camp.

"Willy, don't you get it? We're not going to build a German work camp anywhere. Only God knows what will happen from here. All we can do is wait."

"How can you sleep?"

"Sleep is the only thing keeping me from crying."

"Do you think this is bad? Is this really bad?"

"I'm afraid it may be, Willy. We'll know when we get there. Try and rest. There's no use getting upset about something out of your control."

He knew Max was right, but his mind raced nonstop. *Where were they going? What would be there once they arrived? How was Mara?* He couldn't stop the questions entering his head, driving him into a frenzy. Fear was overtaking him, so he bit his lip to keep from crying out. Max, half-awake, sensed that his friend was nearing the end of his emotional rope. He drew Willy close, kissing him on the cheek. "You are my brother. I love you as much as my own family. No matter what waits for us when we arrive, let's promise to stay together, alright?"

Willy took a deep breath, feeling slightly better. "Alright. I promise. Thank you, Max. I love you, too."

The train suddenly buckled as it slowed to a crawl, entering an area of multiple tracks and several platforms. Willy and Max looked out the window and saw that it was snowing, unusual for September. And it was everywhere, covering the platforms, tracks, and even the buildings in the distance.

"How can it be snowing?" Willy asked.

"I have no idea."

Willy could see masses of people being herded like cattle. Armed guards were everywhere, many holding vicious dogs on leather leashes. As the train came to a stop, guards shouted for everyone to take their belongings and exit onto the platform. Willy, Max, and the others grabbed their bags and followed the throng of men exiting the train. Once out on the platform, they realized it wasn't snow. It was ash. Ashes were falling from the sky, covering everyone and everything. The ashes and the shouting coming from every direction confused the men.

"*Schnell!* Over there, Jews," came an order, accompanied by a sharp jab of a rifle tip in Leo's side. He jumped forward, thrusting the group into a mass of moving humanity, forming lines and following others toward a row of tables where it appeared that doctors were examining each man as he passed. Max, Willy, Leo, Otto, Little Max, and Nol all stood in the same line, some 50 men back from the tables.

Suddenly a loud voice bellowed over the noise. "Look who we have here. Are you not Max Ehrlich, the famous comic?" The guard pulled Max out of the line.

Willy started to follow, but was immediately kept in place by Leo.

The guard took Max away from the tables as other guards surrounded him.

Max looked at Willy, terrified.

"Are you not Max Ehrlich, the comedian from Berlin?"

"Yes, sir," Max said softly, his head lowered.

"Gentlemen, I have seen this Jew several times in Berlin at the KaDeKo. One of the funniest men I have ever heard. Go on, Jew, tell us a joke," he said, goading Max. The other guards joined in. "Yes, a joke! Tell us a joke."

Willy turned to see Max instantly change from terrified man to comic genius. He appeared relaxed as he told a funny story, with an even funnier punchline to the group of guards and officers surrounding him. *Max is truly in his element, even in such terrible conditions*, Willy thought.

The group burst into laughter and applause, making Willy smile as he watched Max's face light up with that ever familiar look of appreciation.

The moment was shattered by a sudden single gunshot through Max's forehead.

Watching his best friend crumble to the ground, Willy cried out and began to run back toward him, but he was held back by Little Max, who covered Willy's mouth with his hand. He whispered into Willy's ear, "You can't help him now. You can only help yourself. Keep your head down."

Willy could barely move. He felt himself being pushed forward toward the table where a doctor was examining Nol. "Over to the right," he said, pointing him to follow the group heading toward a large bunker. Little Max was next and, after a few seconds, was ordered to follow the same route. Willy was pushed up to the waiting doctor. Still unable to speak, the doctor looked at Willy and simply pointed to the left. Willy started to follow Nol and Little Max to the right, but a guard forced him to the left. "Leave your bags here! You can pick them up later!" a guard shouted over and over like a recorded message. Willy kept his bag close, refusing to let go of the one thing connecting him to his past. Page after page of music filled the sachel which he was being ordered to leave behind; his life transcribed into notes on staves and lyrics which illuminated his every emotion. As he pulled it even closer, it was grabbed off his shoulder in one swift motion followed by a punch to the head.

"I said drop your bag!"

Stunned, Willy fell in line with the others walking toward a large brick building with smokestacks. He looked around and he saw no one and he saw everyone. Hundreds of faces were staring just as he was, looking but not seeing, blindly following whoever was in front of them. He looked back at the line in time to see Leo and Otto sent to the right. He really was alone. He followed the crowd to a large wooden building next to the brick smokestacks, where a guard ordered them all to remove their clothing. "It will be waiting here for you. You are going to be disinfected first. Off to the showers. *Schnell!*"

Willy undressed, still trying to wrap his head around what he had just seen. He had promised Max that he would stay with him. Now, he was standing naked in a room with several hundred other men and small boys, all equally stunned and silent.

"This way! *Schnell!*"

Willy followed the mass as it made its way through a narrow stone passage and into a large, cavernous room with nearly three dozen large showerheads attached to the ceiling.

"The water will begin to flow in a minute. When you are finished, you will exit the rear doors and collect your things."

Willy heard a steel door slam shut with a deafening sound. He looked around at the men in the room. Some were just children; others weak looking, but most were older like him. No one spoke. Rather, the silence created a change that permeated throughout the room. The faces of the men began to harden, their eyes widen, as they understood what was to come next.

Willy heard a loud thump that shook the metal pipes of the shower system, followed by what sounded like small marbles or pellets descending through three metallic mesh pillars placed evenly throughout the large narrow space. Seconds later, he heard a hissing sound, followed by screams and moans coming from the men nearest the pillars. Men climbed upon men in a vain attempt to reach what appeared to be an air vent, but to no avail. Willy watched as those closest to the developing gas plumes collapsed onto the hard, concrete floor of their human cage. He looked to his left to see an older man gently pushing the head of who appeared to be his son down onto the floor. Willy began to cough uncontrollably as he continued to watch the man guide the youngster's face toward the intersection of the wall and the floor. Willy's coughing became uncontrollable; he couldn't breathe... His lungs began to burn as he started to lose consciousness. Terrified, he watched the old man shield the boy from the cloud of gas that was quickly falling around them. Willy's eyes began to water as he fell onto the stone floor. He continued to gasp, remaining focused on the old man and his son. As Willy's eyes closed, the room began to turn quiet. He took his final breaths as the old man lovingly whispered to his son, "Keep your head down..."

EPILOGUE

Willy Rosen and Max Ehrlich died in Auschwitz in the late-night hours of September 30, 1944/early-morning hours of October 1. Max's death is given in contrasting accounts. One is written in this book, which was recorded by eyewitnesses. It was also given that he accompanied Willy into the gas chambers. In either case, the two died together, as they had intended to do.

Amalie Rosenbaum was deported to Theresienstadt on December 2, 1942 and was sent on to Sobibor, where she was murdered on March 21, 1943. Willy had no idea that his mother was ever there.

Edith Rosenbaum Maerker, sister of Willy Rosen, returned to Germany after the war where she worked for the Komische Oper Berlin through the 1950s and 1960s. In 1971, Edith moved into a retirement home in Rottach-Egern followed by a move to Bad Griesbach, Germany in 1980. It is rumored that she died in an auto accident in Rottach-Egern, near the Austrian border on September 8, 1980, at age 83, although no record of the accident nor obituary can be located at present.

Lucie Rosenbaum Herzberg and Rudolf Herzberg lived out their years in Brazil where they had two children, Hannelore and Helene.

Elsbeth Hoffman Rosen emigrated to São Paolo, Brazil where she was last heard from in 1967, when she gave a memory statement of her former husband for Will Meisel. Attempts to locate any additional information have been futile.

Mara Krauskopf Rosen was transported to Auschwitz on October 4, 1944, where she was murdered on March 15, 1945.

Helene Krauskopf was sent to Westerbork in April 1943, and immediately sent on to Sobibor, where she was murdered on April 16, 1943. The events surrounding Alexander Krauskopf are vague. He was picked up with his wife, but appears to have died shortly after being taken into custody, having never been sent to a camp.

Charlotte Ehrlich was liberated from Theresienstadt and survived the war. She emigrated to America, working as a masseuse, passing away of natural causes in September, 1978 in West Hollywood, California.

Jetty and Mozes Cantor were sent to Auschwitz where they were both assigned to the orchestra. They survived the war and divorced in 1948, with Jetty resuming her stage and film career, passing away on April 23, 1992 in the Netherlands. Mozes Cantor remained close to Jetty until the end, passing away on August 4, 1954.

Erich Ziegler survived the war, being liberated from Westerbork in 1945. He gave a short account of events in Westerbork to the Allies, after which he never spoke of the internment again. He passed away from natural causes in 1948.

Hans Margules survived the war, being liberated from Westerbork in 1945. His oral testimonies would prove to be critical evidence against Gemmeker and other high-ranking German officers in Westerbork. He emigrated to the United States, living most of his life in New York City, returning to Germany shortly before he passed away from natural causes on February 15, 2016 in Munich.

Camilla Spira and her family moved back to Amsterdam following her release from Westerbork. Upon the war's end, she and her family relocated back to Berlin where she built a very successful film career in both East and West Germany. She only spoke of events in Westerbork much later in her life and in no great detail, passing away from natural causes on August 25, 1997.

Heintje Davids survived the war by hiding out in a mental hospital in the Dutch countryside, and she resumed her professional career after the war. She passed away from natural causes on February 14, 1975.

Otto Aurich and his wife Lisl Frank were deported to Auschwitz on September 29, 1944. Otto was moved from Auschwitz to Buchenwald, miraculously surviving the war, dying of natural causes in Amsterdam on March 23, 1961. His wife, Lisl Frank, was murdered on a death march from Auschwitz to Christianstadt during January 1945.

Leo Kok was relocated from Auschwitz to Mauthausen and then to Ebensee doing hard labor. He was liberated from Ebensee on March 7, 1945 and sent to a field hospital in Sankt Wolfgang where he died five days later. His wife, Kitty, was liberated from Theresienstadt and survived the war, passing away from natural causes on April 13, 2018.

Hermann Feiner was transported to Auschwitz on October 1, 1944, where he was killed on October 3, 1944.

Esther Philipse was transported to Auschwitz on October 6, 1944 and killed on October 8, 1944. Her husband, Salomon Zwaap, was killed along with Willy and Max on September 30/October 1, 1944.

Flip Sanders was also transported to Auschwitz on October 6, 1944 and killed on October 8, 1944. He was only 12 years old.

Ulla (Ursula) Gross was transported to Auschwitz on October 23, 1944. She survived the war, passing away from natural causes in The Hague in 2008.

Nol van Wesel (Johnny) and his second cousin Max Kannewasser (Jones) were transported from Auschwitz to Sachsenhausen, Ohrdruf, and finally to Bergen-Belsen. Max died from exhaustion on March 20, 1945. Nol died from exhaustion on April 15, 1945, the day the camp was liberated. Nol's wife Gerda died on a death march on February 28, 1945. Max's wife Suzanne survived the war and remarried, emigrating to the United States. Additional information couldn't be located.

Otto Wallburg was transported from Theresienstadt to Auschwitz on October 28, 1944 where he was murdered.

Albert Konrad Gemmeker was captured by the Allies shortly after the liberation of Westerbork, on April 12, 1945. He was imprisoned in Assen and given a sentence of ten years but was released for good behavior on April 20, 1951. He maintained his ignorance of the Jewish pogrom for the duration of his life which ended on August 30, 1982 in Düsseldorf of natural causes.

BRIEF BIBLIOGRAPHY

Arnborm, Marie-Theres, *War'n Sie schon mal in mich Verliebt?,* Böhlau Verlag Wien, 2003

Bergmeier, *Chronologie der deutschen Kleinkunst in den Niederlanden 1933-1944,* Hamburg, 1998

Busch, O. H., *On Camp Westerbork,* Interview Notes, Ascona, 5 May 1944

Budzinski, Klaus, *"Text und Music – Von Mir"* *Erinnerungen an den Chanson-und-Schlager-Entertainer Willy Rosen.* Program from May 18, 1947, Minerva Pavilion, Amsterdam

Davids, Henriette, *Mijn Levenslied,* N.V. Johan Mulder´s Uitgevers-Maatschappij, Gouda, 1948

Forster, Verona, *"Obgleich man ja nie weiß, was weiter wird. Ein wichtiger Fund: Handschriften von Willy Rosen",* In: *Zwischenwelt. Zeitschrift für Kultur des Exils und des Widerstands.* Nr. 4, Vienna, March 2008, pp. 26–31.

Grohs-Martin, Silvia, *Silvie*, Welcome Rain Publishers, 22 May 2002

Hett, Benjamin Carter, *The Death of Democracy*, Henry Holt Co., New York, 2018

Jelavich, Peter, *Berlin Cabaret*, Harvard University Press, Cambridge, 1993

Klösch, Christian and Thumser, Regina, *"From Vienna" – Exilkabarett in New York 1938 bis 1950*, Picus Verlag, Vienna 2002

Koban, Ilse, *Routine zerstört das Stück – Zum 50jährigen Bestehen der Komischen Oper Berlin*, Märkischer Verlag Wilhelmshorst, 1997

Koch, Alexander, *Diversity Destroyed – Berlin 1933-1938*, Deutsches Historisches Museum Exhibition Book, Berlin, 2013

Kühn, Volker, *Totentanz, Kabarett im KZ*, Edition Mnemosyne, Neckargemünd, 2003

Large, David Clay, *Berlin*, Basic Books, New York, 2000

Levie, Walter J., *Gestapo Interview with Dr. Walter Levie*, Amsterdam, 23 June 1941

Mathijsen, H, *De entertainer van Westerbork*, VRU Nederlands, 2 May 1992, Utrecht

Mathijsen, H.H.J.M, *Radio Documentary notes on Willy Rosen*, Amsterdam, 13 September 1989

Morgan, Paul, *Stiefkind der Grazien*, Universitas Deutsche Verlags-Aktiengesellschaft, Berlin, 1928

Pelger, Lies and Waale Renee, *Die mooiste liedjes van Louis Davids*, Uitgeverij De Harmonie, Amsterdam, 1980

Polak-Daniels, A, *A Report on the Camp Theresienstadt* Compiled for the United Nations War Crimes Commission, Netherlands Charges Against German War Criminals, Charge No. 117

Raber, Ralf Jörg, *Wir sind wie wir sind*, Männerschwarm Verlag, Hamburg, 2010

Rees, Laurence, *Auschwitz – A New History*, Public Affairs, New York City, 2005

Rosen, Elsbeth, *"Mein Mann, Willy Rosen"*, in Rudolph Schröder *"Text und Musik von Mir"*, Willy Rosen, Verlag Meisel, Berlin 1967

Schröder, Rudolph, *100 Jahre Will Meisel*, Edition Meisel, Berlin, 1996

Seeber, Ursula, *Asyl Wider Willen – Exil in Österreich 1933-1945*, Picus Verlag, Vienna, 2003

Stompor, Stephan, *Jüdisches Musik-und Theaterleben unter dem NS-Staat*, Europäisches Zentrum für Jüdische Musik, Hannover, 2001

Van der Veen, Harm, *Westerbork 1939-1944*, Herinneringscentrum Kamp Westerbork, 2008

Van Vree, Frank (Ed), *Site of Deportation, Site of Memory – The Amsterdam Hollandsche Schouwburg and the Holocaust*, Amsterdam University Press, Amsterdam, 2013

Veigl, Hans, *Weit von Wo – Kabarett im Exil*, Verlag Kremayr und Scheriau, Vienna, 1994

Veigl, Hans and Fink, Iris, *Verbannt, Verbrannt, Vergessen und Verkannt-Kurzbiographien zum Thema Verfolgung und Vertreibung Österreichischer Kabarett-und Kleinbühnenkünstler 1933-1945*, Österreichisches Kabarettarchiv, Graz, 2012

ABOUT THE AUTHOR

Dr. Casey J. Hayes earned his bachelor and Master of Music in music education from Butler University in Indianapolis, IN and PhD in music education from the Steinhardt School of Education, New York University (2009). His doctoral research focused on educational outreach within Lesbian / Gay / Bisexual / Transgender choral ensembles. His studies of the LGBTQI+ Choral Movement led him to be the co-music director of the New York City Gay Men's Chorus. In 2007, Casey founded the Gay Men's Chorus of Manhattan, an ensemble which raised funds for not-for-profit organizations in need across the tri-state area; the first ensemble of its kind in the United States.

He currently serves as professor and the A.J. Thurston Chair of Music, music department chair, and director of choral activities at Franklin College in Franklin, Indiana. He also serves as the Artistic Director of the Quarryland Men's Chorus, an ensemble of gay, bisexual, and transgender men and their straight allies located in Bloomington, IN. Dr. Hayes has addressed audiences on issues surrounding LGBTQI+ Rights and Culture at conferences around the globe and remains in high demand on issues involving Education, the Roman Catholic Church, and their intersection within the paradigm of human rights.

Dr. Hayes' interest in Weimar Germany and its brief yet beautiful emergence of LGBTQI+ culture grew out of his interest in music written to disseminate gay culture, such as Mischa Spoliansky's *Das Lila Lied*. His desire to learn more about this vibrant, yet largely unknown period of music history led him to discover the music of Willy Rosen and his fascinating but largely unknown life.

In 2021, Casey was selected as an Austrian Fulbright scholar and was named the Fulbright-Botstiber Visiting Professor of Austrian-American Studies at the University for Music and Performing Arts, Vienna. His research topic, *Rosa Wien; Gay Rights, Schlager and Self-Exile: 1918-1938* focused upon the plight of Vienna's LGBTQI+ and Jewish cabaret communities during the Anschluss, and their recreation of Viennese cabaret in the United States. Through the eyes of gay Weimar cabaret performer Paul O'Montis, his research re-examined the role Europe played in the early days of emerging LGBTQI+ Rights in Berlin and Vienna. Currently, Dr. Hayes' developing partnership with Literaturhaus Wien enables him to continue his research of Vienna's cabaret history throughout the coming years.

Dear Reader,

If you have enjoyed reading my book,
please do leave a review on Amazon or Goodreads. A few kind words would be enough. This would be greatly appreciated.

Alternatively, if you have read my book as Kindle eBook you could leave a rating.

That is just one simple click, indicating how many stars of five you think this book deserves.
This will only cost you a split second.
Thank you very much in advance!

NOTES

Chapter 17

1. Rudolph and Herbert Nelson, a father and son duo, were the top talent agents for Amsterdam and the leaseholders of the Joodsche Schouwburg. Their final large-scale production—the Rudolf Friml operetta *De Czardasvorstin*—had no fewer than 65 actors and a production value unlike anything previously seen. During this time, the Nazi decree that all Jews must wear the Star of David was declared, which meant the badge had to be sewn onto every costume. Cast members were shaken to their core because this was the first visible infringement of the Nazis on their creative process.

Chapter 24

1. "The Buffoon."

AMSTERDAM PUBLISHERS FURTHER READING

The Series **Holocaust Survivor True Stories WWII** by Amsterdam Publishers consists of the following biographies:

1. Among the Reeds. The true story of how a family survived the Holocaust, by Tammy Bottner

2. A Holocaust Memoir of Love & Resilience. Mama's Survival from Lithuania to America, by Ettie Zilber

3. Living among the Dead. My Grandmother's Holocaust Survival Story of Love and Strength, by Adena Bernstein Astrowsky

4. Heart Songs - A Holocaust Memoir, by Barbara Gilford

5. Shoes of the Shoah. The Tomorrow of Yesterday, by Dorothy Pierce

6. Hidden in Berlin - A Holocaust Memoir, by Evelyn Joseph Grossman

7. Separated Together. The Incredible True WWII Story of Soulmates Stranded an Ocean Apart, by Kenneth P. Price, Ph.D.

8. The Man Across the River. The incredible story of one man's will to survive the Holocaust, by Zvi Wiesenfeld

9. If Anyone Calls, Tell Them I Died - A Memoir, by Emanuel (Manu) Rosen

10. The House on Thrömerstrasse. A Story of Rebirth and Renewal in the Wake of the Holocaust, by Ron Vincent

11. Dancing with my Father. His hidden past. Her quest for truth. How Nazi Vienna shaped a family's identity, by Jo Sorochinsky

12. The Story Keeper. Weaving the Threads of Time and Memory - A Memoir, by Fred Feldman

13. Krisia's Silence. The Girl who was not on Schindler's List, by Ronny Hein

14. Defying Death on the Danube. A Holocaust Survival Story, by Debbie J. Callahan with Henry Stern

15. A Doorway to Heroism. A decorated German-Jewish Soldier who became an American Hero, by Rabbi W. Jack Romberg

16. The Shoemaker's Son. The Life of a Holocaust Resister, by Laura Beth Bakst

17. The Redhead of Auschwitz. A True Story, by Nechama Birnbaum

18. Land of Many Bridges. My Father's Story, by Bela Ruth Samuel Tenenholtz

19. Creating Beauty from the Abyss. The Amazing Story of Sam Herciger, Auschwitz Survivor and Artist, by Lesley Richardson

20. Painful Joy. A Holocaust Family Memoir, by Max J. Friedman

---

The Series **Holocaust Survivor Memoirs World War II** by Amsterdam Publishers consists of the following autobiographies of survivors:

1. Outcry - Holocaust Memoirs, by Manny Steinberg

2. Hank Brodt Holocaust Memoirs. A Candle and a Promise, by Deborah Donnelly

3. The Dead Years. Holocaust Memoirs, by Joseph Schupack

4. Rescued from the Ashes. The Diary of Leokadia Schmidt, Survivor of the Warsaw Ghetto, by Leokadia Schmidt

5. My Lvov. Holocaust Memoir of a twelve-year-old Girl, by Janina Hescheles

6. Remembering Ravensbrück. From Holocaust to Healing, by Natalie Hess

7. Wolf. A Story of Hate, by Zeev Scheinwald with Ella Scheinwald

8. Save my Children. An Astonishing Tale of Survival and its Unlikely Hero, by Leon Kleiner with Edwin Stepp

9. Holocaust Memoirs of a Bergen-Belsen Survivor & Classmate of Anne Frank, by Nanette Blitz Konig

10. Defiant German - Defiant Jew. A Holocaust Memoir from inside the Third Reich, by Walter Leopold with Les Leopold

11. In a Land of Forest and Darkness. The Holocaust Story of two Jewish Partisans, by Sara Lustigman Omelinski

12. Holocaust Memories. Annihilation and Survival in Slovakia, by Paul Davidovits

13. From Auschwitz with Love. The Inspiring Memoir of Two Sisters' Survival, Devotion and Triumph Told by Manci Grunberger Beran & Ruth Grunberger Mermelstein, by Daniel Seymour

14. Remetz. Resistance Fighter and Survivor of the Warsaw Ghetto, by Jan Yohay Remetz

---

The Series **Jewish Children in the Holocaust** by Amsterdam Publishers consists of the following autobiographies of Jewish children hidden during WWII in the Netherlands:

1. Searching for Home. The Impact of WWII on a Hidden Child, by Joseph Gosler

2. See You Tonight and Promise to be a Good Boy! War memories, by Salo Muller

3. Sounds from Silence. Reflections of a Child Holocaust Survivor, Psychiatrist and Teacher, by Robert Krell

4. Sabine's Odyssey. A Hidden Child and her Dutch Rescuers, by Agnes Schipper

---

The Series **New Jewish Fiction**, by Amsterdam Publishers, consists of the following novels, written by Jewish authors. All novels are set in the time during or after the Holocaust.

1. Escaping the Whale. The Holocaust is over. But is it ever over for the next generation? by Ruth Rotkowitz

2. When the Music Stopped. Willy Rosen's Holocaust, by Casey Hayes

3. Hands of Gold. One Man's Quest to Find the Silver Lining in Misfortune, by Roni Robbins

4. The Corset Maker. A Novel, by Annette Libeskind Berkovits

5. There was a garden in Nuremberg. A Novel, by Navina Michal Clemerson

CPSIA information can be obtained
at www.ICGtesting.com
Printed in the USA
BVHW031048180122
626500BV00006B/110